THE ULTIMATE Cricket
Fact & Quiz Book

THE ULTIMATE
Cricket
Fact & Quiz Book

SCYLD BERRY

PETER WYNNE-THOMAS

CRIS FREDDI

Illustrations
JIM HUTCHINGS

STOPWATCH

PUBLISHED BY STOPWATCH PUBLISHING LIMITED

THIS EDITION PUBLISHED 1999

PRINTED AND BOUND IN FINLAND

COMPILED BY COMMUNIQUÉ PLUS LTD

© STOPWATCH PUBLISHING LTD
1-7 SHAND STREET, LONDON SE1 2ES

ISBN 1-900032-03-1

INTRODUCTION

Welcome to the Ultimate Cricket Fact and Quiz Book. It's a massive compendium of cricketing knowledge and know-how, brought together as a celebration of the game for fans and followers of the sport from eight to 80.

We've included a series of quizzes on each of the County teams, the Test sides, the One Day Internationals and World Cups. Each quiz section is complimented by a selection of fascinating facts that may offer some help to those in search of assistance with some of the more demanding questions.

Dip in, to either challenge and quiz family and friends alike or test your own knowledge about all the aspects of the game; including the players, the grounds, the commentators and the characters, as well as all the information on the Tests and Leagues from the early years right up to the present day.

Good luck and enjoy!

CONTENTS

POT LUCK

POT LUCK

1 How was Hunter Scott Thomas Laurie Hendry better known?
2 Apart from Leicestershire which other counties has Chris Lewis played for?
3 Who captained Surrey as well as England in 1932 and 1933?
4 Who was the last player to be out 'obstructed field' in English first-class cricket?
5 Who was Man of the Match in the 1996 NatWest Trophy final?
6 Which country set a record by beating India by an innings and 336 in 1959?
7 Who has made the highest first-class score of 274 for Derbyshire: Kim Barnett, George Davidson, Peter Kirsten?
8 Who was the last Warwickshire bowler to take ten wickets in a first-class innings?
9 Which Yorkshire bowler was banished by Lord Hawke from first-class cricket for urinating on the ground when drunk?
10 Which West Indian fast bowler broke Mike Gatting's nose during the 1985-86 tour?
11 Who is Lancashire's coach?
12 Who achieved a hat-trick for Pakistan v West Indies at Sharjah in October 1989?
13 Which current Leicestershire player formerly played for Middlesex?
14 Who was the last Northamptonshire allrounder to do the double of 1000 runs and 100 wickets in a first-class season?
15 Against whom did England play their first home five match ODI series?

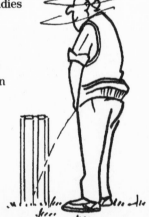

Quiz 2
POT LUCK

1 Which Zimbabwean was the only bowler to dismiss a 14-year-old in Test cricket?

2 Which pace bowler made his England debut in the 2nd Test of the 1998-99 Ashes series?

3 What is Nottinghamshire's highest total: 690 v The Pakistanis in 1936, 739-7 dec v Leicestershire in 1903, 746 v. Derbyshire in 1990?

4 Which country won the toss ten times in a row in 1959-60?

5 Which South African scored a Test century in 80 minutes in 1902?

6 Which Australian played in 71 consecutive Tests from 1966 to 1976?

7 Which current player scored a century on his first-class debut in 1985?

8 Which Kent fast bowler went on the 1994-5 England tour of Australia?

9 Who scored a record seven Test centuries against New Zealand?

10 Which New Zealander lost his first 6 Tests as captain before achieving a draw at Lord's in 1994?

11 Which New Zealander dismissed Herbert Sutcliffe with the first ball of a Test series?

12 What record was broken at Clifton College in 1899?

13 Which Pakistani took four wickets in five balls against the West Indies?

14 Who in 1970 became the first player to hit five successive fours in a Test match?

15 Name the New Zealand captain who hit 239, sharing three record partnerships, to set up New Zealand's first ever win over India.

POT LUCK

1   Which Kent batsman had the nickname 'Kipper'?

2   Who was the last player to captain England while wearing glasses?

3   Name the West Indian fast bowler who in 1989 was dismissed by the first ball he faced in Test cricket.

4   Who captained Australia when they lost the 1978-79 Ashes series, without their Packer players, 5-1?

5   Who in 1921 took the best bowling analysis in an innings for Derbyshire?

6   Who was the leading run scorer in the Sunday League in 1998?

7   Which Australian wicketkeeper bowled ten overs without taking a wicket against Pakistan in 1980?

8   Who said 'The Star pay me a lot of money and they want interesting articles. They won't pay me a brass farthing to write a lot of pap. They'll find someone else.'

9   Who dismissed Don Bradman for 0 in his last Test innings at The Oval in 1948?

10 Who took 61 catches for Australia against England?

11 Which Pakistani batsman faced 15 balls from the West Indies fast bowlers with his broken arm in plaster?

12 Which country dismissed Sri Lanka for 71 in a home Test in 1994?

13 Which Essex batsman is the only England player to have been dismissed 'handled the ball' in a Test?

14 Who took 6-54 against the 1997 Australians?

15 Who took 200 first-class wickets in his first full season?

POT LUCK

1   Apart from Ray Booth which other Worcestershire wicketkeeper has made 100 dismissals in a first-class season?

2   Which Indian Test captain was known as 'The Noob'?

3   Which two Worcestershire players went on England's 1995-6 tour of South Africa?

4   Who scored a double-century on his first-class debut in 1997?

5   In which country was Dipak Patel born?

6   Name the West Indian leg-spinner who took 0-191 at Trent Bridge in 1995 and had a bowling average of 74.38 in his five Tests.

7   Which New Zealand wicketkeeper equalled a world record by making 23 dismissals in a series?

8   Who set a Test record by scoring fifty in only 28 minutes against Australia in 1895?

9   Who was the leading run scorer in the 1997 Sunday League?

10 Of whom was it said by Bob Taylor: 'He must have put more backsides on seats than any other English cricketer since Denis Compton'?

11 Name the captains in the 1978-79 series, Pakistan's first against India for 17 years.

12 Which West Indian won the 1992-93 series in Australia with a spell of seven wickets for one run?

13 Name the West Indian cousins who shared an unbroken record partnership of 274 to save the 2nd Test in 1966.

14 Of bowlers who have played for Somerset, who has taken the most first-class wickets?

15 Which current player joined Surrey from Essex?

1 Hugo Yarnold. 2 Nawab of Pataudi Jnr. 3 Graeme Hick and Richard Illingworth.
4 Mike Powell. 5 Kenya. 6 Rajindra Dhanraj. 7 Artie Dick. 8 Jack Brown. 9 Matthew Hayden.
10 Ian Botham. 11 Mushtaq Mohammad and Bishan Bedi. 12 Curtly Ambrose.
13 David Holford and Garry Sobers. 14 Tom Richardson (mainly Surrey).
15 Nadeem Shahid.

POT LUCK

1   Which Glamorgan and West Indian fast bowler was crippled when he fell out of a tree in St Vincent?

2   Which Derbyshire fielder took two catches as a sub for England in the Edgbaston Test against South Africa in 1998?

3   Who was the first England cricketer to do the Test double of 1,000 runs and 100 wickets?

4   Which Warwickshire bowler has taken 100 wickets in a first-class season most times?

5   Who was chiefly responsible for the 1980 Code of Laws?

6   Which Pakistani was the first Test player born in Kuwait?

7   Which 'Anglo-Kiwi' took 6 wickets to help beat New Zealand in 1997?

8   Which former West Indies fast bowler was paralysed in a fall from a tree in 1997?

9   Name either of the two Indian batsmen who averaged over 100 in the 1992-93 series against England.

10   When Peter Pollock was injured in his last Test, who took 6-73 to win the match then spent three days in bed with flu?

11   Which non-championship team beat Gloucestershire in the 1980 B and H Cup: Ireland, Minor Counties, Scotland?

12   Name the New Zealand opener who made a pair in his second Test, against England in 1992.

13   What individual player's feat links Trent Bridge in 1938 and 1947 and Lord's in 1939?

14   Which Indian opener batted through the entire 60 overs in a 1975 World Cup game, but scored only 36?

15   Which Glamorgan player previously represented three other counties?

Quiz 6
POT LUCK

1   Which country celebrated the centenary of Tests at the Adelaide Oval with a victory by 191 runs?

2   Which Warwickshire batsman set a record, since broken, of 17 sixes in a first-class match when batting against Lancashire at Blackpool in 1959: Rohan Kanhai, Mike Smith, Jim Stewart?

3   Which Worcestershire player went on England's 1985-6 tour of the West Indies?

4   Which Somerset player has represented Holland in the ICC Trophy?

5   Who are the only two Durham players to have scored 500 runs and taken 50 wickets in a first-class season?

6   Which New Zealander hit 9 sixes in an innings of 120 against Zimbabwe in 1996?

7   Who completed 4,000 ODI runs at Leeds in May 1988?

8   Who plays on Broad Halfpenny Down?

9   Who took over 2000 first-class wickets yet never played a Test for England: George Dennett, Tom Goddard, Charlie Parker?

10   Who took 83 wickets in 1998 in his debut season for Warwickshire?

11   Which substitute wicketkeeper conceded a record 37 byes in a Test innings in 1934?

12   Who was the last teenager before 1994 to play Test cricket for the West Indies?

13   Who has scored the highest first-class innings for Sussex?

14   Which Englishman took 38 wickets in one series and hit a century in another?

15   Which New Zealand bowler was once described as 'neither one thing nor another?'

---

1 West Indies. 2 Jim Stewart. 3 David Smith. 4 Adam Parore. 5 Anderson Cummins and Manoj Prabhakar. 6 Chris Cairns. 7 Gordon Greenidge. 8 Hambledon. 9 George Dennett. 10 Ed Giddins. 11 Frank Woolley. 12 Elquemedo Willett. 13 KS Duleepsinhji, 333. 14 Maurice Tate. 15 Bob Cunis.

POT LUCK

1   Against whom did Mike Gatting hit his only ODI century?
2   Which South African scored 142 at Lord's in 1955 after being dropped six times?
3   Which umpire's autobiography was called, 'How's That'.
4   Which Indian batsman took 5-107 in 56 overs and scored 56 and 172 not out against the West Indies in 1962?
5   Which New Zealander's nickname is Bogo?
6   Who was the first English batsman to score a century in the World Cup?
7   Which was the first country to win a Test series in Pakistan?
8   Who were the first country to win a series against South Africa after their return to Test cricket in 1992?
9   Who was Man of the Match in the 1990 NatWest Trophy final?
10 Which West Indian scored his 1,000th Test run during the 1997 series against India?
11 Which New Zealander took his 100th Test wicket in 1987 twelve years after his first?
12 Which Englishman reached a Test hundred with a six at Delhi in 1976?
13 Which Pakistani batsman had innings of 102 not out against India in both 1984 and 1989?
14 Who scored the most Test centuries (12) against Australia?
15 Which Australian opener scored 311 in almost 13 hours at Old Trafford in 1964?

1 India at Poona in 1984. 2 Roy McLean. 3 Frank Chester's. 4 Polly Umrigar. 5 John R Reid.
6 Dennis Amiss 137 at Lord's June 7, 1975. 7 Australia. 8 Australia. 9 Phil DeFreitas.
10 Curtly Ambrose. 11 Ewen Chatfield. 12 Dennis Amiss. 13 Salim Malik. 14 Jack Hobbs.
15 Bobby Simpson.

POT LUCK

1 Which country were all for 66 in 1996, the lowest innings total against South Africa?

2 Which 20-stone Australian captain was known as 'The Big Ship'?

3 Name the two Sussex seamers who dismissed South Africa for 30 in 1924.

4 Which New Zealander scored the then slowest first-class century in Australia while batting for 11 hours in a Test innings?

5 Which Australian fast bowler was banned from football for life after breaking a referee's nose?

6 Which Pakistani had his thumb broken by Dennis Lillee in his debut Test innings?

7 Who captained Australia exactly 50 times?

8 Who shared a record second wicket partnership of 285* against Minor Counties South in the B&H Cup in 1973?

9 Who was Allan Border's vice-captain in 37 Tests?

10 Why did Oxford University play their 'big' matches at the Christ Church Ground rather than the usual ground in The parks?

11 In which town did John Wisden (in partnership with George Parr) open a cricket ground?

12 Whose only two wins as captain were enough to make him the last England skipper to win an Ashes series?

13 Two non-Test playing countries competed in the 1975 World Cup, Sri Lanka was one, which was the other?

14 When did the Logan Cup become a first-class competition?

15 Who alienated parts of the East Indian population by referring to the West Indies' 'African' team?

---

1 India. 2 Warwick Armstrong. 3 Arthur Gilligan and Maurice Tate. 4 Mark Greatbatch.
5 Jeff Thomson. 6 Talat Ali. 7 Mark Taylor. 8 Gordon Greenidge and David Turner.
9 Geoff Marsh. 10 Because they couldn't take gate money at the latter. 11 Leamington Spa.
12 Mike Gatting. 13 East Africa. 14 1993/94. 15 Viv Richards.

POT LUCK

1   Who said 'Well he was the captain, but he wasn't the captain, if you know what I mean. Jack Hobbs was the captain.'

2   Who has hit most sixes in a first-class innings for Northamptonshire?

3   Which Australian bowler was an overseas player for Kent in 1984: Terry Alderman, Dave Gilbert, Jeff Thomson?

4   Who scored 230 not out in 9 hours against India in 1955, a New Zealand record at the time?

5   Which Kent allrounder has done the double of 1000 runs and 100 wickets in a first-class season most times?

6   Name the Englishman who in 1947 took a wicket with his first ball in Test cricket.

7   Which Sri Lankan player was killed in a motor cycle accident less than a year after the 1979 World Cup competition?

8   Which Pakistani took 5-46 to win the 3rd Test and the series against Zimbabwe in 1995?

9   When Australia were dismissed for 200 by the West Indies in 1984, their highest score was 36. By whom?

10   Who captained the first England team to go into a Test without a recognised spinner?

11   Which county did Lancashire beat in the 1998 NatWest semi-finals?

12   Which England cricketer scored 455 runs at 56.87 in Australia in 1970-71 and took Sunil Gavaskar's wicket the following summer.

13   Name the Indian opener who in 1995 scored 59 and 73 in only his fourth Test in four years.

14   Name the Australian cricketer who had cataracts removed in time to take 144 Test wickets?

15   Which World Cup competition first involved floodlit games?

1 Harold Larwood about Percy Chapman. 2 Roger Harper,12. 3 Terry Alderman.
4 Bert Sutcliffe. 5 Frank Woolley, 8. 6 Dick Howorth. 7 DLS de Silva, aged 23. 8 Aamir Nazir.
9 Extras. 10 Douglas Jardine in 1932-33. 11 Hampshire. 12 Brian Luckhurst. 13 Ajay Jadeja.
14 Bill O'Reilly. 15 1992.

Quiz 10
POT LUCK

1 Who said 'Fender was the type of captain who wins many battles, but never a war.'

2 Who did Surrey play in the Peter May Memorial Cup match in 1995?

3 Which West Indian played his 200th ODI at Kingston, March 1994?

4 Who was the only New Zealand bowler to concede 200 runs in a Test innings?

5 Which fielder has taken most first-class catches in a season for Worcestershire: Tom Graveney, Graeme Hick, Dick Richardson?

6 Which Australian leg-spinner set a Test record by being dismissed for five consecutive ducks in 1985?

7 Who has taken most wickets in a first-class season and career for Kent?

8 Name the bowler who began his England career in 1951, took a record number of Test wickets, and made a comeback with 5-40 in 1965.

9 Which England allrounder was booed at Trent Bridge for wanting to leave Nottinghamshire?

10 Who put on 385 with Steve Waugh against South Africa in 1997?

11 Who took 8-53 for Derbyshire before lunch on his twentieth birthday?

12 Which England bowler took 27 Test wickets in the West Indies in 1967-68 and 31 in Australia in 1970-71?

13 Which two Worcestershire players went on England's 1987-8 tour of New Zealand?

14 Name the only batsman to score 2,000 Test runs without making a century.

15 Who played Test cricket for Pakistan at the age of 44 after having played for India?

QUIZ 11

POT LUCK

1. Name the much-vaunted South African batsman who suffered at the hands of Shane Warne and averaged only 5.20 in the 1993-94 series.

2. Who in 1985-86 became the first country to win two series against Australia in the same season?

3. Which Australian bowler dismissed Len Hutton when he made his record 364 in 1938?

4. Which South African made a pair at Lord's in 1955 and two hundreds in the next Test?

5. Who took 61 catches for England against Australia?

6. How did 1965 break the pattern of Test cricket in England?

7. Who said 'Pringle is like a London bus between the wickets – all right once he has got under way.'

8. Who is the only player to have done the double of 2000 runs and 200 wickets in a first-class season?

9. Who captained Australia most times in Tests before Allan Border?

10. Which Pakistani took 5-53 on his Test debut against Zimbabwe in 1996?

11. What competition was staged at the Don Valley Stadium in 1991?

12. Name the English spinner who made his highest score with the bat in his last Test, against the West Indies in 1968?

13. Who hit the first ball of the 1994-95 Ashes series for four?

14. How was England captain Albert Neilson Hornby better known?

15. Both English openers in the 1979 World Cup were subsequently awarded OBEs. Name them?

1 Daryll Cullinan. **2** New Zealand. **3** Bill O'Reilly. **4** Jackie McGlew. **5** Ian Botham.
6 There were two separate Test series for the first time. **7** John Woodcock on Derek Pringle.
8 George Hirst, 1906. **9** Greg Chappell. **10** Shahid Nazir. **11** A floodlit cricket contest
between three counties. **12** Tony Lock. **13** Michael Slater. **14** 'Monkey'.
15 Mike Brearley and Geoff Boycott.

Quiz 12
POT LUCK

1   Which England bowler twice took 11 wickets in a match during the 1946 series against India?

2   What links Lancashire and Somerset with the B&H Cup?

3   Who scored over 100 runs in his last Test as England captain?

4   What is Gloucestershire's highest position in the Sunday League?

5   Who said 'Like Cleopatra's nose and Mistinguette's legs, that perfect left elbow alone is worth a poem.'

6   Which Pakistani scored a Test century in 74 balls in 1976?

7   Who was the first Hampshire player to do the double of 1000 runs and 100 wickets in a first-class season: Alec Kennedy, Charles Llewellyn, Jack Newman?

8   What was the name of the Trophy competed for in 1987?

9   Who said 'Cowdrey was long one of the world's greatest bats, yet had he given full play to his natural abilities he could have been even greater.'

10 Which Glamorgan batsman and captain became cricket correspondent of the 'Sunday Telegraph'?

11 Who hit the fastest fifty in 1998 Texaco Series? – it was hit off 31 balls at Headingley.

12 Who was the first New Zealand bowler to take 7 wickets in an innings against England?

13 What book links Harry Altham, John Arlott, Desmond Eagar and Roy Webber?

14 Which England wicketkeeper made 6 dismissals on his Test debut in 1994?

15 Which future Leicestershire captain made his first-class debut at 16?

1 Alec Bedser. 2 They are the only counties to win the trophy two years running.
3 Stanley Jackson. 4 Second. 5 Chris Wordsworth on Graeme Hick. 6 Majid Khan.
7 Charles Llewellyn. 8 Reliance Cup. 9 Bob Arrowsmith in 1980. 10 Tony Lewis.
11 AD Brown. 12 Lance Cairns. 13 Joint authors of the Official History of Hampshire
CCC in 1957. 14 Steve Rhodes. 15 Nigel Briers.

POT LUCK

1 Name the West Indian brothers who played Test cricket, one before and one after the War.

2 Who hit three successive 100s for Pakistan in 1982/83?

3 Which English bowler took 8-34, the best figures for a Lord's Test, and hit a hundred in the same game?

4 Which New Zealander improved his highest Test score four times in one series against England?

5 Which South African captain won all five tosses in the 1927-28 series against England?

6 Which Indian scored 642 runs at an average of 80.25 in the 1970-71 series in the West Indies?

7 How many Surrey players were taken on England's 1998-9 Test tour of Australia?

8 Which Indian made his highest score in his last Test after being hit in the chest by a Gubby Allen bouncer?

9 Which Kent and England bowler had the nickname 'Plank'?

10 Who is England's coach?

11 Who has made the highest score for Hampshire in all matches?

12 Who was the youngest player to represent Glamorgan at 16 years 99 days: Alan Lewis Jones, Tony Lewis, Javed Miandad?

13 Which English batsman averaged 61.25 against Australia in 1985 but only 9.00 in the West Indies the following winter?

14 When was the last first-class match played at Prince's?

15 Which New Zealander scored 176 and 175 in consecutive Test innings against England?

1 Cyril and Bob Christiani. 2 Zaheer Abbas. 3 Ian Botham. 4 Ian Smith. 5 Hubert 'Nummy' Deane. 6 Dilip Sardesai. 7 Five. 8 CK Nayudu. 9 Richard Ellison. 10 David Lloyd. 11 Francis Lacey, 323* v Norfolk in 1887. 12 Alan Lewis Jones. 13 Tim Robinson. 14 September 11, 12, 1878. 15 Bev Congdon.

Quiz 14
POT LUCK

1   Which England bowler took 11 wickets in a Test against New Zealand in 1969 and 12 against them in 1971?

2   How was England captain Robert George Canning better known?

3   Which Indian took 4-69 and 7-59 to beat Sri Lanka in 1994?

4   Where did Zimbabwe play its first home Test?

5   Who scored the most championship runs for Hampshire in 1998?

6   Which Englishman's name has the anagram Trying Ego?

7   Which wicket keeper captained Hampshire in 1979?

8   Who was included in an England squad in 1902 but played in fifteen Tests for South Africa?

9   Which Pakistani took 22 wickets in the three-Test series against Australia in 1982-83?

10 Which Sussex bowler has produced two volumes of poetry: Tony Buss, Vasbert Drakes, John Snow?

11 When New Zealand were struck down by a mystery virus in 1988 and forced to field five substitutes, who were their opponents?

12 What catastrophe occurred on July 29, 1825?

13 Which country in 1998 became the first to win in Durban since England in 1964?

14 Which Pakistani's last Test was his brother's first?

15 Which Hampshire cricketer had a son and a grandson who played for the county?

HAMPSHIRE

GRANDDAD · DAD · SON

1 Derek Underwood. 2 Lord Harris. 3 Anil Kumble. 4 Harare Sports Club. 5 Giles White.
6 Tony Greig. 7 Bob Stephenson. 8 Charlie 'Buck' Llewellyn. 9 Abdul Qadir. 10 John Snow.
11 India. 12 The pavilion at Lord's was burnt to the ground and many cricket records lost as
a result. 13 Pakistan. 14 Hanif Mohammad. 14 Charles Fry.

POT LUCK

1   Name the Pakistani wicketkeeper who made 104 Test dismissals from 1982 to 1990.

2   Name the West Indian pace bowler who conceded 26 no-balls on his Test debut in 1996.

3   Which Pakistani bowled 75 overs against the West Indies despite a broken bone in his hand?

4   Who said 'Chandigarh is like Milton Keynes after massive cuts in the municipal sanitation budget, but the cows are holy rather than fake.'

5   Which Australian medium pacer made his highest first-class score and maiden Test fifty during the 1998-99 series?

6   Which New Zealander hit 7 sixes against South Africa in 1953 with his head bandaged?

7   Which bowler other than Graham McKenzie played for Leicestershire and took more than 200 Test wickets?

8   Who was the first batsman to reach four 100s in ODI matches?

9   In South Africa's first ever Test against Sri Lanka, which pace bowler had Test-best figures of 4-57 on his 23rd birthday?

10   What happened in Colombo on February 17, 1996?

11   Which current Kent and England player is the son of a former Kent captain?

12   Which Northamptonshire batsman was described in 1976 as 'A bank clerk going to war'?

13   Name either of the West Indian batsmen who scored exactly 100 in the 5th Test of the 1958-59 series in India?

14   Who made five stumpings in India's first ever win over England?

15   Who said 'Boon is now completely cleanshaven – except for his moustache.'

---

1 Salim Yousuf. 2 Patterson Thompson. 3 Abdul Qadir. 4 Matthew Engel. 5 Damien Fleming. 6 Bert Sutcliffe. 7 Andy Roberts. 8 DL Amiss. 9 Brett Schultz. 10 Australia failed to turn up, Sri Lanka given a walk over. 11 Mark Ealham. 12 David Steele. 13 Collie Smith and Joe Solomon. 14 Khokar Sen. 15 Graham Dawson on David Boon.

POT LUCK

1 Which England cricketer in 1993 made a duck in his first Test innings for five years?

2 Which two Antiguans played for Somerset in 1980?

3 Which two Gloucestershire players made their Test debuts against Sri Lanka at Lord's in 1988?

4 What occurred between 1956 and 1962 at Cowes?

5 Which Indian twice reached a Test century by hitting a six?

6 Which Indian pace bowler took most Test wickets for any country in 1996?

7 Who shared a record first wicket opening stand of 311 against Scotland in the 1997 NatWest Trophy?

8 Which New Zealander gave up wicketkeeping to make his Test debut as an opening bat in 1993?

9 Which South African all-rounder averaged 98.66 with the bat in the 1996-97 home series against India?

10 Which current player joined Surrey from Warwickshire?

11 Which Maharaja scored a century against England in his maiden Test innings?

12 Which South African wicketkeeper completed 50 dismissals in only his 10th Test in 1998, breaking Dave Richardson's world record?

13 Who was Man of the Match in the 1972 Gillette Cup final?

14 Who kept wicket for England in all the 1983 World Cup matches?

15 Which West Indian was out hit wicket after a Test innings of exactly 250?

Quiz 17
POT LUCK

1 What 44 year old bowler made his ODI debut for England in 1985?

2 For which county did Northants' Raman Subba Row formerly play?

3 What is Essex's highest total: 648, 761-7, 812?

4 Which outstanding close fielder played in three Tests before presenting Sunday cricket on BBC?

5 Which Australian made his Test debut against England in 1928-29 at the age of 46?

6 Who took 3,278 first-class wickets but played in only one Test?

7 Which wicketkeeper has made the most dismissals in a first-class season and career for Lancashire?

8 Who has taken most first-class wickets for Essex?

9 Which New Zealander batted for over an hour without scoring against England in 1958 and averaged only 10.06 in his eight Tests?

10 When did Gloucestershire win the Benson and Hedges Cup?

11 Who was the first England player born in the West Indies?

12 Which Englishman dismissed Garry Sobers first ball in successive Test innings in which he bowled to him?

13 For whom did GP Bilby and N Puna make their Test debuts in 1966?

14 Which New Zealand opener took 239 balls to reach fifty against England in 1997?

15 Who was the last Middlesex bowler to take 100 wickets in a first-class season?

POT LUCK

1   Who has played the most first-class matches for Derbyshire: Kim Barnett, Derek Morgan, Denis Smith?

2   Zimbabwe's first partnership in Test cricket was worth exactly 100, shared by Grant Flower and which other opener?

3   Which Middlesex batsman scored 184 for England against Australia?

4   Which West Indian pace bowler has a bullet hole in his cheek, apparently the result of a changing room prank?

5   What feat did David Lloyd achieve at Trent Bridge in 1974?

6   When Kapil Dev took his 432nd Test wicket, a new record, who took the catch?

7   Where is the Arnos Vale Test match venue?

8   Which overseas player scored over 2000 runs for Derbyshire in 1991?

9   Which current player made his debut for Kent 16 years after his first-class debut?

10 Who has taken most wickets in a first-class season and career for Surrey?

11 Who was England's first professional captain?

12 Name the two seamers who dismissed India for 58 at Old Trafford in 1952.

13 Which current player has the nickname 'The Cat'?

14 Which Derbyshire player has played over 100 ODIs for England?

13 Phil Tufnell. 14 Phillip DeFreitas.
11 James Lillywhite in 1877 (not Len Hutton in 1952). 12 Alec Bedser and Fred Trueman.
8 Mohammad Azharuddin. 9 Alan Wells. 10 Tom Richardson, 252 and 1775.
batsman to carry his bat through the full 50 overs. 6 Sanjay Manjrekar. 7 St Vincent.
1 Derek Morgan. 2 Kevin Arnott. 3 Denis Compton. 4 Winston Benjamin. 5 He was the first

POT LUCK

1   Who was the last Somerset bowler to take 100 wickets in a first-class season?

2   What makes 1899 important in Worcestershire's history?

3   Who was the first allrounder ever to score 1000 runs and take 200 wickets in a first-class season: Bernard Bosanquet, Frank Tarrant, Albert Trott?

4   Why did James Lillywhite and Dave Gregory become significant figures in cricket history in 1877?

5   Which county did Chris Balderstone come from?

6   Name the fast and fiery West Indian bowler who was sent home from the 1958-59 tour of India for bowling beamers.

7   Which Pakistani averaged 108.00 with the bat against India in 1952-53 and took 5-37 and 6-42 to win Pakistan's first ever Test against New Zealand?

8   Who said 'He is a temperamental cricketer, and temperamental cricketers depend on the stars being right for them.'

9   Which Indian batsman scored his maiden Test fifty in the same Test as he achieved his best Test bowling figures of 6-132?

10 Which New Zealander dismissed Len Hutton in 1949 with his first ball in a Lord's Test?

11 Which county has played major matches at both Lloyds Bank ground and Midland Bank ground since 1946?

12 Name the Australian cricketer suspended for throwing his bat in the same Test in which he made his 300th Test dismissal.

13 Which Australian Test player represented Somerset from 1971 to 1972?

14 Who was the opening batsman who left Nottinghamshire at the end of the 1998 season to join Worcestershire?

15 Who was the first Indian pace bowler to take 7 wickets in a Test innings?

1 Andy Caddick, 1998. 2 The County joined the Championship. 3 Albert Trott. 4 They were the captains in the first ever Test. 5 Yorkshire. 6 Roy Gilchrist. 7 Zulfiqar Ahmed. 8 Alan Ross in 1963. 9 Manoj Prabhakar. 10 Tom Burtt. 11 Kent. 12 Ian Healy. 13 Kerry O'Keefe. 14 Paul Pollard. 15 Ladha Amar Singh.

POT LUCK

1 Name either of the New Zealand openers who both scored hundreds in the 2nd Test in Australia in 1973-74.

2 How many grounds in Colombo have staged Test Matches?

3 Which future Test cricket captain played rugby for England against Wales in 1956?

4 Where is the Fenner Trophy staged?

5 Which country dismissed England for 45, their lowest ever total?

6 Name the flamboyant West Indian opening batsman who played in his first Test in 1991 and his second in 1998, both against England.

7 Who has captained Derbyshire for the most seasons?

8 Which Pakistani scored a Test double century in 241 balls in 1982?

9 Who took a hat-trick in the B and H semi-final to help Gloucestershire into that final?

10 Who has taken 100 wickets in a first-class season most times?

11 When England won by two wickets in Durban in 1948, name either of the batsmen who ran a leg bye off the very last ball.

12 Which Kent and England bowler had the nickname 'Deadly'?

13 Which New Zealander took exactly 100 Test wickets, the last 39 with a displaced vertebra?

14 Name the 19-year-old New Zealander who top-scored in each innings, including a century in the first, against South Africa in 1932.

15 Which country dismissed New Zealand for 70 in 1955?

POT LUCK

1 Who was the first bowler to take 70 Test wickets in a calendar year?

2 Which county did Adrian Pierson come from?

3 Who said 'No Lancashire player has been so abundantly Lancashire, no stumper has been more nimble and certainly none more vocal.'

4 Who was the last Glamorgan player to do the double of 1000 runs and 100 wickets in a first-class season: Geoff Holmes, John Steele, Peter Walker?

5 Which Australian completed 3,000 ODI runs v India in March 1990?

6 Who was head groundsman at Kennington Oval for 20 years, ending in 1965?

7 Which Australian took a record 31 wickets in the 1991-92 series against India?

8 Which English spinner bowled 87 overs without taking a wicket in the 1998 series against South Africa but still went to Australia the following winter?

9 Of the bowlers who took 8 wickets in a Test innings, who conceded the most runs (143)?

10 Who represented Pakistan International Airways from 1986-8 while playing for Sussex: Rehan Alikhan, Imran Khan, Javed Miandad?

11 Which county other than Leicestershire did Gordon Parsons play for?

12 Which Pakistani cricketer carried his bat for 188 against India in 1999?

13 Who said 'Taylor could do no wrong – again. He should try walking on water.'

14 Which South African was Essex's overseas player in 1987: Ken McEwan, Hugh Page, Garth Le Roux?

15 Which Pakistan Test player has taken the most first-class wickets for Northamptonshire?

POT LUCK

1   How many Test runs did Dennis Lillee score with his notorious metal bat?

2   How many Somerset batsmen scored 750 or more runs in the championship in 1998?

3   How did the World Cup 1983 fixtures differ fundamentally from those of 1975 and 1979?

4   Jeff Dujon made 272 Test dismissals. How many were stumpings?

5   Who was the last Sussex batsman to score 1000 first-class runs in his debut season?

6   How was England captain Henry Dudley Gresham Leveson-Gower better known?

7   South Africa were the first country to lose a Test by over 500 runs. Against which country?

8   Which English batsman, now a Test umpire, took 22 Tests and almost ten years to score his 1,000th Test run?

9   Name the two seamers who dismissed India for 42 at Lord's in 1974.

10 Name the Australian leg-spinner who took only 6 wickets in the 1972-73 series in the West Indies, all in the same Test, which Australia won.

11 England played two Test series at the same time in 1929-30. In which countries?

12 Who was called up by England for The Oval Test against Sri Lanka and allowed to return to Cardiff during the match to attend the birth of his first child?

13 Why was the inclusion of HW Dalton on the tour to Australia in 1954/5 a new departure?

14 Where is the Amblecote Ground, used for 61 first-class matches?

15 What was without precedent concerning the Man of the Match award in the New Zealand v West Indies game at Georgetown in April 1996?

MATERNITY

---

1 3. 2 None. 3 The teams played each other twice, rather than once. 4 5. 5 Jamie Hall, 1990.
6 'Shrimp'. 7 Australia. 8 Peter Willey. 9 Geoff Arnold and Chris Old. 10 Kerry O'Keeffe.
11 New Zealand and the West Indies. 12 John Jameson. 13 The First time a masseur had been sent with an England team. 14 Stourbridge. 15 It was given to the whole New Zealand team.

POT LUCK

1 Who was the last man to play cricket and soccer for England?

2 Who was the last Somerset batsman to score 2000 runs in a first-class season?

3 Who was the first England wicketkeeper to do the Test double of 1,000 runs and 100 dismissals?

4 When did Yorkshire finish bottom of the championship for the first time?

5 When did Gloucestershire win the Gillette/NatWest competition?

6 Which Pakistani batsman averaged 103.00 in the 1989-90 series against India?

7 Who was Man of the Match when Warwickshire won the 1993 NatWest Trophy final?

8 What remarkable event took place on November 29, 1996?

9 Which Indian scored 774 runs at an average of 154.80 in the 1970-71 series in the West Indies?

10 Who holds the records for the highest innings for Hampshire in all three one-day competitions?

11 Who was the oldest man to score a maiden Test century?

12 Which England bowler took 7-34 against the West Indies in 1954 and 7-44 against them in 1957?

13 Name the England bowler who was twice on a hat-trick in taking 4 wickets for 7 runs against New Zealand in 1955.

14 Name the England batsman who was Garry Sobers' first Test victim and later wrote his biography.

15 Who was originally signed as Yorkshire's first overseas player?

1 Arthur Milton. 2 Jimmy Cook, 1991. 3 Godfrey Evans. 4 1983. 5 1973.
6 Shoaib Mohammad. 7 Asif Din. 8 The Derbyshire cricketer, Jim Hutchinson, celebrated his
100th birthday. 9 Sunil Gavaskar. 10 Gordon Greenidge. 11 AW 'Dave' Nourse (42).
12 Trevor Bailey. 13 Bob Appleyard. 14 Trevor Bailey. 15 Craig McDermott.

POT LUCK

1 Which Indian cricketer didn't win one of his first 20 Tests as captain before breaking the duck in England?

2 Which England captain made his only Test century while facing a kind of Bodyline bowling?

3 Who scored 177 against Glamorgan in the 1975 Gillette Cup: Gordon Greenidge, Barry Richards, David Turner?

4 Name the Englishman who in 1991 took a wicket with his first ball in Test cricket.

5 Name the Australian-born batsman who broke a finger on his Test debut for England in 1995.

6 Which two Sussex players still hold the record for the highest 7th wicket partnership in the county championship?

7 Who shared with England's Bill Edrich the record among Test players of having five wives?

8 Who was the first player born in East Pakistan to play in a Test match?

9 What was illegal about Courtney Walsh's dismissal of Salim Jaffer at Sharjah in November 1986?

10 How many times have Yorkshire won three or more championships in succession?

11 For which county did Northamptonshire's Roy Virgin formerly play?

12 Which ground witnessed the first tied Test?

13 Who took a record number of Test wickets despite being known as 'Irongloves' in his first series because the ball kept bouncing out of his hands?

14 Which Pakistani batsman averaged only 7.66 with the bat in the 1990-91 series against the West Indies?

15 Which former Test ground is now a railway station?

15 Old Wanderers, Johannesburg.
11 Somerset. 12 Woolloongabba, Brisbane. 13 Rod Marsh. 14 Javed Miandad.
already bowled nine overs and was in the process of a tenth. 10 Five.
6 KS Ranjitsinhji and William Newham, 344. 7 Hugh Tayfield. 8 Niaz Ahmed. 9 Walsh had
1 Kapil Dev. 2 Douglas Jardine. 3 Gordon Greenidge. 4 Richard Illingworth. 5 Jason Gallian.

POT LUCK

1 Which Pakistani batsman hit two double centuries against India?

2 Which Englishman batted for over 27 hours against West Indies fast bowling in the 1995 series ?

3 Which cricketer with a seasonal name played for both England and Australia?

4 Which South African had a gap of 14 years in his Test career?

5 Which Pakistani batsman hit two consecutive centuries in the 1989-90 series against India?

6 Who captained Harold Larwood for Notts as well as for England?

7 Which wicketkeeper took a record 10 catches in a Test in 1980?

8 Who has scored most runs off a first-class over for Sussex?

9 Which cricket journalist and broadcaster was the first batsman to score a fifty for a minor county against Hampshire in the Gillette Cup: Henry Blofeld, Brian Johnston, Christopher Martin-Jenkins?

10 Name the bespectacled Indian spinner who took 114 Test wickets, the first when he was 32.

11 Who was Yorkshire's first overseas player?

12 Name the fast bowler who partnered Harold Larwood for Nottinghamshire and on the Bodyline tour of 1932-33.

13 Which South African wicketkeeper's 120th Test dismissal was his first stumping?

14 Which Englishman made his Test debut in Perth in 1998/9?

15 Name the 20-year-old Indian student who scored his only Test century on his debut, at Old Trafford in 1959.

Quiz 26
POT LUCK

1 Who, in his last season, led Middlesex to the championship in 1920?

2 Who led Middlesex to the championship in 1947: Bill Edrich, George Mann, Walter Robins?

3 Whose Test career stretched from 1931 to 1953, including a tour of Australia as captain?

4 Of the batsmen who played in ten Tests, Don Bradman had the best average (99.94). Which New Zealander lies in second place with 65.72?

5 Who reached 4,000 runs in LOI matches whilst batting in the World Cup on October 13, 1987?

6 Which England captain won the toss in 26 Tests in the 1950s and '60s?

7 Which South African Test batsman scored 32 League goals for Charlton Athletic?

8 Name the England captain who won a boxing gold medal at the 1908 Olympic Games.

9 Who was the leading run scorer for India in the 1996 World Cup?

10 Who was Man of the Match when Warwickshire won the 1968 Gillette Cup final?

11 Who headed Hampshire's bowling averages in 1998?

12 How did John Arlott title the biography he wrote of Freddie Trueman?

13 Which English batsman, who hadn't yet made a Test century, was left marooned on 96 when rioting stopped play at Karachi in 1969?

14 Which non-championship team beat Middlesex in the 1997 B and H Cup: Cornwall, Devon, Ireland?

15 Who had to eat his words after intending to make the West Indies 'grovel'?

POT LUCK

1 Why was the third final of the B&H Cup in 1979/8 cancelled?

2 When Ian Botham scored his famous unbeaten 149 not out at Headingley in 1981, whose bat was he using?

3 Name the batsman who top-scored in each innings of a Test in the West Indies and never played for England again.

4 Who was the last Northamptonshire player to score 1000 first-class runs in his debut season?

5 When Colin Cowdrey won his 92nd cap in 1967, whose world record did he break?

6 Which was the title of Don Mosey's autobiography?

7 Which Zimbabwean scored an unbeaten 203 against New Zealand in 1997?

8 Who held the record for the most first-class dismissals by a wicketkeeper until Bob Taylor broke it?

9 Which English wicketkeeper was arrested in New Zealand for causing an affray?

10 Who said 'He charmed the crowds by the way he used to wave his bat. He just captivated them'.

11 Which left-arm spinner lost his bowling after taking 65 first-class wickets in 1995: Andy Afford, Richard Bates, Jimmy Hindson?

12 Which New Zealander's maiden Test century took less than 90 minutes and was completed with a six?

13 Who set a record of 917 in a Sunday League season in 1991?

14 Who was the first leg spinner to take 4 wkts in an innings in ODI matches – at Adelaide in December 1981?

15 Which spinner took 8 wickets to help New Zealand beat South Africa in 1994?

15 Matthew Hart.
Compton. 11 Jimmy Hindson. 12 Bruce Taylor. 13 Tom Moody. 14 Wasim Raja for Pakistan.
7 Guy Whittall. 8 John Murray, 1527. 9 Ted Pooley in 1876/7. 10 Colin Cowdrey on Denis
3 David Smith. 4 Brian Crump, 1960. 5 Godfrey Evans. 6 The Alderman's Tale.
1 Because West Indies had already beaten England in the first two. 2 Graham Gooch.

POT LUCK

1   Why did the result of the World Cup match at Trent Bridge on June 9 1983 cause a sensation?

2   Whose selection for the 1968-9 England tour of South Africa led to the cancellation of that tour and ultimately to the ban on South Africa from Test cricket?

3   Why was January 1928 significant in the career of Don Bradman?

4   Who said 'But Bill was a popular cricketer not so much for his successes as for his repeated triumphs over prejudice and adversity.'

5   Which Australian Test player represented Somerset from 1968 to 1969?

6   Who was the last white player to represent the West Indies in a Test?

7   Which New Zealand opener made an unbeaten 267 in 10 hours against Sri Lanka in 1997?

8   For which Australian state did Michael Bevan make his maiden first-class century?

9   Name the England batsman who was run out when Colin Bland rolled the ball under his feet in 1965.

10 Which Kent and England bowler had the nickname 'Picca'?

11 Who said 'Broad's reaction to dismissal has long since ceased to bear any guide to its authenticity.'

12 Which New Zealander was hit for 21 in an over by Sri Lanka's Asanka Gurusinha in 1991?

13 Name the slow left-armer who took 9 wickets to set up New Zealand's first win in India.

14 Which England captain made his highest Test score of 99 in 1947?

14 Norman Yardley.
10 Graham Dilley. **11** Alan Lee in February 1988. **12** Chris Cairns. **13** Hedley Howarth.
5 Greg Chappell. **6** Geoff Greenidge, in 1973. **7** Bryan Young. **8** South Australia. **9** Jim Parks.
2 Basil D'Oliveira. **3** He recorded his first Test century. **4** Ralph Barker on Bill Edrich.
1 Zimbabwe beat Australia – the first time a non-Test country had beaten a Test team.

POT LUCK

1 Which great England batsman played Test cricket with one arm shorter than the other after breaking it during the last War?

2 Who was the youngest player to represent England in the 1979 World Cup?

3 Who went with the 1928/9 side to Australia, but was sent home without appearing in a match?

4 Why was Garry Sobers first three figure innings in Test cricket completely outstanding?

5 Which country were all for 75 in 1950 but still beat South Africa by 5 wickets?

6 Which Glamorgan batsman became a government minister in Guyana?

7 Who said after being hit on the head by Dennis Lillee: 'No good hitting me there, mate. Nothing to damage'?

8 Which Indian wicketkeeper scored a century while opening the batting against the West Indies in 1967?

9 Who was the only man to play Test cricket in five different decades?

10 Which Middlesex batsman scored 173 for England against Australia?

11 Who was Man of the Match when Warwickshire won the 1966 Gillette Cup final?

12 Where on 'The Park' did Derbyshire play home games between 1923 and 1986?

13 Who made 46 stumpings in Test cricket, the record for an England wicketkeeper?

14 Which New Zealander improved his Test best bowling figures in three successive Tests in 1992?

15 Which two batsmen shared a stand of 369 against New Zealand at Headingley in 1965?

Quiz 30
POT LUCK

1 When Jim Laker took his 19 wickets at Old Trafford in 1956, which 6' 5" close fielder held five catches in his last Test?

2 Name the lionhearted English fast bowler of the 1890s who took 5 wickets in an innings 11 times in his 14 Tests.

3 How many matches were played in the 1992 competition, 33, 39, 45 or 49?

4 What unique bowling feat took place at Headingley in July 1932?

5 Which Worcestershire player has done the double of 1000 runs and 100 wickets in a first-class season most times: Ted Arnold, Martin Horton, Ray Howorth?

6 When Ken Wadsworth made his 52nd Test dismissal in 1973, whose national record did he break?

7 Which batsman nearly died after being hit by a ball from Bob Willis at the Adelaide Oval in 1979?

8 Which Worcestershire wicketkeeper was the last to make 100 dismissals in a first-class season?

9 Which Nottinghamshire spinner toured Zimbabwe with England A in 1989-90 but never played a Test?

10 Who hit the record of 16 sixes in a first-class innings against Glamorgan at Abergavenny in 1995?

11 Which Pakistani batsman averaged 70.42 in his first 21 Tests?

12 Who scored 160 on his Sunday League debut for Worcestershire?

13 On what ground did Brian Lara score his record 501*?

14 Which Indian batsman was out hit wicket for 96 in the second innings of a Test after making a century in the first?

15 Which Zimbabwean took his 50th Test wicket in only his 11th Test?

15 Heath Streak.

10 Andrew Symonds. 11 Javed Miandad. 12 Tom Moody. 13 Edgbaston. 14 Chandu Borde.

5 Ted Arnold. 6 Artie Dick. 7 Rick Darling. 8 Roy Booth. 9 Andy Afford.

1 Alan Oakman. 2 Tom Richardson. 3 39. 4 H Verity took 10 wkts for 10 runs.

WORLD CUP CRICKET

QUIZ 1

WORLD CUP CRICKET

1   For which team did Kevin Arnott make his Cup debut in 1987?

2   What record was performed at New Plymouth on Feb 23, 1992?

3   Who took three wickets in seven balls for Zimbabwe v West Indies at Hyderabad on Feb 16 1996?

4   Which two Worcester batsmen added 149 for the 3rd wicket at Edgbaston June 7 1975?

5   Of the eight 1979 captains, which was the only specialist wicketkeeper?

6   Which Somerset bowler took five wickets on his home ground in a 1985 cup game?

7   Name the umpire whose 100th LOI match was at Ahmedabad on October 27 1987?

8   Which former Australian Test player hit the winning run for South Africa in the latter's first ever cup game?

9   Who played his 200th LOI match for India at Cuttack on February 18 1996?

10 Name the three brothers who represented New Zealand in 1975?

11 Two countries fielded unchanged sides throughout the 1979 cup – which two?

12 Who conceded 105 runs off his 12 overs in the 1985 cup?

13 Who was run out off his first ball on his Australian debut at Chandigarh on October 27 1987?

14 Who captured his 150th LOI wicket at Hobart on Feb 27 1992?

15 Which two brothers, opening the batting were both run out v Sri Lanka at Colombo Feb 21 1996?

1 Zimbabwe. 2 Both teams – Sri Lanka and Zimbabwe totalled over 300. 3 Paul Strang.
4 Glenn Turner and John Parker – for New Zealand. 5 BM Mauricette (Canada). 6 Viv Marks took
5-39 v Sri Lanka. 7 Dicky Bird. 8 Keppler Wessels. 9 M Azharuddin. 10 BG, DR and RJ Hadlee.
11 India and West Indies. 12 Martin Snedden playing for New Zealand v England at The Oval.
13 Mike Veletta. 14 Wasim Akram (Pakistan). 15 Andy and Grant Flower.

Quiz 2

WORLD CUP CRICKET

1   Which two Sri Lankan batsmen retired hurt at The Oval on June 11 1975 and were taken to St Thomas's Hospital?

2   Two Somerset players represented West Indies in the 1979 cup, one was Viv Richards, name the other?

3   Who hit 175 not out, going in at no.6 at Tunbridge Wells on June 18 1983?

4   Who, in 1987, achieved the first World Cup hat-trick?

5   Who headed England's bowling averages in the 1992 cup?

6   The Kenya v Zimbabwe 1996 game at Patna was started twice, due to rain, what change did Zimbabwe make for the second game?

7   Which spinner returned figures of 12-8-6-1 at Headingley on June 11 1975?

8   Who was West Indies oldest player in the 1979 cup series?

9   England used 12 men in the 1983 cup, but one player made a solitary appearance. Name him?

10   Who was the 'Little Master' who hit 103* at Nagpur in 1987?

11   Which country reached the semi-finals in the first five cups?

12   What record did Mark Taylor achieve v India at Bombay in 1996?

13   Who kept wicket for England in all their 1975 matches?

14   In the 1979 series, Gavaskar's opening partner was the son of an Indian Test cricketer, who was he?

15   New Zealand included two keepers in their 1983 squad, name them?

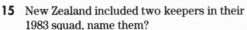
ST. THOMAS'S HOSPITAL

---

1 S Wettimuny and D Mendis. 2 Joel Garner. 3 Kapil Dev. 4 Chetan Sharma for India v New Zealand.
5 Dermot Reeve, avge 15.75. 6 In the first they won the toss and chose to bat, in the second they
chose to field. 7 Bishen Bedi for India v East Africa. 8 Deryck Murray born 20.5.1943.
9 Norman Cowans of Middlesex. 10 Sunil Gavaskar. 11 England. 12 He hit a century, having also
scored one in the preceding game. 13 Alan Knott. 14 AD Gaekwad. 15 Warren Lees and Ian Smith.

WORLD CUP CRICKET

1   Who completed 4,000 LOI runs for Pakistan at Hyderabad in 1987?

2   Who made the highest score and captained his side in the 1992 Final?

3   Why was West Indies all out total of 93 at Pune in 1996 so sensational?

4   Which Australian bowler dismissed the first five England batsmen for single figures at Headingley in 1975?

5   For which county did the 1979 Indian captain play?

6   Which Pakistan batsman arrived in England for the 1985 cup holding the world 1st wkt record partnership?

7   England required 91 off the final 10 overs to beat West Indies at Gujranwala in 1987, which batsman made 67 to win the game?

8   Who coached the 1992 Zimbabwe Cup team?

9   What did Richie Richardson say in a press statement after hitting 97 v Australia at Jaipur in 1996?

10 Who captained West Indies to victory in all five 1975 games?

11 Which 1979 Indian player gained a blue at Cambridge?

12 Three 1983 West Indies players appeared for Hampshire, one was Gordon Greenidge, who were the others?

13 Who hit a new World Cup record score v Sri Lanka at Karachi on October 15 1987?

14 Who was the oldest member of the 1992 England squad?

15 How many matches did West Indies win in the 1996 cup?

WORLD CUP CRICKET

1 How much money did the 1975 Cup winners receive, £25,000, £8,000, £4,000?

2 Name the two brothers-in-law in the 1979 Indian squad.

3 For which English county did DAG Fletcher of Zimbabwe play?

4 Who hit 50 off 51 balls on his debut for West Indies at Lahore on October 16 1987?

5 One county supplied three players for the 1992 England squad, which one?

6 Which country was used for World Cup games for the first time in 1996?

7 Which famous player was originally selected for the 1975 West Indies squad, but did not take part?

8 Only one cricketer surnamed Chappell took part in the 1979 series – who was he?

9 Which South African Test player appeared in the 1983 Cup?

10 When England opposed Sri Lanka on October 17 1987, one Notts player was dropped and replaced by another. Name them?

11 Only New Zealand did not use all their 14 1992 cup squad. Who was the unlucky player?

12 Who was the only 1996 UAE player with first-class experience?

13 Who managed England in 1975?

14 Which match was totally washed out in the 1979 cup?

15 Who was the only captain to lead his side in all the first three World Cup competitions?

Quiz 5
WORLD CUP CRICKET

1   Who was the first English batsman to score a century in the World Cup?

2   Both English openers in the 1979 Cup were subsequently awarded OBEs. Name them?

3   How did the 1983 fixtures differ fundamentally from those of 1975 and 1979?

4   What was the name of the Trophy competed for in 1987?

5   How many matches were played in the 1992 competition, 33, 39, 45 or 49?

6   Who was the leading run scorer for India in the 1996 cup?

7   Two non-Test playing countries competed in the 1975 cup, Sri Lanka was one, which was the other?

8   Who was the youngest player to represent England in the 1979 cup?

9   Who kept wicket for England in all the 1983 matches?

10 Who reached 4,000 runs in LOI matches whilst batting in the World Cup on October 13, 1987?

11 Which World Cup Competition first involved floodlit games?

12 What happened in Colombo on February 17, 1996?

13 Which Indian opener batted through the entire 60 overs in a 1975 cup game, but scored only 36?

14 Which Sri Lankan 1979 player was killed in a motor cycle accident less than a year after the competition?

15 Why did the result on June 9 1983 of the match at Trent Bridge cause a sensation?

---

1 Dennis Amiss 137 at Lord's June 7, 1975. 2 Mike Brearley and Geoff Boycott. 3 The teams played each other twice, rather than once. 4 Reliance Cup. 5 39. 6 Sachin Tendulkar with 523 runs. 7 East Africa. 8 David Gower, born 1.4.1957. 9 Ian Gould. 10 Allan Border. 11 1992. 12 Australia failed to turn up, Sri Lanka given a walk over. 13 Sunil Gavaskar v England at Lord's. 14 D.L.S.de Silva, aged 23. 15 Zimbabwe beat Australia – the first time a non-Test country had beaten a Test team.

QUIZ 6
WORLD CUP CRICKET

1   Who was the first player to reach 1,000 World Cup runs?

2   Which 1992 Pakistan player spent the preceding summer with Hampshire?

3   Who created a new individual batting record at Rawalpindi on Feb 15 1996?

4   Who was the 1975 cricketer of the series?

5   Which was the only team to score more than 1,000 runs in the 1979 series?

6   Why were Zimbabwe chosen to take part in the 1985 Cup?

7   Whose final over in the 1987 semi-final was a wicket maiden?

8   Two Pringles played in the 1992 Cup, one was Derek of England, who was the other?

9   Which former Warwickshire player represented New Zealand in the 1996 World Cup?

10 The 1975 final saw the first three out of four Australian batsmen run out, who was the fielder involved in each dismissal?

11 Who scored most runs in the 1979 Cup?

12 Greg Chappell was selected for the 1985 Australian squad, but did not play, why dot?

13 Who stumped Boon, whilst acting as temporary keeper for Pakistan in the 1987 semi-final?

14 Which two countries staged the 1992 cup?

15 Why did India fail to complete their innings v Sri Lanka in the 1996 semi-final?

WORLD CUP CRICKET

1   Which two Warwickshire batsmen opened England's innings in the first 1975 cup match?

2   Who took most wickets in the 1979 cup?

3   Name the 1983 Indian player whose father played Test cricket?

4   Who kept wicket in the 1987 cup matches for Australia?

5   Who was the only ever present player for England in both 1987 and 1992 cup matches?

6   Only one country failed to obtain at least one Man of the Match award in 1996. Name the country?

7   Who captained England in the 1975 cup matches?

8   Why were Sri Lanka and Canada chosen to take part in the 1979 cup?

9   Name the 1983 Pakistan player whose father played Test cricket?

10   What were the venues for the two 1987 semi-finals?

11   How many overs were allotted to each side in the first three cup series?

12   Which two England players gained Man of the Match awards in the 1996 cup?

13   Who was the only England player to appear in both the 1975 and 1979 cup?

14   Which English batsman took twice as many wickets as he scored runs v Australia at Lord's on June 9 1979?

15   Who was injured during the 1979 Lord's Final when the mob invaded the ground and had his leg put in plaster as a result?

1 John Jameson and Dennis Amiss. 2 Mike Hendrick(England). 3 Mohinder Amarnath.
4 GC Dyer. 5 Phil DeFreitas. 6 Holland. 7 Mike Denness. 8 They were the finalists in the ICC
Trophy that year. 9 Mudassar Nazar. 10 Gaddafi Stadium, Lahore and Wankhede Stadium,
Bombay. 11 60. 12 Graeme Hick and Neil Smith. 13 Chris Old. 14 Geoff Boycott took 2
wickets, but only scored a single. 15 Michael Holding.

WORLD CUP CRICKET

1   Who gained the Man of the Match award in the 1987 final?

2   Two English players each gained two Man of Match awards in the 1992 cup, who were they?

3   Three 1992 Australians reappeared in 1996, two were Healy and McDermott, who was the third?

4   Who were the two Sussex players in the 1975 England squad?

5   Who took 4 wickets in 8 balls for England v Pakistan at Headingley in 1979?

6   Who was called up to captain Australia in a vital match v India in 1983?

7   Who scored the most runs in the 1987 cup?

8   Name the only Indian to gain a Man of the Match award in 1992?

9   Who was co-opted into the Australian squad when McDermott was injured in the 1996 cup, but did not in fact play in a match?

10 The oldest player in the England 1975 squad was a fast bowler. Who was he?

11 Who hit 16 off the first over, bowled by Hogg, of the match Australia v Canada at Edgbaston in 1979?

12 Who was the substitute who brilliantly caught out Coney in the New Zealand v Sri Lanka match of 1983?

13 Who was the only batsman to hit two hundreds in the 1987 cup?

14 Who was the only player to gain three Man of the Match awards in the 1992 cup?

15 Ten Sri Lankan players sppeared in every match in 1996, who shared the eleventh place with GP Wickramasinghe?

WORLD CUP CRICKET

1   Australia fielded the same ten men in every game in 1975, the eleventh place was split between Gilmour and who else?

2   Which match resulted in the only win of the 1979 cup by a non-Test team against a Test team?

3   The oldest player in the 1983 competition played at Taunton on his birthday, June 11, who was he?

4   Only two bowlers took more than 15 wickets in the 1987 cup. Name them?

5   In the 1992 cup the two 'veterans' (both born in the 1950s), added 137 for the 3rd Pakistani wicket in the Final, who were they?

6   Three countries were used for the 1996, but only one team played in all three. Name it?

7   Who were the two brothers in Pakistan's 1975 squad?

8   Who gained the Man of the Match award in the 1979 Final?

9   Which batsman, who was famous for his fielding, was part of the 1985 England squad, but was never picked for a match?

10 Who, in the first 1987 match at Hyderabad, hit his 9th successive fifty in LOI matches?

11 Who was the only player over 40 in the 1992 South African squad?

12 Who presented the 1996 Trophy to the winning captain?

13 Asif Iqbal led Pakistan in the first 1975 game, who captained the side in the remaining matches?

14 Who kept wicket for the 1979 Australians?

15 Why was the England v New Zealand match on June 15 1983 particularly notable?

England for the first time.
12 Pakistan PM Benazir Bhutto. 13 Majid J Khan. 14 KJ Wright. 15 New Zealand beat
Mohammad. 8 Viv Richards. 9 Derek Randall. 10 Javed Miandad. 11 Omar Henry.
and Imran Khan. 5 Imran Khan and Javed Miandad. 6 Sri Lanka. 7 Sadiq and Mushtaq
1 Ashley Mallett. 2 Sri Lanka beat India at Old Trafford. 3 DS de Silva. 4 Craig McDermott

Quiz 10
WORLD CUP CRICKET

1   Whose 'slow medium dobbers' dismissed Gooch, Gatting and Pringle at Gujranwsla on October 9, 1987?

2   Which New Zealand player of 1992 had a father playing in the 1975 cup?

3   Who hit a century in the 1996 Finsl?

4   Warwickshire had three players in the 1975 West Indies' squad Deryck Murray and Rohan Kanhai were two, name the third?

5   Which member of the 1979 Australian squad never played Test cricket?

6   Who in 1983'hit Pakistan's first ever World Cup hundred?

7   Who had the best batting average in the 1987 series?

8   Which teenager represented New Zealand in the 1992 cup?

9   In which of the six Finals did the side batting second win?

10 How many members of the 1975 Australian cup squad played in 1979?

11 Which team did Canada surprisingly beat in the ICC Trophy to qualify for the 1979 World Cup?

12 Which Windward Islander bowler produced the best ever World Cup bowling figures?

13 No less than four Indians exceeded 50 v Australia at Delhi on October 22 1987. Name two?

14 For the 1992 Final England dropped one South African born player in favour of another, who was involved?

15 Who was the only player to gain four Man of the Match awards in 1996?

WORLD CUP CRICKET

1   Three Australians of 1975 also played in 1983, name two of them?

2   Who was the England physio for the 1979'squad?

3   Which two West Indian batsman created a new partnership record of 195 v Zimbabwe at Worcester in 1985?

4   Which Irish passport holder represented Zimbabwe in the 1987 cup?

5   Which famous Pakistani fast bowler failed a fitness test just prior to the 1992 World Cup competition?

6   156) Who was the match referee in the Indis v Sri Lanka 1996 semi-final – he was called upon to make a major decision?

7   Who was the first bowler to take five wickets in an innings in World Cup cricket?

8   Which Middlesex batsman was in the 1979 England squad, but did not play in any matches?

9   Who was the leading wicket-taker in the 1985 cup?

10 In 1987 England picked four wicketkeepers for their overseas teams, Downton, French, Russell and Richards, which one played in the World Cup?

11 Who coached the 1992 Australians – a former Test captain?

12 Which firm sponsored the 1996 World Cup?

13 Who hit 50 off 50 balls for England v India in 1975?

14 Which famous fast bowler was in the 1979 West Indies squad, but was not picked for any match?

15 Which 1983 England player had a brother in the 1983 FA Cup?'

1 Rodney Marsh, Dennis Lillee, Jeff Thomson. 2 Bernard Thomas. 3 Gordon Greenidge and Larry Gomes. 4 Kevin Curran. 5 Waqar Younis. 6 Clive Lloyd. 7 Dennis Lillee v Pakistan in 1975. 8 Mike Gatting. 9 Roger Binny. 10 Paul Downton. 11 Bobby Simpson. 12 Wills. 13 Chris Old. 14 Malcolm Marshall. 15 Mike Gatting.

Quiz 12
WORLD CUP CRICKET

1   How many centuries were scored in the 1975 World Cup?

2   Which two countries remained in England after the 1979 World Cup to play a programme of first-class matches?

3   Which was the last World Cup to be sponsored by Prudential Assurance?

4   What links Graham Gooch and Craig McDermott in the 1987 Cup?

5   Who was the South African manager in the 1992 Cup?

6   Graham Gooch had an unusual opening partner throughout the 1992 Cup. Name him?

7   How many countries took part in the 1996 Cup?

8   Who rallied his side with: 'You're a cornered tiger; you've got nowhere to go. Forget all those worries about no-balls and wides and just go out and fight?

9   Who made Australia's highest individual score in the 1975 Cup?

10   Who managed the 1979 Sri Lankan side?

11   Which pair opened for England in all their 1983 Cup matches?

12   Who were the brothers who played for New Zealand in the 1987 Cup?

13   Why did the organisers have to completely rejig the fixtures at the eleventh hour for the 1992 Cup?

14   Which opening batsman kept wicket for New Zealand when Ian Smith was injured at Wellington in the 1992 Cup?

15   Who managed England's 1996 World Cup squad?

---

1 six. 2 Sri Lanka and India. 3 1983 4 Both won Man of the Match Awards in the Semi-Finals.
5 Mike Procter. 6 Ian Botham. 7 Twelve. 8 Imran Khan. 9 Alan Turner. 10 Maj-Gen Russell
Heyn. 11 Graeme Fowler and Chris Tavare. 12 Martin and Jeff Crowe. 13 South Africa were
late entrants. 14 Mark Greatbatch. 15 Ray Illingworth.

WORLD CUP CRICKET

1   Who hit the most fifties in the 1992 Cup?

2   What was the common factor between Anura Tennekoon, Harilal Shah and Majid Khan in the 1975 Cup?

3   Name the Indian wicketkeeper omitted from their 1979 cup squad, but recalled for 1983?

4   Who was Canada's highest scorer in the 1975 Cup?

5   Which wicketkeeper achieved most dismissals during the 1992 Cup?

6   Who won the award for the "Most Valued Player" of the 1996 competition?

7   Two Pakistani bowlers each took more than 15 wickets during the 1992 Cup, who were they?

8   Which two countries failed to gain a single victory in the 1987 Cup?

9   Who opened Australia's batting in all their 1979 Cup matches?

10 Who umpired the first World Cup Final of 1975?

11 Who played in every West Indies match in the 1979 series, but was never dismissed?

12 Which Australian batsman hit a century in his first innings of the 1992 Cup and another in his last?

13 Who was Sri Lanka's wicketkeeper during the 1983 Cup?

14 Who were New Zealand's opening batsmen through the 1975 Cup?

15 In terms of runs what was the largest margin of victory in a World Cup Final?

MOST VALUED PLAYER AWARD

---

1 Javed Miandad. 2 They captained their respective countries. 3 Syed Kirmani.
4 GR Sealy. 5 David Richardson. 6 S Jayasuriya. 7 Wasim Akram and Mushtaq Ahmed.
8 Sri Lanka and Zimbabwe. 9 Andrew Hilditch and Warwick Darling. 10 Arthur Fagg and
Tom Spencer. 11 Colin Croft. 12 David Boon. 13 Ronald De Alwis. 14 Glenn Turner and
John Morrison. 15 92 runs by West Indies in 1979.

WORLD CUP CRICKET

Jeff Thomson's first over in World Cup cricket – Australia v Pakistan at Headingley 1975 contained five no-balls, one of which was also a wide.

The Canadian team opposing Pakistan at Headingley in the 1979 World Cup contained no less than seven players born in the West Indies.

The Pakistan v Sri Lanka match at Swansea in 1983 was not concluded until 8.15 pm.

The umpire who changed his mind during the Australia v India game at Madras in October 1987 effectively decided the contest. He changed a four into a six: Australia won by one run.

The first ever World Cup match at Mackay in Australia – India v Sri Lanka lasted just two balls, due to rain. About 3,000 spectators came to watch the proceedings.

Guy Whittall (Zimbabwe) was run out when he tripped over the heel of bowler, Ian Bishop, who was awaiting the return from the outfield in the 1996 Cup Match.

A helicopter was employed to dry the ground for the Kenya v Zimbabwe game at Patna, but its action blew away the covers and the game, during the 1996 Cup, was abandoned.

The match on February 27, 1996 in Bombay was the first floodlit game played in that city.

Very few spectators turned out to watch the Australia v New Zealand 1996 game at Nagpur, because earlier in the season a serious accident on the ground had killed nine people.

England dismissed Pakistan at Adelaide in the 1992 World Cup for just 74, their lowest total to date; rain then arrived and England were robbed of victory.

The first day's play in the Australia v New Zealand 1987 game at Indore was washed out – the first time in 35 years that rain had fallen on that city during October.

Three records were broken in Swansea in 1983 – highest team total, Pakistan 338-5; highest total for team batting second, Sri Lanka 288-9; Highest match aggregate, 626 runs.

WORLD CUP CRICKET

Javed Miandad and Imran Khan hit 96 in nine overs off the Sri Lanka attack Swansea in 1983.

England's three principal seam bowlers in the 1979 semi-finals v New Zealand – Mike Hendrick, Ian Botham and Bob Willis all suffered strains.

The Sri Lanka v West Indies game of 1975 was completed in just 58 overs, so the two sides set up an exhibition match to entertain the crowd for the rest of the day.

When Andy Roberts joined Deryck Murray in the 1975 game at Edgbaston, West Indies needed 64 to beat Pakistan with one wicket left. The pair won the game with two deliveries remaining.

Alvin Kallicharran hit 10 consecutive deliveries from Dennis Lillee for 35, viz 4,4,4,4,4,1,4,6,0,4, at The Oval in 1975.

A meeting 24 hours prior to the start of the 1979 World Cup agreed that declarations would be banned – a few days earlier in a B&H Cup game, Somerset, to help their run rate had declared after one over, and caused mayhem.

Bob Willis was no-balled during the 1983 England v Pakistan match at Old Trafford, because there were insufficient fielders inside the 30 yds circle.

The biggest stand for Sri Lanka v England at Headingly in 1983 was 33 for the 10th wicket by Ratnayake and Vinothen John.

David Houghton scored 141 for Zimbabwe v New Zealand at Hyderabad in very hot conditions and reputedly lost a stone in weight in the course of his innings.

Three players, Michael Whitney, Moin Khan and Aamer Sohail, were each fined 250 dollars for causing disputes when Pakistan played Australia at Perth in March 1992.

Sanath Jayasuriya and Romesh Kaluwitharana hit 42 off the first three overs for Sri Lanka v India at Delhi in March 1996.

WORLD CUP CRICKET

The closing ceremony at Kanpur on March 6, 1996 during the India v Zimbabwe game, was briefly disrupted when a dog decided to do a 'lap of honour'.

Graham Thorpe, fielding in the slips, dropped both openers in the England v New Zealand match at Ahmedabad in 1996 – England lost by 11 runs.

In the 1996 semi-final of 1996, Australia, batting first, collapsed to 15 for 4, but recovered so well that they made 207 for 8 and won the game.

A military guard had to be placed round the home of Azharuddin, the Indian captain, after India's defeat in the 1996 semi-final.

No less than eight of the final squad of 14 for England's 1992 World Cup bid were born outside the British Isles.

Phil Defreitas , who was suffering an upset stomach, stopped in the middle of his run up, in order to be sick, during the England v West Indies game at Gujranwala in October 1987.

Graeme Wood, the Australian opener, was stretchered unconscious off the field during the 1983 Australia v West Indies game at Headingley, he had been struck by a ball from Michael Holding.

In the 1979 Final at Lord's, England commenced with an opening stand of 129, but were all out for 194.

Only one of the 14 players selected for the 1975 West Indian squad had not played in County cricket – Maurice Foster.

England in 1996 failed for the first time in six Cup Competitions to reach the semi-finals.

The 1996 Pakistan v New Zealand match in Lahore was scheduled as a day/night match but had to be switched to a daytime game because the lights were not ready on time.

The opening ceremony for the 1996 World Cup was so badly handled that the Indian Government contemplated arresting the organiser on a charge of wasting public money.

WORLD CUP CRICKET

Australia were quoted as 1996 World Cup favourites by all the leading bookmakers, prior to the start of the matches.

Kenya were coached by the former Indian Test batsman, Hanumant Singh, in preparation for the 1996 Cup.

Shane Warne was among the Australian squad for 1996, who received death threats. The Australian Board stated they would support any player who, similarly threatened, wished to withdraw from the squad. Warne was involved in the Pakistan bribery scandal.

Dave Richardson, South Africa's principal wicketkeeper, missed out on the 1996 Cup, when he broken a finger shortly before the squad was to be announced.

On January 31, 1996, Tamil terrorists exploded a bomb in Colombo, killing many innocent passers by. As a result, the Australian and West Indian teams refused to play their matches in Sri Lanka.

England's beer supply arrived at their base in Lahore a few days before the 1996 World Cup began, Mike Atherton stated:"It is important we should have the right attitude."

No less than nine of the Australian 1987 cup squad survived to play in 1992; in contrast England had just four survivors.

Javed Miandad caused a rumpus, when arging with the umpire's decision to give him out leg before wicket, in the Pakistan v England game of 1987 at Rawalpindi.

When India opposed Zimbabwe at Leicester on June 11, 1983, many of the tannoy announcements were made in Urdu – several thousand Indians watched the match.

Australia took the drastic step of dropping both Jeff Thomson and Dennis Lillee for their 1983 game v India at Trent Bridge. Australia won by 162 runs.

When Graeme Porter was picked for the 1979 Australia World Cup squad he had played in only 14 first-class matches.

WORLD CUP CRICKET

A few weeks before the 1979 World Cup, a mini-indoor version was staged at the Wembley Arena. Ian Botham and Derek Randall won the contest for England; Richard Hadlee and Geoff Howarth, for New Zealand, came second.

Mushtaq Mohammad, who led Pakistan v Australia in 1978/79, stated he did not wish to captain Pakistan in the 1979 World Cup. The task was given to Asif Iqbal.

A man with an iron bar attacked Viv Richards in Antigua a few weeks before the 1979 World Cup. Richerds suffered a broken finger and damaged jaw, but was fit by the time the matches came to be played.

The rift between the Packer cricketers and the Australian officials was healed in April 1979, but Australia had already selected its World Cup squad from non-Packer men. In contrast the West Indies squad included ten Packerites.

In the fortnight prior to the 1979 cup, the 14 lesser cricketing nations fought a knock-out contest in England – the finalists would qualify for the World Cup.

In reporting England's squad for the 1979 World Cup, the press were surprised only by the choice of Wayne Larkins, the 25 year old Northants batsman.

Sri Lanka's highest scorer in the 1975 World Cup was Sunil Wettimuny, brother of the much better known Sidath. The latter played 23 Tests for Sri Lanka.

'Indian Stodge follows England's Spice' ran the Sunday Telegraph headline after Sunil Gavaskar's infamous innings of 36 not out in 1975.

Seven of the 1975 Pakistani squad, Sadiq, Majid, Zaheer, Mushtaq, Asif Inbal, Imran Khan and Sarfarz, were experienced county cricketers, in contrast to Australia's single county man Greg Chappell.

To make certain of a place in the 1979 World Cup, Sri Lanka overwhelmed Denmark in the final preliminary game of the ICC Trophy: Sri Lanka 328-8; Denmark 110 all out.

WORLD CUP CRICKET

Franklin Dennis was the only Canadian batsman to master the England attack in the 1979 cup game between the two sides. He was eventually dismissed, when a Willis bouncer hit him on the head and he toppled backwards on to his wicket.

'Reflecting on the Second World Cup I feel that though it could not be called a failure, it was less gripping than the First. The novelty was wearing off.' Alan Gibson reviewing 1979.

Ladbroke's offered 100-1 on India beating West Indies in the 1983 final – India won by 43 runs.

During the 1983 Cup only two matches went the full 120 overs both were staged on June 9, at Swansea and Trent Bridge.

Imran Khan suffered a serious hairline fracture of his left shin in the run up to the 1983 World Cup. He was still picked to play for Pakistan, but only as a batsman.

Greg Chappell announced his retirement as Australia's captain on ta April 12, 1983, but was chosen for the 1983 World Cup squad. However he later withdrew from the team.

Nine of the 1983 Sri Lanka side played in every match during the tournament. Granville de Silva and Edward Fernando of their squad of 14 did not play in any games.

The 1983 Australian squad was managed by Phil Ridings, a first-class cricketer, though he never played any major cricket in England.

England reached 206 for 4, needing 240 to beat Pakistan at Rawalpindi in October 1987. They were all out 221, three batsmen being run out.

Imran Khan, on receiving the cheque as the winning captain of the 1992 Cup side, pledged the proceeds to the cancer hospital planned in his mother's memory.

Roger Twose, the Devon-born batsman, who emigrated to New Zealand played six seasons in New Zealand first-class cricket, before qualifying for his adopted country and representing them in the 1996 Cup.

WORLD CUP CRICKET

Shane Lee, picked for the Australian 1996 cup squad, was described as Australia's answer to Ian Botham. During the Cup he scored 9 runs and failed to take a wicket.

The Indian-born, American-based, entrepreneur, Mark Mascarenhas was reported to have paid 10 million dollars for the TV rights for the 1996 Cup.

One reporter described the UAE 1996 World Cup squad as:"A bunch of failed first-class cricketers who went to the Gulf in search of oil wealth and their lost youth."

South Africa's debut in the World Cup – v Australia at Sydney in 1992 was an enormous success. Australia all out 170; South Africa 171 for 1.

Courtney Walsh was given a hand woven carpet as a present, when he sportingly warned Jaffer for backing up too far in the West Indies v Pakistan game at Lahore in 1987.

Pat Patterson of West Indies broke the off stump in half when he bowled Tim Robinson of England at Jaipur in 1987.

South Africa wanted 22 to win off 13 balls v England at Sydney in 1992. A shower interrupted play and after some fiendish mathematics it was decided that South Africa now needed 21 off one ball. In disgust the batsman patted the ball for a single.

The UAE side of 1996 comprised eight Pakistanis, two Sri Lankans, one Indian, one New Yorker and two from Dubai.

Kim Hughes, Clive Lloyd, plus the two umpires, David Constant and David Evans, reported both the pitch and the medical facilities as inadequate following the 1983 Australia v West Indies game.

With one run still needed by India to beat England at Old Trafford in 1983, a spectator rushed on to the pitch and tried to grab a stump. Only prompt action by umpire Don Oslear saved the situation. The police then came to the rescue.

WORLD CUP CRICKET

As a gesture against the refusal of West Indies and Australia to go to Colombo for their 1996 Cup matches, a joint India & Pakistan team opposed Sri Lanka there. About 25,000 spectators attended.

Graham Thorpe dropped a catch off batsman Nathan Astle, when Astle was 1, he went on to score 101 for New Zealand.

Roland Lefebvre, the Dutch seam bowler in the 1996 Cup, had played as a professional in New Zealand, South Africa, Australia and England.

The captain of the 1996 UAE team began his batting career in the Cup by being struck on the head first ball – the ball delivered by the formidable Allan Donald – he survived a further eight balls, then succumbed for 0.

The West Indies 1985 Cup team wanted to play a warm-up game against Yorkshire, but this request by Clive Lloyd was rejected by the West Indian Board, as Geoff Boycott and Arnie Sidebottom of Yorkshire had toured South Africa.

Zimbabwe were bowled out for 91 in the their 1983 warm up game with Derbyshire. Ole Mortensen, the Danish bowler, on his debut for Derbyshire, conceded just 15 runs off 10 overs.

Sir Garfield Sobers, coach to Sri Lanka in 1985 commented after his side lost to Pakistan, after being in a very strong position:"We just threw it away. They played like maniacs. They just lost their heads. I'm puzzled."

Aamer Sohail batting for Pakistan v Australia in the 1992 Cup was caught off a no-ball before he had scored, but went on to make 78 and win the Man of the Match award.

David Houghton had his foot broken while batting for Zimbabwe v New Zealand in a Test Match just prior to the 1996 World Cup and was therefore unable to take part.

In the run up to 1985 Cup, the West Indian fast bowler, Michael Holding, was the subject of protracted arguments over qualification for county cricket, between Derbyshire and the TCCB.

WORLD CUP CRICKET

Kapil Dev, whose brilliance in the 1983 World Cup was partially responsible for India's success, was frequently seen on Indian TV – advertising bicycles.

Martin Crowe of New Zealand averaged a scoring rate of 90.66 runs per 100 balls through the 1992 Cup series.

In a warm-up match for the 1983 Cup at Cambridge, between Zimbabwe and Sri Lanka Asantha de Mel took five wickets for six runs in 4.4 overs. Zimbabwe were all out for 72.

Commenting on the England squad for the 1983 Cup, Mike Carey said: "Wicketkeepers everywhere will be saddened that their art has again been demeaned by the choice of Ian Gould, who, despite other considerable merits, is not the best available".

Tony Greig's comment while watching England v Sri Lanka at Taunton in 1983,"A bit dull in this white gear, isn't it?" Greig was a major figure in Packer's Circus.

Kim Hughes, on the eve of the 1985 Cup stated:"West India are the team to beat, you can shuffle the rest." Australia were then immediately beaten by Zimbabwe.

"If England do not beat UAE by something approaching the length of Oxford Street tomorrow in Peshawar, they should seriously consider packing their bags and coming home." commented Peter Deeley.

Pakistan's fixtures in the 1996 Cup were arranged so that they avoided Ramadan and the Eid Holiday celebrations.

Hansie Cronje the 1996 South African captain noted:"At the end of this trip if you don't have a degree in United Nations relationships, you haven't learnt anything."

Sultan Zarawani, the UAE player, was probably the only participant in the 1996 Cup to own both a Lamborghini and a Ferrari.

In Kenya, soccer, athletics and boxing are the big sports, there only about 1,500 cricketers in the whole country.

WORLD CUP CRICKET

Owing to his university exams, Imran Khan was forced to remain in Oxford, rather than play for Pakistan v West Indies at Edgbaston in the 1975 Cup – West Indies won by one wicket.

"Deryck Murray's innings of 61 not out v Pakistan said more about his character than a hundred visits to the psychiatrist's couch" noted Tony Lewis when Murray saved West Indies in 1975.

Mark Rampraskash was co-opted into the 1996 England team When Neil Fairbrother returned home with a torn hamstring. Ramprakash, in fact did not play.

"All England have got to take back with them to the old country are bad memories and gaudy carpets." Derek Pringle at the end of the 1996 cup.

Rats burrowed under the pitch at Calcutta prior to the 1996 semi-finals and gnawed away the stump-vision camera cables.

Prior to the 1996 Final, there had been 328 ODI matches between Australia and Sri Lanka, Australia had won 22, Sri Lanks 8 and two were abandoned.

In the six Cup Finals, the side batting first had won five times, the team batting second once – in 1996.

An embarrassing faux pas at the start of the 1996 Final was that the Australian National Anthem was played, then to welcome the Sri Lankan side, the South African anthem blared out.

Sixteen centuries were hit in the 1996 cup in comparison with only eight in 1992.

The East African side of 1975 comprised six Kenyans, two Zambians, two Ugandans and one player from Tanzania.

Glenn Turner was selected as New Zealand's captain for the 1975 cup, when Bev Congdon had to give up the leadership for business reasons.

WORLD CUP CRICKET

Dav Whatmore, the coach of the 1996 Sri Lankan side, was born in Sri Lanka, but moved to Australia when he was eight. He was head coach to the Victoria Institute of Sport, when he took the job of coaching his native country in April 1995.

A curiosity of the 1996 Cup was that up to the Final, there had been 17 wins for the side batting first and 17 for the side batting second.

For the World Cup each country picks a squad of 18 players. This is reduced to 14 prior to the start of the Cup. If a player is injured during the cup he can only be replaced by one of the omitted four.

Only Graham Thorpe and Graeme Hick reached 200 runs for England during the 1996 competition.

During a press interview in the 1996 competition, Mike Atherton called a journalist a buffoon. The England captain, who had earned the title 'Capt Grumpy' was made to apologise.

On learning of Kenya's historic win over West Indies in the 1996 cup, most of Nairobi seemed bemused. A typical comment was "It's really great, I didn't know Kenya even had a team."

As the crowd booed Jeff Thomson off the field following some aggressive bowling during a 1975 game, the Australian manager, Fred Bennett, responded with, "What do you expect Thomson to do, bowl underarm?"

Doug Walters the Australian middle order batsman learnt he had been awarded the MBE on the day of the Australia v West Indies match in 1975.

On the morning of the Australia v England game at Headingley in 1975, Ian Chappell decided to omit Mallett and include Gilmour. The latter returned figures of 12-6-14-6.

During the last wicket stand between Lillee and Thomson in the 1975 cup, Thomson was caught off a no-ball. Spectators not hearing the no-ball called rushed on to the ground. The ball was lost. Would the batsmen be able to run the 21 required for victory?; Fortunately the umpire remained calm and called 'Dead ball'.

ONE DAY INTERNATIONALS

ONE DAY INTERNATIONALS

1 Who was the highest scorer in the first ever ODI?

2 Who captained England in the 3 matches v South Africa in 1998?

3 Where was the ODI Singer Cup series played in April 1996?

4 Which South African hit 26 off a single over at Centurion Park in February 1994?

5 What was odd about the way the ODI Zimbabwe v New Zealand at Harare on November 8, 1992 was scheduled?

6 Who took 4 wkts in an innings in three successive matches in Sharjah in May 1990?

7 Who made his debut in ODI v Pakistan at Sharjah in October 1989 he had the same surname as his country's captain?

8 Who carried his bat through the full 50 overs on his 100th ODI appearance?

9 Who returned figures of 4-3-3-1-5 in 1986?

10 Who was the first player to complete 1,000 runs and take 100 wickets in ODI matches?

11 Which Australian batsman was out first ball of the match at Melbourne in 1985 and had to retire hurt in the next ODI?

12 What record was created in the New Zealand v England game at Auckland on February 19, 1983?

13 Who did Jeff Dujon replace as West Indies wicketkeeper in the middle of the 1981/2 B&H World Series?

14 Which Derbyshire bowler took 5 wkts in an innings v Australia at The Oval in August 1982.

15 Where did David Gower hit his maiden ODI Hundred?

---

1 John Edrich with 82. 2 Alan Hollioake. 3 Singapore. 4 Adrian Kuiper. 5 It was sandwiched in the middle of a five day Test. 6 Waqar Younis. 7 Robert Haynes. 8 Gordon Greenidge. 9 Courtney Walsh v Sri Lanka. 10 Ian Botham in June 1985. 11 Graeme Wood. 12 A new record attendance for any match in New Zealand. 13 David Murray. 14 Mike Hendrick. 15 Kennington Oval in 1978.

ONE DAY INTERNATIONALS

1 What linked David Lloyd and Majid Khan at Trent Bridge in 1974?

2 Who won the first ever ODI?

3 Which player was nicknamed 'Kid Dynamite' during the 1996/7 ODI series in Australia?

4 What did the Sri Lanka v West Indies match at Port of Spain in April 1996 celebrate?

5 In what season did UAE first compete in official ODI matches?

6 Who had his 200th ODI appearance for Pakistan in December 1992?

7 Who hit fifty off 18 balls for Australia in Sharjah in May 1990?

8 What event did the 18 match series in India in 1989/90 commemorate?

9 Which two venues on the same day in the same country staged their initial ODIs in October 1988?

10 With which famous international sporting event was the Perth B&H Challenge of 1986/87 designed to coincide?

11 Why was the Pakistan innings v West Indies at Karachi on December 6, 1985 reduced in overs?

12 Who was the first West Indies bowler to obtain 100 ODI wickets?

13 Why did Sarfraz Nawaz refuse to play for Pakistan v West Indies at Sydney on January 12, 1982?

14 Pakistan used three wicketkeepers in the three ODI matches v West Indies in 1980/1, Taslim Arif and Ashraf Ali were two, name the third?

15 How many Australians made their ODI debuts v West Indies at St John's in February 1978?

ONE DAY INTERNATIONALS

1   What record did Pakistan achieve in the 1974 Prudential Trophy tournament in England?

2   What was the venue of the first ever ODI?

3   Who created a new record for the fastest ODI hundred in Nairobi in October 1996?

4   Name the captains in the Australia v Zimbabwe match at Colombo in August 1996?

5   Who was the first batsman to be adjudged 'hit wicket' by the third (video) umpire in a ODI match (in October 1994)?

6   Who returned figures of 10-8-3-4 for West Indies at Sydney in 1992?

7   Which Australian reached 3,000 ODI runs at Perth on December 9, 1990?

8   What was odd about the selection of W Larkins for England in October 1989?

9   Who was the first bowler to capture 150 wickets in ODI matches?

10   Which was the first ground to stage 50 ODI matches?

11   Who was the first New Zealander to complete 1,000 runs and take 100 wickets in ODI matches?

12   Who was the first Sri Lankan batsman to reach 1,000 ODI runs?

13   When was the first tied ODI match?

14   Why did the number of overs vary per innings through the three match India v England series of 1981/2?

15   Who created a new individual batting record for Australia which stood for ten years – at Sydney in November 1980?

1 The first country to beat England two-nil. 2 Melbourne. 3 Shahid Afridi – in 37 balls. 4 Ian Healy and ADR Campbell. 5 Keith Arthurton. 6 Phil Simmons. 7 David Boon. 8 It was nearly 10 years since he had played in ODI matches. 9 Kapil Dev in October 1988. 10 Melbourne in January 1987. 11 Richard Hadlee. 12 Roy Dias in 1985. 13 February 11, 1984, Australia v West Indies, Melbourne. 14 The number was governed by the overs bowled prior to lunch in each match. 15 Greg Chappell – 138.

ONE DAY INTERNATIONALS

1 Who hit a century on his ODI debut for West Indies v Australia at St John's in February 1978?

2 What was most unusual about the New Zealand v England ODI series of 1974/75 in New Zealand?

3 Name England's captain in the first ever ODI?

4 Which pair of batsmen created a new 4th wkt ODI record in Nairobi in September 1996?

5 What was remarkable about Nick Knight's 100 v Pakistan at Trent Bridge on September 1, 1996?

6 Who was the first Indian batsman to complete 5,000 ODI runs?

7 Which was the 100th venue to stage an ODI match – the game was the first in that particular country?

8 Who was the first Australian to appear in 200 ODI matches?

9 Which Australian hit three successive sixes off the bowling of GC Small in Hyderabad in October 1989?

10 Who returned figures of 9-0-21-5 including 4 wkts in 15 balls for India at Dacca in October 1988?

11 When did Eden Gardens, Calcutta stage its first ODI?

12 How many 100s did Sunil Gavaskar hit in his 108 ODI matches?

13 Why was Graeme Wood booed as he left the field, having hit 104* for Australia at Adelaide in January 1985?

14 Who was the first Pakistani bowler to take 5 wkts in an innings?

15 Which country did Sri Lanka oppose for the first ODI match on February 13, 1982?

ONE DAY INTERNATIONALS

1   Who took a wicket with the first ball of the first ODI match played at Perth on December 9, 1980?

2   Which India captain took his batsmen off the field in protest at the bumpers bowled by Sarfraz Nawaz in 1978?

3   Who was the first New Zealander to take 5 wkts in an innings in ODI matches?

4   Who scored the first ever ODI century?

5   When did Kenya first stage an official ODI match?

6   Where was the Sahara Friendship Cup of ODI matches staged?

7   Who was seriously injured when he ran into his brother in law during the Pakistan v Sri Lanka match in December 1994?

8   Who did South Africa play in their first ODI match?

9   Who was the first fielder (other than wicketkeepers) to hold 100 ODI catches?

10   Where and when did Sri Lanka beat West Indies in an ODI match?

11   Who reached 3,000 runs in the same match as he took 5 for 27, in December 1988?

12   Who was the first batsman to reach 5,000 ODI runs?

13   Who achieved a hat-trick for Australia v New Zealand at Sydney in 1986?

14   Where and against whom did Larry Gomes hit his only ODI 100?

15   Who was the first English bowler to take 5 wkts in an ODI match?

1 Richard Hadlee dismissed Sunil Gavaskar. 2 Bishen Bedi. 3 Richard Collinge v India 1975/76. 4 Dennis Amiss, 103 in 1972. 5 September 28, 1996 in Nairobi. 6 Toronto, Canada. 7 Salim Malik. 8 India. 9 Allan Border. 10 At Rajkot in October 1989. 11 K Srikkanth. 12 Viv Richards. 13 Bruce Reid. 14 At Perth v Sri Lanka in February 1985. 15 Vic Marks – at Wellington in February 1984.

ONE DAY INTERNATIONALS

1 What was odd about the captaincy in the Pakistan v Sri Lanka match in Karachi on March 31, 1982?

2 Why was the match scheduled for Perth on January 8, 1981 Australia v India – switched to Sydney?

3 Where did Allan Border make his ODI debut?

4 Did Alan Knott captain England in ODI matches?

5 Which company sponsored the first ODI matches in England?

6 Who made his first ODI century in May 1997 on the same ground as he hit his maiden Test century?

7 Who hit 19 fours in his innings for South Africa v New Zealand at Centurion Park on December 11, 1994?

8 Who was the first player in ODI matches to be suspended for swearing at the umpire – he received a one match ban?

9 Who took 6 for 50 for West Indies v Australia in March 1991?

10 Which English batsman reached 3,000 ODI runs at Kanpur in October 1989?

11 Which batsman hit 100 off 62 balls for India v New Zealand at Baroda in December 1988?

12 Who was the first player to score 100 and take 5 wkts in the same ODI match?

13 Who was the first batsman to be dismissed 'handled ball' in ODI matches?

14 How many 100s did Allan Border hit in ODI matches?

15 Who was the first bowler to take 5 wkts on his ODI debut?

1 Both official team captains were injured and both teams were led by their deputies.
2 An airline strike. 3 Sydney in 1979. 4 Yes, once v West Indies in 1976. 5 Prudential.
6 Siv Chanderpaul. 7 David Callaghan. 8 Aqib Javed. 9 Anthony Gray. 10 Allan Lamb.
11 M Azharuddin. 12 Viv Richards at Dunedin in 1986/87. 13 M Amarnath in 1986.
14 Three. 15 SHV Karnain in March 1984.

ONE DAY INTERNATIONALS

1   What family record was created in the ODI match at Trent Bridge in July 1982?

2   What tactics caused a change in the laws after the Australia v New Zealand match at Melbourne in February 1, 1981?

3   Which Yorkshireman kept wicket for England for the first time in ODI matches at Melbourne in January 1979?

4   When and where was the first official floodlit ODI match?

5   What was notable about Van Holder's 5 wkts v England in 1976?

6   Who was the first Australian to gain a Man of Match award?

7   What was notable about Ken Wadsworth's 100 v Australia in 1974?

8   What linked Greg Chappell and Gary Cosier at Edgbaston in June 1977?

9   Which West Indies bowler was the first to take 5 wkts in an innings in ODI matches?

10 Who was omitted from the 1981/2 Australian squad because of his dour batting, was recalled in an emergency and hit 117 off 159 balls?

11 Who was the first batsman to hit five 100s in ODI matches?

12 Why was the India v Australia match at Sialkot abandoned after 40 overs in 1984?

13 When was the first ODI match staged in Barbados?

14 Who reached 3,000 runs in his 100th ODI match in November 1986?

15 Who was the chief beneficiary of the Sharjah Tournament of 1987/88?

---

15 Lal Amarnath, the former India Test cricketer.
December 1982. 12 Due to the assassination of Mrs Gandhi. 13 April 1985. 14 Javed Miandad.
9 Andy Roberts at Adelaide in 1980. 10 Bruce Laird at Sydney v West Indies. 11 Zaheer Abbas – in
7 It was the first 100 in ODI matches by a wicketkeeper. 8 Both took 5 wkts in the match v England.
5 It was the first such feat by a West Indian in ODI matches. 6 Greg Chappell at Lord's in 1972.
2 Underarm bowling was banned from ODI matches. 3 David Bairstow. 4 November 1979 at Sydney.
1 Derek Pringle became the first son of an ODI player to also appear in ODI matches.

ONE DAY INTERNATIONALS

1 Where did England play their first tied ODI match?

2 Which Indian made his 100th ODI appearance at Christchurch on March 3, 1990?

3 Which wicketkeeper made his ODI debut for England at Lord's in May 1992?

4 Where did Brian Lara hit his first ODI century?

5 Who was the first Zimbabwean bowler to take 5 wkts in an innings in ODI matches?

6 Who took 4 wickets in 5 balls for Pakistan in 1996/97?

7 Who captained England to victory in his first ODI was leader in February 1997?

8 Which South African scored 50 and took 4 wkts on his ODI debut at Cape Town in January 1996?

9 Who hit his 8th ODI century at East London in February 1993?

10 Name the match referee involved in the ball tampering incident at Lord's in 1992?

11 Who took two wickets in his first over on his ODI debut for New Zealand in March 1990?

12 Who hit a then record eight sites in a single innings at St John's in March 1989?

13 Which West Indies bowler took 4 wkts in both his first and second ODI matches – in 1988?

14 From whom did Javed Miandad take over wicketkeeping duties during the match v West Indies at eeshawar in October 1986?

15 Which country announced a national holiday when its cricketing hero was chosen to captain West Indies in ODI matches?

1 Trent Bridge in May 1989. 2 M Azharuddin. 3 Richard Blakey. 4 Durban in February 1993.
5 ACI Lock in 1996 v New Zealand. 6 Saqlain Mushtaq. 7 Nasser Hussain. 8 Shaun Pollock.
9 Javed Miandad. 10 Deryck Murray. 11 SA Thomson. 12 Gordon Greenidge.
13 Curtly Ambrose v Pakistan. 14 Anil Dalpat. 15 Antigua.

QUIZ 9

ONE DAY INTERNATIONALS

1 Why did the match between India and Australia at Jamshedpur start late in October 1984?

2 Which two Pakistani batsman hit 100s in the ODI match v India at Multan on December 17, 1982?

3 Who was the first wicketkeeper to take 5 catches in an innings in ODI matches – at Leeds in 1981?

4 Who took 4 wkts for 7 runs in 20 balls on his ODI England debut at Sydney in January 1980?

5 Why was the pitch at Old Trafford for the ODI England v Australia in 1977 'underprepared'?

6 How many ODI appearances did Garfield Sobers make for West Indies?

7 Who was the first England captain to win a Man of the Match award?

8 When was the first ODI match staged in Sharjah?

9 Who took three wickets in four balls at Christchurch in February 1985?

10 What was unusual about the umpiring of the Sri Lanka v Pakistan match at Colombo in March 1986?

11 Who was the first England player to make 100 ODI appearances?

12 Who captained England in their three matches in Sharjah in 1986/87?

13 Who was the first twins to appear together in an ODI match?

14 Which New Zealand batsman hit 50s in every one of the five matches v Pakistan in 1988/89?

15 Who was the first batsman to reach 6,000 ODI runs – in January 1989?

1 The lorry carrying the players' kit got lost. 2 Mohsin Khan and Zaheer Abbas. 3 Rodney Marsh. 4 Graham Stevenson. 5 The groundsman resigned three days before the game. 6 One. 7 Mike Denness in 1973. 8 April 6, 1984. Pakistan v Sri Lanka. 9 Richard Hadlee. 10 Neutral umpires were used for first time. 11 David Gower. 12 John Emburey. 13 Mark and Steve Waugh in December 1988. 14 Andrew Jones. 15 Viv Richards.

ONE DAY INTERNATIONALS

1 Both captains were leading their countries for the 100th time at Melbourne on January 3, 1990. Name them?

2 Which two batsmen were involved in a 200 run 1st wicket partnership for Pakistan v Australia in February 1989?

3 What caused a great rumpus during the England v Pakistan ODI match at Lord's in August 1992?

4 Who captained South Africa in their first ODI match?

5 One bowler on either side took 5 wkts in an innings during the India v England game at Bangalore in February 1993. Name them?

6 Who is the youngest batsman to reach 3,000 ODI runs?

7 Who hit a century on his ODI debut for Pakistan v Sri Lanka in 1995?

8 Name the umpire who no-balled Muralitharan for throwing at Brisbane in January 1996?

9 Who reached 300 ODI wickets in October 1996?

10 Who was the first batsman to hit 150 runs in an innings in ODI matches?

11 What new record did the ODI match between Pakistan and New Zealand at Siakot in 1976 produce?

12 Who captained New Zealand in their first ODI – in February 1973?

13 Which was the first non-Test match venue used for ODIs in the UK?

14 What was the result of the 1973 ODI at Old Trafford?

15 What bowling record did Colin Croft achieve at St Vincent v England in February 1981?

---

1 Imran Khan (Pakistan) and Allan Border (Australia). 2 Ramiz Raja and Saeed Anwar.
3 Accusations of ball tampering. 4 Clive Rice. 5 J Srinath and Paul Jarvis. 6 Sachin Tendulkar.
7 Salim Elahi. 8 Ross Emerson. 9 Wasim Akram. 10 Viv Richards in December 1979.
11 The first ODI win by one run. 12 Bev Congdon. 13 St Helen's, Swansea. 14 It was the first ODI
in England to be washed out. 15 First West Indian to take 6 wkts in an innings.

Quiz 11

ONE DAY INTERNATIONALS

1   What did Viv Richards and Michael Holding achieve together for West Indies v England at Old Trafford in 1984?

2   Which 18 year old bowler took 5 for 21 on his ODI debut, at Melbourne in February 1985?

3   Who scored 81 for England when his 10 colleagues could only muster 55 between them – in March 1985.

4   Which was the first country to take part in an ODI match except during the World Cup, and never to have played Test cricket?

5   Who returned the analysis of 10-4-9-4 in SharJah in April 1986?

6   Which Victoria bowler took 5 wkts on his ODI debut in 1988?

7   Who was the first New Zealand player to hit 3,000 ODI runs?

8   What landmark did Desmond Haynes reach as a batsman in December 1991?

9   Who reached 200 ODI wickets for India at SharJah in October 1991?

10 Which two brothers added 121 for the 1st wkt in an ODI match in February 1993?

11 Who hit the first ODI century for South Africa?

12 Where did Zimbabwe achieve their first series win over England?

13 In which match did the Hollioake brothers play together for the first time?

14 Who was the first Indian batsman to reach 6,000 ODI runs?

15 Name the third set of brothers to represent Zimbabwe in ODI matches?

---

14 M Azharuddin in September 1996. 15 John and Gavin Rennie.
11 Andrew Hudson. 12 At Harare on January 1, 1997. 13 At Lord's on May 25 1997 v Australia.
7 John Wright in December 1988. 8 7,000 ODI runs. 9 Kapil Dev. 10 Andrew and Grant Flower.
4 Bangladesh in March 1986. 5 Abdul Qadir v New Zealand. 6 Tony Dodemaide at Perth.
1 They added 100 for the 10th wicket. 2 Wasim Akram. 3 Allan Lamb v Pakistan.

ONE DAY INTERNATIONALS

1 Which batting landmark did Javed Miandad reach at Rawalpindi in January 1992?

2 Who was the first player to appear in 200 ODI matches?

3 Who returned the analysis of 7-4-4-O for India at Port of Spain in March 1989?

4 Who was given out 'obstructing field' with his score on 99?

5 Who was the first New Zealander to appear in 100 ODI matches?

6 In which country in 1986 where two ODI competitions being staged concurrently?

7 What milestone did DB Vengsarkar reach in 1984?

8 Which double did Rodney Marsh achieve in 1983/84?

9 Who bowled the first hat-trick in an ODI match?

10 Who recorded the first century for Sri Lanka?

11 Where did 'West Indies play their first home ODI?

12 Alec Stewart was the 6th English player to reach what ODI milestone in May 1998?

13 Who hit the then fastest 150 in October 1995?

14 What was remarkable about the five match rubber between the West Indies and India in 1983/84?

15 Who made the highest score in the 1998 Texaco Trophy matches?

1 6,000 ODI runs. 2 Allan Border – in February 1990. 3 Kapil Dev. 4 Ramiz Raja.
5 Richard Hadlee – January 1988. 6 Sri Lanka – Asia Cup and John Player Tournament.
7 First Indian to score 1,000 ODI runs. 8 1,000 runs and 100 dismissals. 9 Jalaluddin in
1982/83. 10 Roy Dias. 11 Albion Sports Complex in Berbice. 12 100 ODI appearances.
13 Brian Lara. 14 West Indies won all five matches. 15 Nick Knight – 64.

ONE DAY INTERNATIONALS

PA de Silva refused to leave the field when given out 'obstructed; field' in the Sri Lanka v New Zealand match at Wellington in 1977. Under pressure the umpire was persuaded to reverse his decision.

In the West Indies v England match at Scarborough, a throw from the boundary by Michael Holding hit one set of stumps and went on to hit the other set. The batsmen were out of their creases, but the umpire was too confused to give either 'out'.

Having not played in ODI for 4 years, Ian Chappell marked his return by hitting 63 off 65 balls and gaining the Man of the Match award.

For three successive years Melbourne broke the attendance record for ODI matches: 78,142 in 1982, 84,153 in 1983 and 86,133 in 1984.

After Pakistan were defeated at Adelaide in January 1984, Mohsin Khan announced his retirement, but it was not long before he made a comeback.

A swarm of bees caused bedlam among the capacity crowd watching West Indies play New Zealand at Berbice in April 1985.

Imran Khan permitted a specialist keeper, D Williams, to stand behind the stumps when PJL Dujon retired hurt – Williams then caught out Imran.

Carl Rackemann missed the last delivery when Australia needed two to beat England in 1989, but the batsmen scrambled a bye and the game was tied.

Ramiz Raja was dropped three times in his 90s on the way to scoring 116* for Sri Lanka v Pakistan in February 1990.

David Boon broke his bat in two whilst playing for Australia v New Zealand at Adelaide in December 1990.

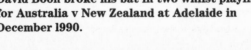

ONE DAY INTERNATIONALS

A cyclone occurred just after the match between Australia and West Indies at Brisbane on January 12, 1992 ended.

England lost their last seven wickets for 10 runs against India at Gwalior on March 4, 1993.

During the New Zealand v England series in New Zealand in 1996/7 each player was accompanied to the crease with his favourite tune. Jack Russell chose "How much is that doggie in the window."

Ken Wadsworth hit 52 in just 25 minutes for New Zealand v India at Eden Park on February 22, 1976. six months later he died of cancer.

Geoff Boycott confused both scorers and umpires when he took strike at the wrong end, following a drinks interval, England v Australia at Sydney, December 1979.

The game between Australia and Pakistan at Sydney arranged for December 8, 1981 had to be postponed due to a power workers strike.

70 spectators were arrested for drunken behaviour during the Australia v West Indies match at Sydney in January 1984.

Larry Gomes suffered a broken nose and the loss of two teeth whilst batting for West Indies v Sri Lanka at Melbourne in February 1985.

David Boon hit 15 fours during his innings of 122 for Australia v Sri Lanka at Adelaide in January 1988.

The 1998/89 Sharjah Cup Tournament was staged for the benefit of Abdul Qadir, who unfortunately injured his hand whilst attempting a caught and bowled in the first game and could not play thereafter.

PA de Silva attempted a reverse sweep, but the ball shot up and hit him in the face. The wound required stitching, during the 1989/90 ODI matches in Australia.

William Watson was on a hat-trick in the New Zealand v Australia match at Sydney in November 1990, when rain ended Australia's innings – Watson had only the last ball of the over to deliver.

ONE DAY INTERNATIONALS

David Boon was the first Tasmanian to hit a century in ODI matches, a feat he achieved in his native state – at Hobart in December 1991.

Kapil Dev, who was the bowler, ran out Peter Kirsten, whilst the latter was backing up during the South Africa v India ODI match in Port Elizabeth in December 1992.

In the Zimbabwe v England match at Harare in January 1997, A Flower, CN Evans and ADR Campbell were all reprimanded by the match referee for excessive appealing.

Australia and West Indies were the finalists in the 1975 world cup; later in the same year they were met again – this time however the result was reversed.

Mike Brearley, when West Indies required three to win off the last ball of the match, stationed all the fielders, including the wicketkeeper on the boundary – England won by two runs.

Wasim Raja took four wickets for Pakistan on December 5 in the B&H World Cup series of 1981/82, but in the match the following day was not even invited to bowl.

The first ODI in which wides and no balls were added to the bowlers' analyses was India v Pakistan at Jaipur on October 2, 1983.

Graeme Wood was forced to retire with a broken finger during the Australia v West Indies match in February 1985, but suitabLy bandaged he returned to the crease later and with Simon O'Donnell made a record stand for the 9th wicket.

Because of the extremely hot weather, drinks intervals were allowed every two overs in the Australia v New Zealand match at Melbourne in January 1988.

Des Haynes and Gordon Greenidge completed 15 century partnerships in ODI matches for West Indies.

Sri Lanka lost their last six wickets for 8 runs off 371 balls in the game v Australia at Melbourne in January 1990.

ONE DAY INTERNATIONALS

Pakistan did not win a home series against West Indies until 1990/91.

The first ODI match in which both sides lost all ten wickets and both had the same total was West Indies v India at Perth on December 6, 1991.

Mark Waugh was run out four times in five innings in ODI matches in 1992.

During the India v New Zealand at Nagpur on November 26, 1995, a wall collapsed killing 12 people and injuring dozens more.

India's first two ODI matches in England were both rain affected. The last overs of the first game were played in an increasing downpour; in the second game the match had to be extended to the second day.

David Bairstow was run out attempting a sixth run from a hit by Mike Brearley – England v Australia at Melbourne in February 1979.

The match between New Zealand and India at Auckland on February 14, 1981 was the first in New Zealand in which coloured clothing, white balls and black sightscreens were employed.

A storm on April 29, 1983 which ended a four-month drought flooded the Sinhalese Sports Club ground in Colombo causing the match between Australia and Sri Lanka to be abandoned.

The Australia v Sri Lanka game at Adelaide in January 1985 saw a number of records fall, including a record win by 232 runs – and a record partnership of 224 for the 3rd wicket by Dean Jones and Allan Border.

India were fined 15,000 rupees for failing to bowl their allotted overs in the time allowed v West Indies at Rajkot in January 1988.

When the New Zealand v Pakistan Test scheduled for Dunedin in February 1989 was cancelled due to rain, a ODI match was organised for the 4th day of the Test. The pitch was almost unplayable and Richard Hadlee picked up five cheap wickets.

ONE DAY INTERNATIONALS

Both teams were fined for slow overs rates in the Pakistan v Sri Lanka game at Perth December 1989.

Both Richard Hadlee and Ken Rutherford were forced to retire injured whilst batting against Chris Lewis in the match at Kennington Oval in May 1990.

The crowd invaded the pitch in the closing stages of the Pakistan v West Indies match at Karachi. Philo Wallace on his debut was injured by a missile thrown by a spectator.

Security cameras were used for the first time at Melbourne in January 1992 in order to pick out trouble makers in the crowd.

Moin Khan hit the final three balls of the innings for six the bowler Ian Bishop of West Indies, conceded 27 in the over – at Sharjah October 1995.

In the early ODI matches in New Zealand six prizes were given to players when the match ended – each team received v batting, bowling and fielding individual trophies.

India refused to continue the match against Pakistan when Sarfraz Nawaz bowled four successive bumpers and the umpire took no action. The game was at Sahiwal in 1978/79.

Kapil Dev hit 75 off 51 balls, including three sixes and nine fours: India v New Zealand at Brisbane in December 1980.

The ODI match between Australia and New Zealand on March 17 1983 was arranged for the Australian Bushfire Appeal Fund.

25,000 spectators turned up to watch England play its first ODI match at Chandigarh. Unfortunately a violent thunderstorm flooded the ground. In order to placate the crowd a 15 over game was staged in unplayable conditions.

ONE DAY INTERNATIONALS

Ramiz Raja was caught off a no-ball, but, failing to hear the umpire's call, left his crease to return to the pavilion. He was then given out 'run out' by the square leg umpire. Pakistan v England at Perth in January 1987.

Richie Richardson was caught by Mark Waugh bowled Steve Waugh in the West Indies v Australia match at Sydney, January 1988.

The ODI at Perth on December 30, 1989 had to be reduced in overs to make up for time lost, because the groundstaff had forgotten to mark out the fielding circle before the game.

Waqar Younis marked the 50th ODI played at Sharjah by returning figures of 10-1-26-6, but he failed to get the Man of the Match award.

Two Indian fielders were injured, when spectators threw stones during the India v South Africa game at Gwalior in November 1991.

Mark Taylor was given the Man of the Match award in the game between Australia and West Indies at Sydney in 1992/93 for his captaincy – he made only 9 with the bat.

The 1000th ODI was played at Kennington Oval on May 25 1995 when England beat West Indies by 25 runs – Michael Atherton scored 92.

Roy Fredericks and Alvin Kallicharran created a new ODI record partnership when they added 143 for the 2nd wicket v England at Kennington Oval in 1973.

In the first ODI between India and Pakistan – at Quetta in October 1978, Sarfraz Nawaz needed to hit the last ball for six to gain victory for his side – India won by 4 runs.

John Bracewell, fielding sub in the New Zealand v Australia match in November 1980, took four catches. At the time this was an ODI record for a non-wicketkeeper.

When the first ODI was played in St George's, the government of Grenada declared a Public Holiday.

ONE DAY INTERNATIONALS

Two spectators were killed and a number suffered severe injuries when a stand collapsed during the India v England game at Nagpur in January 1985.

The famous Wankhede Stadium in Bombay celebrated its first ODI by allowing 588 runs at 7.35 per over – India v Sri Lanka, January 1987.

Javed Miandad's 63 for Pakistan v West Indies at Perth in January 1989 contained 47 singles and only one four.

Owing to a riot, which was followed by police with tear gas, the match between Pakistan and India in Karachi in December 1989 was abandoned, only 4.3 overs being bowled.

Imran Khan over-ruled the umpire, who had given K Srikkanth out lbw in the match between Pakistan and India in December 1989.

Allan Border deliberately stonewalled during the match between Australia and New Zealand in Auckland in March 1990, so that his partner, Dean Jones, could reach 100.

Sri Lanka hit 44 runs off the last 20 balls to beat India by 3 wickets at Sharjah in April 1990.

When Dennis Amiss scored 100 in the ODI match for England v New Zealand in 1973 s he was the first batsman to reach three figures, even though ODI matches had been played since 1971.

Lance Cairns of New Zealand captured four wickets in nine balls as England's last nine wickets fell in ten overs at Scarborough in 1978.

It was reported that 30,000 tickets had been sold for the Pakistan v West Indies match at Sialkot in December 1980 unfortunately there were only 12,000 seats, so squabbles in the crowd rather overshadowed the cricket.

An earthquake during the West Indies v India match at Port of spain in March 1983 caused some injuries among spectators.

ONE DAY INTERNATIONALS

Play was delayed for 25 minutes in the India v England match at Bangalore in January 1985 after the crowd began throwing bottles at the players.

Despite an opening stand of 212 by Geoff Marsh and David Boon, Australia were defeated by seven wickets with six overs to spare by India at Jaipur in September 1986.

Australia required two runs for victory v West Indies at Sydney in December 1988 with one ball remaining. Craig McDermott, the batsman, struck the ball straight into the hands of Viv Richards – Australia lost by one run.

Salim Malik batted through his entire innings of 66 with a runner, when Pakistan opposed England at Nagpur in October 1989.

New Zealand needed 11 to win off the final over v India at Wellington in March 1990 Richard Hadlee hit nine runs off the first four balls, though his partner was run out off the fourth delivery. Hadlee was bowled by the fifth ball and India won by one run.

During the Australia v West Indies match at Perth in December 1992, the home players were greeted with missiles from the crowd apparently because no local player was in the side.

Shane Warne obtained three victims stumped in six deliveries during the Australia v South Africa match at Faisalabad in October 1994.

Allan Border announced his retirement from ODI matches having completed his 100th game as Australia's captain – v South Africa at Sydney in January 1994.

President Robert Mugabe attended: the first ODI match played in Zimbabwe – v India on October 25, 1992.

The first floodlit match in Sri Lanka was staged at the Khattarama Stadium, Colombo on September 5, 1992.

New Zealand staged their first triangular home ODI series in 1989/90, the games involved New Zealand, India and Australia. Australia won the Trophy.

ONE DAY INTERNATIONALS

Viv Richards gained the Man of the Match Award in the West Indies v India game at Bombay on October 30, 1989, despite the fact that he didn't bat and bowled just four overs without taking a wicket.

Players' names appeared on the back of their shirts in ODI matches for the first time when West Indies opposed Pakistan in December 1988.

Javed Miandad won the Pakistan v India match at Sharjah on April 18, 1986 by hitting the last possible ball for six.

When Sri Lanka batted against New Zealand at Moratuwa in November 1984, six Sri Lankan batsmen reached double figures, but none got to 20.

A fast delivery from Richard Hadlee in the Australia v New Zealand game at Melbourne in January 1983 so badly damaged the ear of batsman Rodney Hogg that he required a number of stitches to repair the wound.

Bob Willis's final over for England v West Indies at Lord's in May 1980 produced four wickets for four runs – Willis bowled two batsmen, the other two were run out.

The British Prime Minister, James Callaghan, and Pakistan's head of state, Zia-ul-Haq, watched the ODI match in Lahore in January 1978, but left before the final result.

Peter Coman, who appeared in New Zealand's first ODI was the only one of the 222 players involved not to win a Test cap.

The first floodlit match in Calcutta in November 1993 attracted 90,000 spectators and millions of insects – the latter were dispersed with smoke bombs.

As the last ball was bowled in the West Indies v Pakistan match at Georgetown in April 1993, spectators rushed on to the field and Pakistan complained that their fielders were impeded – West Indies gained the two runs required to tie the game.

A Ranatunga demanded a runner during the final two vital overs v Australia at Colombo in August 1992 – he claimed he had 'stomach cramp'. Sri Lanka won with four balls to spare.

ONE DAY INTERNATIONALS

England scored the then record total of 363-7 off 55 overs, playing against Pakistan at Trent Bridge in August 1992.

Three of the six ODI matches played between West Indies and England in the 1989/90 series were rain affected.

Sri Lanka lost their last six wickets for 11 runs v Pakistan at Lucknow in October 1989.

HD 'Dicky' Bird was so dehydrated by the exceptionally hot weather that he had to retire from umpiring midway through the West Indies v Pakistan match at Sharjah in October 1988.

President Jayawardine of Sri Lanka granted a Public Holiday when Sri Lanka won the John Player Trophy in April 1986.

Lance Cairns hit 26 off the final over of the innings bowled by Vinothen John – New Zealand v Sri Lanka April 1984.

Someone released two pigs on to the playing area during the Australia v England match at Brisbane in 1983. One had 'Botham' painted on its side, the other 'Eddie'.

Jeremy Coney hit his final ball in the New Zealand v West Indies match at Christchurch for four – this gave New Zealand victory by one wicket with two balls to spare and completed Coney's individual 50.

When Geoff Boycott, who was noted as an opening bat, first led England, he dropped himself to no.7 in the order.

The first ODI played on Sunday was staged at Christchurch, New Zealand on February 11, 1973.

Martin Crowe was given 'not out' by the umpire, when playing for New Zealand v Australia at Dunedin in March 1993, but ignoring the umpire's decision returned to the pavilion. He believed he had been caught behind.

ONE DAY INTERNATIONALS

There were no less than six ducks – plus one by the not out batsman, in the Pakistan innings v West Indies,at Cape Town in February 1993.

West Indies beat South Africa by ten wickets in Port of Spain on April 11 1992 – the West Indian openers, Des Haynes and Brian Lara hit off the 153 runs required.

Phil Simmons hit five sixes in the course of his innings for West Indies v South Africa at Kingston in April 1992.

The first cricket match played in the West Indies and televised live to Britain was the West Indies v England match at Port of Spain in February 1990 – unfortunately rain prevented a definite result.

The former Portuguese colony of Goa staged its first ODI match when Australia opposed Sri Lanka at Margao in October 1989.

The match scheduled for Chandigarh on October 25, 1989 had to be moved to Jullundur owing to political unrest.

A streaker held up play at Lord's during the England v Australia match on May 29, 1989.

K Srikkanth hit three sixes off successive balls bowled by Roger Harper in the India v West Indies match at Sharjah on October 16, 1988 – in all his innings included 10 fours and 5 sixes.

No less than five batsmen were run out during the New Zealand innings v Sri Lanka at Sharjah in Match 1988 – only eight wickets fell in all.

Rain ruined all four matches in the Sri Lanka v Pakistan series of 1985/86. The first game was reduced to 25 overs; the second was abandoned after the first side had faced 38 overs; the third was totally washed out; the fourth had the visitors given 24 overs to score 102.

One man was killed and nine injured when the branch of the tree on which they were perched gave way under the weight as they watched Pakistan v Sri Lanka at Gujranwala in 1985.

ONE DAY INTERNATIONALS

Mike Gatting had his nose broken by a ball from Malcolm Marshall whilst batting v West Indies at Kingston in February 1986. The ball unfortunately dropped from his nose on to the wicket.

The first ODI match in Jamaica was not played until April 1984 almost eleven years after West Indies played their first such game.

The final match of the 1982/83 ODI series between Pakistan and Australia at Karachi, had to be abandoned when the spectators pelted the players with rubbish.

The players could hardly hear themselves think during the Australia v England match at Sydney in December 1979 There was a speedway competition then a fireworks display being organised on the adjacent Showground.

In the first ODI match between England and Pakistan at Sahiwal in December 1977, the scores were level with one ball to be bowled. Ian Botham hit that ball for four.

Alan Oakman the Warwickshire coach took over as umpire in the 1972 ODI match at Edgbaston when Arthur Fagg was taken ill on the morning of the game.

Pakistan required four runs to win off the final ball v New Zealand at Sialkot in October 1976, but the batsman, Wasim Bari, only managed two New Zealand won by one run.

Police had to quell rioters with tear gas during the Pakistan v Sri Lanka match at Karachi in March 1982.

A freak hailstorm defeated the wicket covers prior to the ODI match between England and India at Headingley in June 1982, producing damp patches on the wicket.

A boundary overthrow won the West Indies v Australia match at Port of Spain for the latter on March 14, 1984, with two balls to spare.

The Australian team travelled by helicopter to their ODI match v West Indies at Berbice, but were delayed and the game began 30 minutes late.

ONE DAY INTERNATIONALS

Viv Richards hit 64 of his 80 in boundaries, receiving only 39 balls – West Indies v Pakistan at Gujranwala in November 1985.

Ewan Chatfield conceded six runs off his first five overs v India at Sharjah in April 1988 and 51 off his last five.

The three match series arranged between Pakistan and Australia in Sept-Oct 1988 was not a success. The first game was cancelled due to floods, the second due to a riot and the third was moved from Hyderabad to Lahore.

Viv Richards took three wickets in four balls for West Indies v India at Delhi in 1989/90.

The famous Brabourne Stadium in Bombay, which had been starved of international cricket since the early 1970s , staged its first ODI in 1989/90.

M Amarnath was given out 'obstructed field' in the ODI match, India v Sri Lanka at Ahmedabad, when he kicked the ball away to avoid being run out.

Steve Waugh made 87 consecutive ODI appearances for Australia, and was then dropped, only to be replaced by his twin brother.

Allan Border was the second player to complete 5,000 ODI runs and take 50 wickets – he reached the combined target at Adelaide in February 1990.

England were led by Alec Stewart and won all three of the ODI matches v New Zealand in 1991/92.

Phil Tufnell was bombarded with fruit when he returned figures of 10-3-17-0 for England v New Zealand at Auckland in January 1992.

Play in the Pakistan v Sri Lanka match at Rawalpindi was held up for 30 minutes whilst police with tear gas controlled the crowd.

The first ball in both innings of the West Indies v Pakistan game at Cape Town in February 1993 produced a wicket – the unlucky batsmen were Ramiz Raja and Des Haynes.

ONE DAY INTERNATIONALS

Allan Lamb managed to run out both John Morris and Alec Stewart in the course of his innings for England v New Zealand at Sydney in December 1990.

The first ODI match in Tasmania, saw New Zealand defeat Australia by one run, after four of the latter's batsmen were run out.

Allan Border played in 127 successive ODI matches for Australia, the sequence ended on January 13, 1991 at Sydney.

Both India and West Indies withdrew from the 1990/91 Sharjah Tournament due to the Gulf crisis : only Pakistan and Sri Lanka took part.

Kapil Dev performed the hat trick in the 1990/91 final of the Asia Cup v Sri Lanka in Calcutta.

Andrew Jones completed 2,000 ODI runs at Auckland in February 1991.

Curtly Ambrose, bowling the first over the match between West Indies and Australia at Port of Spain on March 10, 1991, delivered four wides and a no-ball, making 11 deliveries in all.

West Indies lost their first international at Bridgetown since 1935, when Australia beat them there in the ODI match of March 13, 1991.

Denis Compton officially opened the Compton and Edrich stands at Lord's during the England v West Indies ODI match in May 1991.

Aqib Javed performed the hat trick – all lbws during the Pakistan v India match at SharJah in October 1991.

South Africa's first ODI game was v India at Calcutta on November 10, 1991.

The last ODI matches played in England and sponsored by Texaco were staged v South Africa in 1998 – the firm's sponsorship had lasted 15 years.

Darren Gough and Jonty Rhodes were chosen as Men of the Series for the England v South Africa ODI matches of 1998.

TEST CRICKET

TEST • POT LUCK

1 Which country did Bransby Beauchamp Cooper and Hampden Stanley Bray Love play for?

2 Which country did Arthur Beaumont Chudleigh Langton play for?

3 Which country did David Johnson play for?

4 Which country did Duncan Sharpe play for?

5 Which country did Imtiaz Ali and Inshan Ali play for?

6 Which country did Iftikhar Ali and Raman Subba Row play for?

7 Which country did Hans Ebeling and Otto Nothling play for?

8 Which country did Russel Arnold and Graeme Labrooy play for?

9 Who in 1995 became the first country to be convicted of ball-tampering in a Test match?

10 Who in 1994 became the 100th bowler to take 100 Test wickets?

11 Which wicketkeeper has taken most dismissals (28) in a Test series?

12 What made its first appearance in a Test match in 1975?

13 Double barrels apart, which Test cricketer had the longest surname?

14 And which had the longest first name?

15 Who was the first Test cricketer with four christian names?

1 Australia. 2 South Africa. 3 India. 4 Pakistan. 5 West Indies. 6 England. 7 Australia.
8 Sri Lanka. 9 Sri Lanka. 10 Phil DeFreitas. 11 Rod Marsh. 12 A streaker. 13 India's Laxman
Sivaramakrishnan (16 letters). 14 Sri Lanka's Ellawalakankanamage De Silva (19 letters).
15 Vernon Peter Fanshawe Archer Royle (England).

QUIZ 2
TEST • POT LUCK

1   Who is the only Test cricketer with five christian names?

2   Who were the only country to win a Test in their first series in England?

3   Who was the first batsman to score a hundred and a double hundred in the same Test?

4   Who was the only bowler from his country to take nine wickets in a Test innings - in the match after he became the first to take eight?

5   Who was the first President of the United States to watch Test cricket?

6   Which country gave away 68 extras in one Test innings in 1977?

7   Name the only two players to do the Test treble of 1,000 runs, 100 wickets and 100 catches.

8   Who has scored most centuries (34) in Test cricket?

9   Who has scored most double centuries (12) in Test cricket?

10   Who has scored most triple centuries (2) in Test cricket?

11   Who was the first batsman to score 1,000 Test runs?

12   Who was the first batsman to score 2,000 and 3,000 Test runs?

13   Who was the first batsman to score 4,000 and 5,000 Test runs?

14   Who was the first batsman to score 6,000 and 7,000 Test runs?

15   Who was the first batsman to score 8,000 Test runs?

Quiz 3
TEST • POT LUCK

1 Who was the first batsman to score 9,000 and 10,000 Test runs?

2 Who is the only batsman to score 11,000 Test runs?

3 Who was the first bowler to take 100 Test wickets?

4 Who was the first bowler to take 200 Test wickets?

5 Who was the first bowler to take 300 Test wickets?

6 Who was the first bowler to take 400 Test wickets?

7 Who took most Test wickets in the 1980s?

8 Name the only bowler to take 40 wickets in a Test series more than once.

9 Which national coach instructed his players to eat 12 jelly babies an hour?

10 Who was the first player to score a double century and take five wickets in an innings in the same Test?

11 Which country has been involved in the closest finishes in Test matches: two ties, a win by one run, two by three runs, one by five runs.

12 Which player was involved in four of the closest finishes in Test matches?

13 Who was the first player to appear in 50 Tests?

14 Who was the first player to appear in 100 Tests?

15 Who is the only player to appear in 150 Tests?

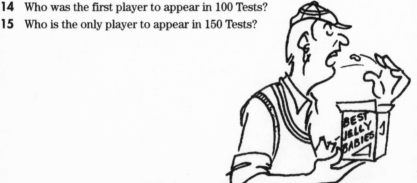

---

1 Sunil Gavaskar. 2 Allan Border. 3 Johnny Briggs. 4 Clarrie Grimmett. 5 Fred Trueman.
6 Richard Hadlee. 7 Malcolm Marshall. 8 Terry Alderman. 9 Bob Woolmer.
10 Denis Atkinson (West Indies). 11 Australia. 12 Allan Border. 13 Syd Gregory.
14 Colin Cowdrey. 15 Allan Border.

TEST • POT LUCK

1. Who was the only bowler to take three wickets in a Test innings without conceding a run?

2. What surname links Derek of England, Chris of New Zealand and Meyrick of South Africa?

3. Who was the first captain to score a Test century?

4. Who was the first captain to score a Test double century?

5. Who was the first captain to make a pair in a Test?

6. Who in 1893 became the first captain to make a declaration in a Test?

7. Who captained his country to a record 36 Test wins?

8. Who in 1995 were the first country since 1888 to win a three-match Test series after being 1-0 down?

9. Who lost a Test match by an innings and 579 runs?

10. Which leading run-scorer's mother once worked for MI5?

11. Who turned up at an England team's fancy dress party dressed as a gorilla to match his nickname?

12. What were WG Grace's christian names?

13. Who was the youngest player to appear in his last Test?

14. Whom did Rodney Hogg describe as having 'a degree in people'?

15. Who took 9 catches in a three-Test series at the age of 43?

1 Richie Benaud. 2 Pringle. 3 Billy Murdoch. 4 Billy Murdoch. 5 Joe Darling.
6 Andrew Stoddart. 7 Clive Lloyd. 8 South Africa. 9 Australia, to England in 1938.
10 David Gower. 11 Ian 'Guy' Botham. 12 William Gilbert. 13 Hasan Raza (14).
14 Mike Brearley. 15 WG Grace.

Quiz 5

TEST • POT LUCK

1   Who scored a century in only 56 balls, the fastest in all Test cricket?

2   Who was the only batsman to score 5 consecutive Test hundreds and 7 consecutive Test fifties?

3   Which opening bowler lost his house in a hurricane?

4   Which famous cricketer had the initials MCC?

5   Which Test batsman appears on the oldest surviving film of a cricketer?

6   Which Test captain broke his leg when he was run over by his own car?

7   Which country declared at 574-8 against Australia in 1972-73 and lost by 92 runs.

8   Which country declared at 547-8 against Australia in 1992-93 and lost by 16 runs?

9   Who was the only batsman to score two hundreds in the same Test three times?

10 Which batsman was dismissed by the first ball of a Test match three times?

11 Who set a Test record by taking 350 balls to reach fifty in 1958?

12 Which Test cricketer became Baron of Maraval and Nelson?

13 Name the match referee, a former Test batsman, who fined Mike Atherton for the 'dirt in the pocket' episode in 1994.

14 Who was the first player to make a pair in his first Test as captain?

15 Which bowler reached 300 Test wickets in the lowest number of balls?

---

1 Viv Richards. 2 Everton Weekes. 3 Keith Boyce. 4 Colin Cowdrey. 5 Ranjitsinhji.
6 Ted Dexter. 7 Pakistan. 8 Sri Lanka. 9 Sunil Gavaskar. 10 Sunil Gavaskar. 11 Trevor Bailey.
12 Learie Constantine. 13 Peter Burge. 14 Mark Taylor in 1994. 15 Malcolm Marshall.

Quiz 6

TEST • POT LUCK

1 What did the following have in common? EJ Smith, Bill O'Reilly, the Nawab of Pataudi jnr, HR Lance.

2 What did the following have in common? WG Grace, Ali Bacher, 'Kelly' Seymour, Jason Vaughan.

3 What did the following have in common? WG Grace, Bishan Bedi, Gundappa Viswanath, Ray Bright.

4 What did the following have in common? Eddie Barlow, Geoff Boycott, Clive Lloyd, MJK Smith, Alf Valentine.

5 What did the following have in common? WG Grace, Peter May, Brian Rose, Hedley Verity.

6 What did the following bowlers have in common? Courtney Walsh, Aqib Javed, Fanie de Villiers.

7 Who scored most Test centuries while captain?

8 Who played in a record 153 consecutive Tests?

9 Who was the only batsman to score 300 runs in a day during a Test match?

10 What kind of delivery is said to have been invented by West Indian Test spinner Ellis 'Puss' Achong?

11 Which wicketkeeper completed a record 52 stumpings in Test cricket?

12 Name the only opening batsman to carry his bat through a Test innings three times.

13 Who took a record 9-95 in an innings during his only Test series?

14 Which country had to wait 26 years and 45 matches for their first win in a Test match?

15 Who was the first player to appear in 100 consecutive Tests?

12 Desmond Haynes, **13** Jack Noreiga, **14** New Zealand, **15** Sunil Gavaskar.

7 Allan Border (15), **8** Allan Border, **9** Don Bradman, **10** Chinaman, **11** Bert Oldfield.

5 Surnames that could be women's christian names, **6** All hit Devon Malcolm with bouncers.

1 All nicknamed 'Tiger', **2** All doctors, **3** All bearded, **4** Played Test cricket in glasses.

QUIZ 7

TEST • POT LUCK

1   Which captain lost the toss in 9 consecutive Tests?

2   Who was the first Man to play Test cricket?

3   Who illegally declared a Test innings closed in 1949?

4   Who had to wait until his 96th Test to captain his country for the first time?

5   Who was the last player to hold Test records for most wickets and catches?

6   Who was the first wicketkeeper to score a century on his Test debut?

7   Which two batsmen shared Test partnerships of 451 and 388 in the same series?

8   Who was the first player to do the Test double of 1,000 runs and 100 wickets?

9   Who was the first player to do the Test double of 2,000 runs and 200 wickets?

10 Who was the first player to do the Test double of 3,000 runs and 300 wickets?

11 Who was the only player to do the Test double of 4,000 runs and 400 wickets?

12 Who completed the double of 1,000 runs and 100 wickets in his last Test as captain?

13 Which Test cricketer was related to a Wimbledon singles champion?

14 Which Test cricketer had the same names as a British Open squash champion?

15 Who scored 258 in his last Test innings?

15 Seymour Nurse.
10 Ian Botham. 11 Kapil Dev. 12 Ian Johnson. 13 Frank Laver. 14 Azam Khan.
6 Brendon Kuruppu. 7 Don Bradman and Bill Ponsford. 8 George Giffen. 9 Richie Benaud.
1 Sunil Gavaskar. 2 Man Sood (India). 3 George Mann. 4 Dilip Vengsarkar. 5 Hugh Trumble.

TEST · POT LUCK

1 Who had to wait 16 Tests before scoring his first Test century, then turned it into a world record score?

2 Who holds the record for most ducks (31) in Test cricket?

3 Who set a record that still stands by taking only 36 Tests to reach 200 wickets?

4 Of the bowlers who took 200 Test wickets or more, who did it most cheaply?

5 Don Bradman once called his players out to watch a marvellous Test innings of 232 in 235 minutes by one of their team mates. Who?

6 Don Bradman has a share in the Test record partnerships for the 5th and 6th wickets. Name either of his partners.

7 Whose innings of 158 in 1968 led to an international incident?

8 Which world-class opener was known as 'Bedser's Bunny' after the England bowler dismissed him 18 times in Tests?

9 Which unfortunately-named slip fielder dropped two important catches against Australia in 1948?

10 Who was on 92 when his captain declared at the MCG in 1971?

11 Who was on 98 when his captain declared at the SCG in 1995?

12 Which future captain of Australia was dismissed by the first ball he faced in Test cricket, in 1894?

13 Who scored a famous 174 in the Centenary Test at Melbourne in 1977?

14 Who batted on every day of the Centenary Test of 1980?

15 Which commentator retired after the Centenary Test at Lord's?

TEST • POT LUCK

1 Who made his Test debut against Australia in 1899 and was still playing Test cricket 30 years later?

2 Who was the first bowler to concede 10,000 runs in Test cricket?

3 Who are the only twins to have played Test cricket?

4 Which fast bowler was the only player to take exactly 200 Test wickets?

5 Which controversial pace bowler was no-balled for throwing against South Africa in 1963 and retired from all levels of cricket?

6 Who was the only batsman to score two hundreds in the same Test twice in the same series?

7 Who shared a record partnership of 451 in his last Test?

8 Which former Test captain once referred to 'scores below single figures'?

9 Which famous all-rounder scored 1,146 Test runs, including two centuries, without wearing batting gloves?

10 How many times was Don Bradman dismissed in the 90s in Test cricket?

11 Who was the first batsman to score 500 runs in a Test series without making a century?

12 Which country set a record of 25 consecutive Tests without defeat?

13 Which country set a record of 26 consecutive Tests without defeat?

14 Which country set a record of 27 consecutive Tests without defeat?

15 Who was the first specialist fast bowler to play in 100 Tests?

1 Wilfred Rhodes. 2 Ian Botham. 3 Mark and Steve Waugh. 4 Jeff Thomson. 5 Ian Meckiff. 6 Clyde Walcott in 1954-55. 7 Bill Ponsford. 8 Richie Benaud. 9 Jack Gregory. 10 None. 11 Clem Hill. 12 Australia. 13 England. 14 West Indies. 15 Courtney Walsh.

QUIZ 10
TEST • POT LUCK

1   Who was the first batsman to score six consecutive Test fifties?

2   Who took a world record 15 catches in a series in 1920-21?

3   Who took a world record 7 catches in a Test in 1974?

4   Who was 90 not out on 27 August 1998?

5   Who was the only batsman to score 150 twice in the same Test?

6   Who was the first batsman to wear a helmet in a Test match?

7   Which country have won all five of their Test matches against Australia in Perth?

8   Who in 1936 held a world record 5 catches in an innings in his last Test?

9   When Clarrie Grimmett took his 190th Test wicket in 1936, whose world record did he break?

10 Who was the first player to score a hundred in his hundredth Test?

11 Who was the first batsman to score four Test centuries before his 21st birthday?

12 Who played in his last Test in 1991 the day after his 41st birthday?

13 Which captain called his own nickname at the toss of the coin?

14 Who scored most hundreds (19) against any one country?

15 Of the players who scored 2,000 Test runs, who has the lowest average (20.49)?

TEST • ASHES

1   Who scored his 7,000th Test run during the 4th Test of the 1998-99 Ashes series?

2   Who took his 100th Test catch during the 1998-99 series?

3   Who played his 100th Test in the 1998-99 series?

4   Who set a world record by taking his 157th Test catch in the 1998-99 series?

5   The leading wicket taker in the 1998-99 series has the same initials as the Sydney Cricket Ground. Name him.

6   Who took 36 wickets (including Mike Atherton's 7 times) in the 1997 series?

7   Who suffered his 20th Test duck during the 1998-99 series, an Australian record?

8   Who took the only hat-trick for England in an Ashes Test in the 20th Century?

9   Who took a hat-trick against England in 1994?

10 Which fast bowler was the easy third victim in that hat-trick?

11 Who took hat-tricks for Australia against England in 1902 and (in his last Test) 1904?

12 Which famous 'Demon' bowler took the first hat-trick in Test history, against England in 1879?

13 Name the bowler who took exactly 100 wickets against England, including 42 in 1981 and 41 in 1989.

14 Name the bowler who took exactly 100 wickets against England, including 33 in 1974-75.

15 Whose 167 wickets are a record for all Ashes Tests?

1 Steve Waugh. 2 Mark Waugh. 3 Mark Taylor. 4 Mark Taylor. 5 Stuart (SCG) MacGill.
6 Glenn McGrath. 7 Glenn McGrath. 8 Darren Gough. 9 Shane Warne. 10 Devon Malcolm.
11 Hugh Trumble. 12 Fred Spofforth. 13 Terry Alderman. 14 Jeff Thomson.
15 Dennis Lillee.

TEST • ASHES

1   Whose 138 wickets are a record for an English bowler in Ashes Tests?

2   In 1985 Australian all-rounder Simon O'Donnell was dismissed by the first ball he faced in Test cricket. Which England all-rounder bowled it?

3   Name the only fast bowler to captain England in an Ashes series since 1936-37.

4   Name England's captain in 1936-37 who refused to bowl Bodyline in 1932-33.

5   Who captained England when they regained the Ashes in 1953 after a record gap of 19 years?

6   Who captained England when they regained the Ashes in 1970-71 after a gap of 15 years?

7   Who captained Australia when they regained the Ashes with a 4-0 win in 1958-59?

8   Whose 188 was the highest score by an England captain in Australia?

9   Which batsman, later a TV commentator, scored 7 centuries for England against Australia from 1964 to 1981?

10 Who scored most Test runs and Test hundreds for England against Australia?

11 Who scored 732 runs in the 1985 series, a record by an English batsman in an Ashes series at home?

12 When Jim Laker took 19 wickets in the Old Trafford Test of 1956, which bowler took the other wicket?

13 When Bob Massie took 16 wickets in the Lord's Test of 1972, which bowler took the other four?

14 In which Australian city have England won only one Test?

15 On which English ground did Australia lose only once in 23 Tests in the 20th Century?

QUIZ 3
TEST • ASHES

1   Which batsman, later the England coach, played his last Test during the 1974-75 series?

2   Whose Test career began in one Ashes series (1954-55) and ended in another (1974-75)?

3   Which England wicketkeeper made his 200th Test dismissal during the 1974-75 series?

4   Name the wicketkeeper who made a record 148 dismissals in Ashes Tests.

5   Which England wicketkeeper took six catches in an innings during the Melbourne Test of 1990-91?

6   Name the 6 foot 8 inch seamer who took 13 wickets for Australia at Melbourne in 1990.

7   Name the batsman, brother of a famous player, who made a pair in his only Test, against Australia in 1880.

8   Which Test record is held by James Southerton, who played in the very first Test match in 1877?

9   Who kept wicket for Australia and England in Tests?

10 What was significant about Billy Murdoch's 211 against England in 1884?

11 What record did Reginald 'Tip' Foster set, relating to football as well as cricket?

12 Who played football for England as well as sharing a famous stand that saved a Test against Australia in 1953?

13 Name the famous player, England captain at both cricket and rugby, who shot himself in 1915.

14 Who scored 98 in his last innings of the 1932-33 Bodyline series and didn't play for England again?

15 Who was the only member of Australia's 1997 squad to have experienced defeat in an Ashes series?

1 David Lloyd. 2 Colin Cowdrey. 3 Alan Knott. 4 Rod Marsh. 5 Jack Russell. 6 Bruce Reid.
7 Fred Grace (brother of WG). 8 The oldest Test debutant (49 years 119 days).
9 Billy Murdoch. 10 It was the first double century in Test cricket. 11 The only player to
captain England at both sports. 12 Willie Watson. 13 Andrew Stoddart. 14 Harold Larwood.
15 Steve Waugh.

TEST • ASHES

1   Whose century in the first match of the 1997 series saved his place in the team?

2   Which England batsman scored his first Test double century in the first match of the 1997 series?

3   In the 1997 series, 19-year-old Ben Hollioake became the youngest England debutant since who?

4   Which England batsman scored his 5,000th Test run in the first match of the 1997 series?

5   Who scored his 5,000th Test run while scoring 196 at Lord's in 1985?

6   Name the only batsman to score 5,000 runs in Ashes Tests.

7   Who in 1957 were the last pair of brothers to play for England before Adam and Ben Hollioake forty years later?

8   How many Australian batsmen were out lbw in the six Tests of the 1970-71 series?

9   At which ground in 1975 was an Ashes Test disrupted by a campaign to free convicted criminal George Davis?

10 Name the batsman, later South Africa's national coach, who took more than six hours to reach a century against Australia in 1975.

11 When Len Hutton made his record-breaking 364 against Australia in 1938, two other England batsmen made centuries. Name either.

12 When Len Hutton made his record-breaking 364 against Australia in 1938, two other England batsmen made one run between them. Name either.

13 Which famous leg-spinner dismissed Hutton in his innings of 364?

14 Which England fast bowler took 11 wickets, including a spell of five without conceding a run, to win the 1961 Headingley Test?

15 Which England fast bowler took one wicket for 160 runs in the first Test of the 1954-55 series before blasting out Australia in the next three?

---

1 Mark Taylor. 2 Nasser Hussain. 3 Brian Close in 1949. 4 Mike Atherton. 5 Allan Border.
6 Don Bradman. 7 Dick and Peter Richardson. 8 None. 9 Headingley. 10 Bob Woolmer.
11 Morris Leyland and Joe Hardstaff Jnr. 12 Denis Compton and Eddie Paynter.
13 Bill O'Reilly. 14 Fred Trueman. 15 Frank Tyson.

TEST • ASHES

1 Which fast bowler took six wickets as Australia dismissed England for 52 in Don Bradman's last Test in 1948?

2 Who bowled Don Bradman for a duck in his last Test innings when he needed only four runs to reach 7,000 runs and average 100 in Test cricket?

3 Name the 'mystery' spin bowler who took 21 wickets to help Australia win the 1950-51 series, the only one he played in.

4 Two batsmen scored 234 in the same innings against England in 1946. Don Bradman was one, who was the other?

5 Who captained Australia in ten consecutive Ashes Tests, winning eight and drawing the other two?

6 Who celebrated his 34th birthday and 20th Test century at Melbourne in 1994?

7 Who scored his first Test hundred during the 1997 series?

8 Who in the 1997 series became only the third batsman to be dismissed for 199 in a Test innings?

9 Name either of the two spinners who hit each other for sixes in the same Test in 1997.

10 Who scored almost two thirds of Australia's runs in one innings of the 1998-99 series?

11 England's Allen Hill set two Test firsts in 1877. What were they?

12 When Ian Chappell said 'the good thing about his bowling is that when he's doing it he's not fielding,' which England spinner was he talking about?

13 Who took 7-66 and 4-27 to win an Ashes Test in 1997?

14 When Geoff Boycott scored a century on his return to Test cricket, at Trent Bridge in 1977, who dropped him when he'd made only 20?

15 Which two captains opposed each other in Ashes series before and after the Second World War?

Quiz 6

TEST • ASHES

1   Who captained Australia in six series against England?

2   Shane Warne took a wicket with his first delivery in Ashes cricket, possibly the most famous ball ever bowled. Who was the batsman he bowled?

3   When David Gower made his infamous flight in a Tiger Moth during the 1990-91 Ashes tour, which other Test batsman was his passenger?

4   Name the grey-haired batsman who was made BBC Personality of the Year in 1975 for his batting against Australia.

5   At one point during the famous Headingley Test of 1981, England were quoted at 500-1 to win. Name the two Australians who put money on them.

6   What was the surname of the three brothers who made their England debuts in the same Test against Australia?

7   When Mike Atherton captained England for the 42nd time during the 1997 series, whose record did he break?

8   Which fast bowler took 41 wickets for Australia in the 1978-79 series?

9   Which fast bowler took 25 wickets for Australia in the 1978-79 series?

10 The record aggregate for runs in Test cricket was broken nine times in 1902, by three different players. Name any one of them.

11 Name the Indian prince who scored 154 not out on his Test debut for England against Australia in 1896.

12 Name the Indian prince who scored 102 on his Test debut for England against Australia in 1932.

13 Which opening batsman remained not out on 99 against Australia in 1980?

14 During the 1902 series, a famous big hitter took just 76 balls to score his only Test century. Name him.

15 Name the wicketkeeper who set a record by taking 97 minutes to score his first run in the Adelaide Test of 1947.

1 Allan Border. 2 Mike Gatting. 3 John Morris. 4 David Steele. 5 Dennis Lillee and Rod Marsh. 6 Grace: Edward, Fred and WG. 7 Peter May. 8 Rodney Hogg. 9 Alan Hurst. Syd Gregory, Clem Hill and Archie MacLaren. 11 Ranjitsinhji. 12 The Nawab of Pataudi senior. 13 Geoff Boycott. 14 Gilbert Jessop. 15 Godfrey Evans.

TEST • ASHES

1 In which year did Australia beat England for the 100th time in Tests?

2 Who put Australia in to bat in Adelaide in 1982, a decision that cost England the match?

3 What current Test record was set by Australian spinner 'Chuck' Fleetwood-Smith during England's mammoth 903-7 in 1938?

4 Who scored a century against Australia on his Test debut in 1993?

5 Which medium pacer missed a Test hat-trick when catches were dropped off three consecutive deliveries in the 1972 series?

6 Don Bradman scored a record number of double centuries in the 1930 series. How many?

7 Who was the first batsman to score his hundredth first-class hundred during a Test match?

8 Who bowled the ball that Boycott hit for four to bring up his hundredth hundred?

9 Who made a pair on his Test debut in the 1975 series, facing only ten balls in all?

10 Which famous opener made his last Test century during the 1932-33 Bodyline series?

11 When Ian Botham scored his swashbuckling 149 not out at Headingley in 1981, who helped him add 117, making his highest Test score of 56?

12 Name the Australian openers who batted throughout a full day's play at Trent Bridge in 1989.

13 Name the bespectacled fast bowler whose only wicket in the 1932-33 series was that of Don Bradman.

14 In 1985 England won successive matches against Australia for the first time since when?

15 Which Australian opener scored 172 in almost ten hours at Trent Bridge in 1985?

14 1956 15 Graeme Wood.

10 Herbert Sutcliffe. 11 Graham Dilley. 12 Geoff Marsh and Mark Taylor. 13 Bill Bowes.

5 Geoff Arnold. 6 Three. 7 Geoff Boycott in 1977. 8 Greg Chappell. 9 Graham Gooch.

1 1989 2 Bob Willis. 3 Most runs conceded in a Test innings (298). 4 Graham Thorpe.

TEST • ENGLAND

1 Who has played in most Tests for England?

2 Which well-known quiz team captain is in second place?

3 Who has scored most runs?

4 Three batsmen have scored a record 22 centuries for England. Name them.

5 Which of the three didn't score a double century?

6 Who has the highest individual innings?

7 Who has taken most wickets?

8 Who has the best bowling figures in an innings?

9 Who has the best bowling figures in a match?

10 Who took most wickets in a series?

11 Two fielders have taken a record 120 catches for England. Name them.

12 Who took a remarkable 87 catches in only 58 Tests?

13 Which wicketkeeper has made most dismissals for England?

14 Who was the first wicketkeeper to make 200 Test dismissals?

15 Who was the first wicketkeeper to score 4,000 Test runs?

15 Alan Knott, in 1977.
Botham. 12 Tony Greig. 13 Alan Knott (269). 14 Godfrey Evans, in 1957.
8 Jim Laker (10-53). 9 Jim Laker (19-90). 10 Sydney Barnes (49). 11 Colin Cowdrey and Ian
Colin Cowdrey and Geoff Boycott. 5 Cowdrey. 6 Len Hutton (364). 7 Ian Botham.
1 Graham Gooch (118). 2 David Gower (117). 3 Graham Gooch (8,900). 4 Wally Hammond,

TEST • ENGLAND

1   Who has captained England most often?

2   Who was England's oldest Test player?

3   Who was the youngest?

4   Who had the longest Test career?

5   Which respected player of fast bowling was dismissed by Curtly Ambrose off the first ball he faced in Test cricket?

6   Who took more first-class wickets than anyone else and was the first fielder to take 50 catches in Test cricket?

7   Who took a hat-trick against the West Indies in 1995?

8   The last England bowler to take a Test hat-trick before 1995, who was suspected of throwing. Name him.

9   Who in 1930 became the first bowler to take a hat-trick on his Test debut?

10   Who was the first player to take 100 catches in Tests?

11   Who in 1994 became the first England batsman to score a century in each innings against the West Indies?

12   When Devon Malcolm took 9-57 against South Africa in 1994, who took the other wicket?

13   Which seam bowler made his Test debut for England at the age of 35 in 1981?

14   Which seam bowler made his Test debut for England at the age of 33 in 1994?

15   Name the England Test batsman who became Bishop of Liverpool.

1 Mike Atherton (52). 2 Wilfred Rhodes (50 years 165 days). 3 Brian Close (18 years 149 days).
4 Wilfred Rhodes (30 years 315 days). 5 Alan Wells. 6 Wilfred Rhodes. 7 Dominic Cork.
8 Peter Loader in 1957. 9 Maurice Allom. 10 Wally Hammond. 11 Alec Stewart.
12 Darren Gough. 13 Robin Jackman. 14 Joey Benjamin. 15 The Rev. David Sheppard.

QUIZ 3

TEST • ENGLAND

1. Name the Test selector who helped pick himself against Australia in 1953.
2. Name the Test selector who helped pick himself against the West Indies in 1956.
3. Name either of the batsmen who were injured against the West Indies in 1984 and won only one cap each.
4. Place Botham, Gooch and Gower in the order in which they were first capped.
5. Which chairman of England selectors referred to Devon Malcolm as Malcolm Devon?
6. Name the England manager who was famous for malapropisms like 'them high-philosophy bullets' and 'a swarm of lotuses.'
7. Who scored 20 centuries for England from 1960 to 1968?
8. The England record for any partnership is 411 against the West Indies in 1957. Name the two batsmen involved.
9. Name the last father and son to captain England.
10. Who took 17 wickets in a Test against South Africa in 1913?
11. After Jim Laker in 1956, who was the next England bowler to take 9 wickets in an innings?
12. Which famous fast bowler took 29 wickets in his debut Test series in 1952?
13. Who in 1929 became the first batsman from any country to score 5,000 runs in Test cricket?
14. Which former England fast bowler reduced Brian Johnston to a fit of giggles on air by saying 'He didn't quite get his leg over'?
15. Who captained England when they lost to New Zealand for the first time, in 1978?

1 Freddie Brown. 2 Cyril Washbrook. 3 Andy Lloyd and Paul Terry. 4 Gooch, Botham, Gower. 5 Ted Dexter. 6 Ken Barrington. 7 Colin Cowdrey and Peter May. 9 Colin and Chris Cowdrey. 10 Sydney Barnes. 11 Devon Malcolm in 1994. 12 Fred Trueman. 13 Jack Hobbs. 14 Jonathan Agnew. 15 Geoff Boycott.

TEST • ENGLAND

1   Name the left-arm seamer who took ten wickets and scored a fifty on his England debut, in India in 1976-77.

2   Which son of a famous father played in five Tests in 1971?

3   Who kept wicket as a substitute against New Zealand at the age of 45?

4   Which great batsman's Test career lasted from 1908 to 1930?

5   Which off-spinner's Test career lasted from 1955 to 1975?

6   Which batsman was recalled at the age of 45 to face the West Indies' fast-bowling battery in 1976?

7   Which much-loved heavyweight batsmen scored 139 in his last Test innings before losing an eye in a car crash?

8   Who was the only batsman to score a triple century and a century in the same first-class match?

9   Whose 1,379 runs in 1974 are the record for England in a calendar year?

10 The fastest triple century in Test cricket took less than five hours. Who scored it?

11 Which spin bowler surprisingly batted for 81 minutes, scoring 2 not out, against India in 1993?

12 Which batsman who scored over 8,000 Test runs was born on April Fool's Day?

13 Who in 1978 hit a boundary off the first ball he received in Test cricket?

14 Who in 1995 hit a boundary off the first ball he received in Test cricket?

15 Which spinner took 6 wickets for only 12 runs against New Zealand in 1971?

Quiz 5
TEST • ENGLAND

1 What were 'Patsy' Hendren's real names?

2 Who took 15 wickets for only 28 runs in a Test in 1889?

3 Name the well-known spinner who in 1952 took a stunning catch with his first touch of the ball in Test cricket.

4 Who in 1990 became the only batsman to score 1,000 Test runs during an English season?

5 Don Bradman scored a record 12 double centuries in Test cricket. Which England batsman lies in second place with 7?

6 Former England captain Ted Dexter was born in which European country?

7 Former England captain Freddie Brown was born in which South American country?

8 Which England wicketkeeper's name was a marine mammal?

9 Name the England batsman with the Indian surname who played a Test against India in 1959.

10 Name the England spinner with the Indian surname who played two Tests against India in 1996.

11 Two players share the England record of 65 consecutive Tests. Name either.

12 Whose entire England career was made up of consecutive Tests: 58 from 1972 to 1977?

13 Which opening batsman scored a match-saving 262 not out against the West Indies in 1974 and 203 against them in 1976?

14 Which famous opening batsman of the 1920s and '30s had an average of 60.83 in his 54 Tests?

15 Who set a Test record by making only two ducks in his 84 Test innings?

1 Elias Henry. 2 Johnny Briggs. 3 Tony Lock. 4 Graham Gooch. 5 Wally Hammond. 6 Italy.
7 Peru. 8 Arthur Dolphin. 9 Raman Subba Row. 10 Min Patel. 11 Alan Knott and Ian
Botham. 12 Tony Greig. 13 Dennis Amiss. 14 Herbert Sutcliffe. 15 Herbert Sutcliffe.

Quiz 6
TEST • ENGLAND

1 In 1987 Nottinghamshire provided England's opening partnership for the first time since 1885. Name either batsman.

2 Who in 1985 scored his first Test hundred in England, in his 40th innings there?

3 Which batsman scored his first Test century in his 26th innings, against Pakistan in 1987?

4 England fielded four captains in the 5-0 drubbing by the West Indies in 1988. Name two.

5 Who was the youngest player to appear in his 100th Test?

6 Which county has provided a record eleven England captains?

7 Which ex- Manchester United footballer played in his only Test in 1985?

8 Which great batsman made a duck in his first Test innings, against New Zealand in 1937?

9 Name the bowler who took 49 wickets in only four matches in 1913-14, still the world record for any Test series.

10 Name the England captain who didn't tell his players to stay on the field because he was watching Wimbledon on TV.

11 Who shared an opening stand of 359 with Len Hutton against South Africa in 1948?

12 Who in 1899 took a wicket with his first ball in Test cricket?

13 Who in 1903 took Victor Trumper's wicket with his first ball in Test cricket?

14 Who in 1923 took a wicket with his first ball in Test cricket?

15 Who in 1924 took a wicket with his first ball in Test cricket?

Quiz 7
TEST • ENGLAND

1 Which England captain won the toss for the 9th successive time in 1962?

2 Which England captain lost the toss for the 6th successive time in 1985?

3 Who retired as England's long-serving physiotherapist in 1986?

4 Whom did Ian Botham succeed as England's record wicket-taker?

5 Name the two batsmen who made double centuries in the same innings against India in 1985.

6 Name either of the openers who made centuries in the same innings against New Zealand in 1983.

7 Which off-spinner returned to Test cricket in 1984 after missing England's previous 86 matches?

8 Who scored a century in each of three successive Tests against the West Indies in 1984?

9 Who was the first player to do the Test double of 3,000 runs and 300 wickets?

10 Which country declared twice at 491-7 and 294-7 in their first Test in England, in 1984?

11 Who batted on all five days of the 2nd Test against the West Indies in 1984?

12 Which medium-pacer, brother of a former England captain, played in two Tests in 1982?

13 Who captained England in his last Test, which was also Sri Lanka's first?

14 Who in 1981 was dismissed by the third ball he faced in Test cricket, made 13 in the second innings, and wasn't capped again?

15 Who was the first England player to score a century and take five wickets in an innings in the same Test?

1 Colin Cowdrey. 2 David Gower. 3 Bernard Thomas. 4 Bob Willis. 5 Graeme Fowler and Mike Gatting. 6 Graeme Fowler and Chris Tavaré. 7 Pat Pocock. 8 Allan Lamb. 9 Ian Botham. 10 Sri Lanka. 11 Allan Lamb. 12 Ian Greig. 13 Keith Fletcher. 14 Paul Parker. 15 Tony Greig.

TEST • ENGLAND

1   Who set a record by scoring a century and taking 13 wickets in the same Test?

2   Against which country in 1982 did England fail to take a wicket during a whole day's play?

3   Name the wicketkeeper who didn't concede a bye in a total of 659-8 in 1946.

4   Name the wicketkeeper who didn't concede a bye in a total of 601-7 in 1989.

5   Which off-spinner took a wicket in his first over in Test cricket, against New Zealand in 1978?

6   Name either of the seam bowlers who made their maiden first-class fifties and put on 128 for the last wicket against the West Indies in 1966.

7   Which off-spinner played in three Tests in 1977-78 either side of bans for throwing?

8   Which opening batsman hit his maiden Test century against South Africa in 1998?

9   Who came out to bat with his broken arm in plaster to save the 2nd Test against the West Indies in 1963?

10 Who went into the last Test of the 1989-90 series in the Caribbean with a broken wrist and made 35 and 34?

11 Name the big England pace bowler who broke his kneecap in New Zealand in 1992.

12 Name the Welsh fast bowler whose entire Test career consisted of five defeats in 1985 and 1986.

13 Which Lancashire slow left-armer took a record 15 Test wickets in a day in 1889?

14 Which Yorkshire slow left-armer took 14 Test wickets in a day in 1934?

15 Which Lancashire off-spinner took 9 Test wickets in a day in 1951?

Quiz 9

TEST • ENGLAND

1   Which strapping young all-rounder played in two Tests against South Africa in 1998?

2   What is Ian Botham's middle name?

3   What is David Gower's middle name?

4   What's Geoff Boycott's middle name?

5   Name the England captain who took the catch that dismissed Garry Sobers first ball at the Oval in 1966?

6   Who was never on the losing side in 19 home Tests as captain?

7   When England won the Triangular Tournament in 1912, which two other countries took part?

8   Name the wicketkeeper whose only two Tests, in India in 1992-93, brought him a total of 6 runs at an average of 1.75.

9   England's bowling coach in 1998 played in four Tests from 1969 to 1973. Name him.

10 Which bowler came closest to 300 Test wickets without getting there?

11 Who famously added the name of a rock star to his own?

12 Whose 310 not out against New Zealand in 1965 included a record 238 in boundaries?

13 Name his cousin, who scored so many runs alongside Denis Compton for Middlesex and England.

14 Who would have been 150 years old on 18 July 1998?

15 Which replacement batsman made 139 at Karachi in 1969 before the Test was abandoned because of a riot?

TEST • ENGLAND

1   Which wicketkeeper took a Test record 11 catches in a match in 1995?
2   Len Hutton's 364 against Australia in 1938 was the longest innings in a Test in England. How many hours did it last?
3   Who scored 256 in 11 hours against Australia in 1964?
4   Who scored 158 in nearly 11 hours against New Zealand in 1978?
5   Whose unbeaten 185 in nearly 11 hours saved a Test in South Africa in 1995?
6   Which slow left-armer bowled 749 balls in a Test in 1929?
7   Which slow left-armer bowled 766 balls in a Test in 1939?
8   Which fast-medium bowler bowled 712 balls in a Test in 1924?
9   Which all-rounder took three wickets in four balls against South Africa in 1947.
10 Which all-rounder surprised a few people by taking 8-68 and 5-70 to win the last Test in the Caribbean in 1973-74?
11 Name the Notts batsman who scored a hundred on his home ground Trent Bridge against South Africa in 1951.
12 Name the stylish slow left-armer who took exactly 100 Test wickets at only 18.63 each.
13 Whose run of 67 innings without a duck ended in 1936?
14 Whose Test record of 78 innings without a duck ended in 1968?
15 Whose Test record of 110 innings without a duck ended in 1989?

TEST • ENGLAND

1 Which England captain knocked down the stumps after being given out during the 1981-82 series in India?

2 Who typically took over 5 hours to score a Test fifty on two occasions?

3 Who scored 273 runs in a day against Pakistan in 1954?

4 Who in 1896 became the first batsman to score a Test hundred before lunch?

5 Who scored a hundred before lunch against Australia in 1921?

6 Who scored a hundred before lunch against South Africa in 1924?

7 Who scored a hundred before lunch against New Zealand in 1933?

8 Who scored a hundred before lunch against South Africa in 1935?

9 Who batted on every day of a Test match in 1977?

10 Who was out for 99 against South Africa in 1960 and Pakistan in 1961?

11 Name the all-rounder and one-day specialist who made 59 and took a wicket with his 8th ball on his Test debut in 1992.

12 Which opening batsman's highest Test score was 99 against New Zealand in 1988?

13 Who made a century and a duck in two different Tests in the 1960s?

14 Who scored a century against Australia in 1929 at the record age of 46?

15 Who scored a century against Australia in 1934 at the age of 45?

1 Keith Fletcher. 2 Chris Tavaré. 3 Denis Compton. 4 Ranjitsinhji. 5 Phil Mead.
6 Jack Hobbs. 7 Wally Hammond. 8 Les Ames. 9 Geoff Boycott (surprise, surprise).
10 Mike (MJK) Smith. 11 Dermot Reeve. 12 Martin Moxon. 13 Colin Cowdrey.
14 Jack Hobbs. 15 Patsy Hendren.

TEST • ENGLAND

1 Who in 1930 equalled a record by scoring six consecutive Test fifties?

2 Whose 140 against the West Indies in 1948 was his maiden first-class hundred, made in his first Test innings?

3 Whose 128 against Australia in 1989 was his maiden first-class hundred?

4 Who scored a century in his first Test innings, against South Africa in 1951?

5 Name the fair-haired batsman who scored an unbeaten hundred on his debut in 1973 but finished with a Test average of only 15.25.

6 Who scored a century on his Test debut, the first ever made for England?

7 Which opening batsman twice scored 4 hundreds in a Test series?

8 Who scored a triple century and a fifty in the same Test, against the West Indies in 1930?

9 Who averaged 60.73 with the bat in his 54 Tests?

10 Who averaged 59.23 with the bat in his 20 Tests?

11 Who averaged 58.67 with the bat in his 82 Tests?

12 Who averaged 58.45 with the bat in his 85 Tests?

13 Who averaged 56.94 with the bat in his 61 Tests?

14 Who averaged 56.67 with the bat in his 79 Tests?

15 Who averaged 50.06 with the bat in his 78 Tests?

1 Patsy Hendren. 2 SC 'Billy' Griffith. 3 Jack Russell. 4 Peter May. 5 Frank Hayes.
6 WG Grace in 1880. 7 Herbert Sutcliffe. 8 Andy Sandham. 9 Herbert Sutcliffe.
10 Eddie Paynter. 11 Ken Barrington. 12 Wally Hammond. 13 Jack Hobbs. 14 Len Hutton.
15 Denis Compton.

TEST • ENGLAND

1   Name the 6'7 pace bowler who took 9 wickets on his Test debut in 1962.

2   Who was the first player to make a pair in three different Tests?

3   Name the bowler, now a journalist, who began his Test career in 1976 with three quality wickets (Fredericks, Richards, Kallicharran) in 20 balls.

4   Which bowler has taken most Test wickets without managing ten in a match?

5   Which bowler took 87 Test wickets from 1974 to 1981 without managing five in an innings?

6   Name the bowler with two fused vertebrae at the top of his spine who took 5-48 to help beat Australia in 1986.

7   Name the wicketkeeper who played as a specialist batsman in the 1976-77 series against India.

8   Which left-arm spinner took 26 wickets at only 13.81 in the 1956-57 series in South Africa?

9   Name the Durham bowler who finished with figures of 2-138 in his only Test, in 1996.

10 Name the bowler who had an important catch dropped off him and finished with figures of 0-89 in his only Test, in 1997.

11 Which future BBC man was captain in his maiden Test, making a duck in the first innings?

12 Which off-spinner continued playing for England after losing three toes in a boating accident?

13 Which respected Derbyshire medium pacer played in only two Tests, 12 years apart?

14 Which two batsmen opened the England innings 54 times together?

15 Who opened the England innings 49 times with Graham Gooch?

1 David Larter. 2 Bobby Peel. 3 Mike Selvey. 4 Bob Willis (325). 5 Mike Hendrick.
6 Gladstone Small. 7 Roger Tolchard. 8 Johnny Wardle. 9 Simon Brown. 10 Mike Smith.
11 Tony Lewis. 12 Fred Titmus. 13 Les Jackson. 14 Len Hutton and Cyril Washbrook.
15 Geoff Boycott.

Quiz 14
TEST • ENGLAND

1 Which Essex team mate opened the England innings with Graham Gooch in his only Test?

2 Len Hutton's 364 in 1938 broke the previous Test best of 336 not out against New Zealand in 1933. Who scored it?

3 Name the pace bowler who played in two Tests in 1959 before being called for throwing in county cricket.

4 The real christian names of which Test wicketkeeper are Robert Charles?

5 Whose only Test century was a quick-fire 185 in 1966?

6 Who, in his only Test, played in his benefit year (1938), dismissed Don Bradman?

7 Which popular Test wicketkeeper killed himself in 1998?

8 Name the wicketkeeper who was bowled for a duck in each innings but didn't concede a bye in his last Test, against South Africa in 1955.

9 Before Alec Stewart's 173 against New Zealand in 1997, who made the highest score by an England wicketkeeper?

10 Name either of the batsmen who scored their first Test centuries against Pakistan in 1996.

11 Who reached his century with a six against Zimbabwe in 1996?

12 Which Yorkshire seamer made his Test debut against Zimbabwe in 1996 after taking only 95 first-class wickets?

13 Who doubled his total of Test wickets by dismissing Wasim Akram in 1996?

14 Who has taken 100 Test wickets most cheaply?

15 When Graham Gooch broke his hand against the West Indies in 1989-90, who took over as captain?

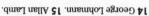

TEST • ENGLAND

1   Who took 236 Test wickets, a world record at the time, and was later chairman of selectors?

2   Who scored his maiden Test century in his 22nd innings, at Bombay in 1993?

3   Which Test all-rounder's surname is a Middle Eastern nationality?

4   Which Test debutant bowled Mohammad Azharuddin for a duck at Edgbaston in 1996?

5   Who played in his first Test for over three years and top-scored in each innings against India in 1993?

6   Whose mother appears in the Births and Deaths section of Wisden?

7   Which fast bowler played his first Test in Fred Trueman's last?

8   George Simpson-Hayward was the last bowler of his type to take wickets in Test cricket. What kind of balls did he bowl?

9   Who scored 753 runs in the 1947 series against South Africa?

10 Which Test all-rounder and radio pundit was known as 'The Barnacle'?

11 Who was the last 40-year-old to play in a Test for England?

12 Who in 1981 scored 104 not out against the West Indies at the age of 40?

13 Which famous left-hander ended a 25-year Test career in 1934?

14 Who captained England at the age of 45 after an 11-year absence from Test cricket?

15 Who was originally chosen for the 1968-69 South African tour in place of Basil D'Oliveira?

1 Alec Bedser. 2 Graeme Hick. 3 Ronnie Irani. 4 Alan Mullally. 5 Mike Gatting.
6 WG Grace. 7 John Snow. 8 Underarm lobs. 9 Denis Compton. 10 Trevor Bailey.
11 John Emburey (42 in 1995). 12 Geoff Boycott. 13 Frank Woolley.
14 George 'Gubby' Allen. 15 Tom Cartwright.

TEST • ENGLAND

1 Which two members of the current England squad are brothers-in-law?

2 Who took 7-43 on his Test debut in 1995?

3 Who averaged only 10.71 in his debut series against the West Indies in 1991?

4 Who passed 20 (but never 30) seven times in his debut series against the West Indies in 1991?

5 Who scored his maiden Test century against the West Indies in 1998?

6 Who captained England for the first time in his 69th Test?

7 Two England Test players were known as 'Hopper.' Name either.

8 Who headed the batting averages against the West Indies in 1995 and played in only one more Test?

9 Who took a record number of Test catches and kept wicket when George Duckworth was injured against South Africa in 1931?

10 Who was the first batsman to score a hundred before lunch in a Test match?

11 Who completed a Test hat-trick in 1892?

12 Who completed a Test hat-trick in 1896?

13 Who completed a Test hat-trick in 1938?

14 Who took 5-41 against South Africa in 1912 and averaged 128.00 with the bat against them 17 years later?

15 Which opening bowler made his debut in England's 100th Test against South Africa, in 1965?

Quiz 17

TEST • ENGLAND

1 When Peter May played in his 52nd consecutive Test, whose world record did he equal?

2 Who was the first Lancashire player to score a Test century at Old Trafford?

3 Who was the first Lancashire player to score a Test century at Old Trafford as England captain.

4 Name the bowler who took 5-20 and 8-51 in the 2nd Test against Pakistan in 1974, a match affected (and shortened) by rain.

5 Who began the 1996 series against New Zealand by scoring 210 and ended it with two ducks?

6 Name the spinner who went to Australia in 1954-55 in place of Laker and Lock but didn't play another Test.

7 Who scored 65 and took 4-47 on his Test debut in 1996?

8 Name the 36-year-old spinner (England's oldest debutant since 1947) who won his only two caps in the 1988 series against the West Indies.

9 Who was the first amateur to score a century for England after the First World War?

10 Who was the first amateur to score a century for England after the Second World War?

11 Which batsman captained England only once, in his 74th Test?

12 Who was invited to play in a Test in 1921 at the age of 49 but refused?

13 Which Kent seamer won his first cap 'as a kind of 17th choice' against Australia in 1989?

14 Which former England captain gave the address at John Arlott's memorial service?

15 Name the 30-year-old seamer whose Test career consisted of two Tests against Pakistan in 1992, in which he took 10 wickets.

1 Frank Woolley. 2 Geoff Pullar. 3 Mike Atherton. 4 Derek Underwood. 5 Graham Gooch. 6 Jim McConnon. 7 Darren Gough. 8 John Childs. 9 SC Wyatt. 10 SC 'Billy' Griffiths. 11 Tom Graveney. 12 CB Fry. 13 Alan Igglesden. 14 Tony Lewis. 15 Neil Mallender.

Quiz 1
TEST • AUSTRALIA

1   Who has played in most Tests for Australia?

2   Who has scored most runs?

3   Who has scored most centuries?

4   Two batsmen have scored 334, the highest individual innings for Australia. Name them.

5   Who has taken most wickets?

6   Who has the best bowling figures in an innings?

7   Who has the best bowling figures in a match?

8   Who took most wickets in a series?

9   Which fielder has taken most catches?

10   Which wicketkeeper has made most dismissals?

11   Who has captained Australia most often?

12   Who was Australia's oldest Test player?

13   Who was the youngest?

14   Who had the longest Test career?

15   Name the opening batsman who captained Australia in 1968 then didn't play another Test until 1977-78 when he was made captain again.

1 Allan Border (156). 2 Allan Border (11,174). 3 Don Bradman (29). 4 Don Bradman and Mark Taylor. 5 Dennis Lillee (355). 6 Arthur Mailey (9-121). 7 Bob Massie (16-137). 8 Clarrie Grimmett (44). 9 Mark Taylor (157). 10 Ian Healy (381). 11 Allan Border (93). 12 Bert Ironmonger (50 years 327 days). 13 Ian Craig (17 years 239 days) 14 Syd Gregory (22 years 32 days). 15 Bobby Simpson.

Quiz 2

TEST • AUSTRALIA

1 Who completed a hat-trick against the West Indies in 1988?

2 Who completed a hat-trick on his Test debut in 1994?

3 Which nightwatchman scored a century against India in 1977?

4 Which whimsical Test leg-spinner entitled his autobiography 'Ten for 66 and all that'?

5 Who averaged exactly one catch per Test, setting a world record in each case?

6 Which pace bowler took his 200th Test wicket in 1993?

7 Who made scores of 0, 2, 0, 0 in his last two Tests after a tearful resignation as Australia's captain?

8 Which seam bowler took 6-15 to dismiss Pakistan for 106 in 1973?

9 Vic Richardson's world record of 6 catches in one Test was broken by his grandson. Name him.

10 What was the surname of the three brothers who played Test cricket for Australia in the 1980s?

11 Whose 193 in 1926 made him the oldest Australian to score a Test century: 43 years 201 days?

12 Australia were the first country to win a Test series 5-0. Who were their opponents?

13 Which country did Australia beat 5-0 in 1931-32?

14 Which ground staged the first Test match in 1877 and the 1,000th in 1984?

15 Which left-hander scored 21 Test centuries for Australia from 1948 to 1963?

1 Merv Hughes. 2 Damien Fleming. 3 Tony Mann. 4 Arthur Mailey. 5 Allan Border (156). 6 Craig McDermott. 7 Kim Hughes. 8 Max Walker. 9 Greg Chappell (Greg, Ian and Trevor). 11 Warren Bardsley. 12 England, in 1920-21. 13 South Africa. 14 Melbourne Cricket Ground. 15 Neil Harvey.

TEST • AUSTRALIA

1   Which fast bowler was known as 'Garth'?

2   Which opening batsman was known as 'Phanto' (The Phantom)?

3   Who was nicknamed 'Tangles' after his bowling action?

4   Which seam bowler wears an ear stud in the shape of a revolver?

5   Which fast bowler bowled twelve bouncers in two overs against the West Indies in 1984?

6   Rod Marsh was the first Australian wicketkeeper to score a Test century. Who was the second?

7   When Greg Chappell took his 121st catch in Test cricket, whose world record did he break?

8   Which former Australian captain made 268, his highest first-class score, against Pakistan in 1983?

9   Name the fair-haired pace bowler who took eleven wickets in one Test in 1983.

10 In Australia's first Test against Sri Lanka (1983), which fair-haired batsman scored his first Test century?

11 Who beat Australia in all four Tests in 1969-70?

12 Who beat Australia in all three Tests in 1982-83?

13 Name the fast bowler whose 5-39 on his Test debut in 1997 improved his best first-class figures.

14 Which opener scored 70 and 113 against the West Indies in 1984 in his first Test for five years?

15 Which pace bowler took 291 Test wickets from 1984 to 1996?

1 Graham McKenzie. 2 Bill Lawry. 3 Max Walker. 4 Paul Reiffel. 5 Rodney Hogg. 6 Wayne Phillips. 7 Colin Cowdrey. 8 Graham Yallop. 9 Carl Rackemann. 10 David Hookes. 11 South Africa. 12 Pakistan. 13 Simon Cook. 14 Andrew Hilditch. 15 Craig McDermott.

TEST · AUSTRALIA

1   Which fast bowler broke two stumps with the same delivery against New Zealand in 1982?

2   Which country won a series against Australia for the first time in 1979-80?

3   Which country won their 8th Test in Melbourne after losing the first seven?

4   Who in 1979 became the first Western Australian to captain Australia?

5   Which pace bowler ran out Pakistan's Sikander Bakht while he was backing up?

6   Which promising batsman scored his only Test century against the West Indies in 1978?

7   Which country lost the decisive last Test of the 1977-78 series despite scoring 445 in their second innings?

8   Name the pace bowler of the 1970s whose real surname was Durtanovich.

9   Name the only bowler to take a hat-trick in each innings of the same Test.

10 Name the bowler who's been hit for six 67 times in Tests, which seems to be a record for any country.

11 Name the bespectacled batsman who scored a century on his Test debut, against England in 1981.

12 Name the man with the walrus moustache who took 212 Test wickets from 1985 to 1993.

13 Which great batsman was 50 not out on 7 August 1998?

14 Name the bearded Australian wicketkeeper who played in 35 Tests from 1877 to 1894, a world record at the time.

15 Who was the first Australian wicketkeeper to do the Test double of 1,000 runs and 100 dismissals?

1 Jeff Thomson. 2 Pakistan. 3 West Indies. 4 Kim Hughes. 5 Alan Hurst. 6 Peter Toohey. 7 India. 8 Len Pascoe. 9 Jimmy Matthews. 10 Shane Warne. 11 Dirk Wellham. 12 Merv Hughes. 13 Greg Chappell. 14 Jack Blackham. 15 Bert Oldfield.

Quiz 5

TEST • AUSTRALIA

1   Who scored over 300 runs and took exactly 20 wickets in two series against the West Indies in the 1950s?

2   Which record-breaking bowler was born in New Zealand on Christmas Day 1891?

3   Who was the first Australian to do the Test double of 1,000 runs and 100 wickets?

4   Who was the first Australian to do the Test double of 2,000 runs and 200 wickets?

5   Who took 12 catches in the 1979-80 series against India and was later Sri Lanka's national coach?

6   Name the wicketkeeper who didn't concede a bye in a total of 551 in 1897.

7   Three Australian wicketkeepers have made 9 dismissals in a Test. Rod Marsh and Ian Healy were two. Who was the first?

8   Name the wicketkeeper who made 22 dismissals in his first Test series, against India in 1977-78.

9   Which off-spinner bowled 571 balls in a Test innings in 1964?

10   Which all-rounder took 7-17 and 6-60 in a Test in 1901-02?

11   Who took 11 wickets for 79 runs to dismiss the West Indies for 99 and 107 in 1932?

12   Who took 11 wickets for 24 runs to dismiss South Africa for 36 and 45 in 1932?

13   Who took 4-12 and 2-6 to dismiss New Zealand for 42 and 54 in 1946?

14   Who took 5-2 and 6-29 to dismiss India for 58 and 98 in 1947?

15   Who shared a stand of 382 with Bill Lawry against the West Indies in 1965?

1 Keith Miller. 2 Clarrie Grimmett. 3 George Giffen. 4 Richie Benaud. 5 Day Whatmore.
6 Jim (JJ) Kelly. 7 Gil Langley in 1956. 8 Steve Rixon. 9 Tom Veivers. 10 Monty Noble.
11 Bert Ironmonger. 12 Bert Ironmonger. 13 Ernie Toshack. 14 Ernie Toshack.
15 Bobby Simpson.

TEST • AUSTRALIA

1 Who shared a stand of 336 with Bill Lawry against the West Indies in 1969?

2 Which pace bowler made 5 ducks in the 1977-78 series against the West Indies?

3 Which pace bowler made 6 ducks in the 1978-79 series against England?

4 Name the 6'6 bearded giant who scored a hundred in a hundred minutes against England in 1885.

5 Who scored a hundred before lunch against England in 1902?

6 Who scored a hundred before lunch against South Africa in 1902?

7 Who scored a hundred before lunch against South Africa in 1912?

8 Who scored a hundred before lunch against England in 1926?

9 Who scored a hundred before lunch against England in 1930?

10 Who scored a hundred before lunch against South Africa in 1935?

11 Who scored a hundred before lunch against New Zealand in 1982?

12 Who scored a hundred between lunch and tea against the West Indies in 1973?

13 Who made a hundred and a duck in two different Tests, in 1932 and 1948?

14 Which big red-haired batsman made a century in his first Test innings, against the West Indies in 1975?

15 Which opening batsman scored four consecutive Test hundreds in 1936?

11 Greg Chappell. 12 Doug Walters. 13 Don Bradman. 14 Gary Cosier. 15 Jack Fingleton.
6 Clem Hill. 7 Warren Bardsley. 8 Charlie McCartney. 9 Don Bradman. 10 Stan McCabe.
1 Doug Walters. 2 Wayne Clark. 3 Alan Hurst. 4 George Bonnor. 5 Victor Trumper.

Quiz 7

TEST • AUSTRALIA

1   Name the fast bowler who formed a fearsome partnership with Jack Gregory in the early 1920s and died in a bizarre road accident.

2   Who carried his bat through a Test innings in 1890?

3   Who carried his bat through a Test innings in 1902?

4   Who carried his bat through a Test innings against England in 1928 and 1933?

5   Who carried his bat through a Test innings against England in 1938?

6   Who carried his bat through a Test innings in 1969 and 1971?

7   Who carried his bat through a Test innings at Auckland in 1974?

8   Who carried his bat through a Test innings at Auckland in 1986?

9   Who scored 834 runs in the 1952-53 series against South Africa?

10   Who averaged 201.50 with the bat in the 1931-32 series against South Africa?

11   Who averaged 216.00 with the bat in the 1993-94 series against New Zealand?

12   Who averaged 362.00 with the bat and 8.50 with the ball in the 1995-96 series against Sri Lanka?

13   Who averaged 63.05 with the bat in his 13 Tests?

14   Who averaged 53.86 with the bat in his 87 Tests?

15   Who averaged 51.62 with the bat in his 20 Tests?

TEST • AUSTRALIA

1   Who was taken to hospital with heat exhaustion after scoring 210 in eight hours at Madras in 1986?

2   Against Pakistan in 1976, Jeff Thomson dislocated his collarbone while colliding with which team mate?

3   When Australia lost 2-1 in India in 1997-98, which bowler's 10 wickets cost 54.00 each?

4   Which versatile bowler made his Test debut in 1998 at the age of 34?

5   When Mark Taylor made his 334 against Pakistan in 1998, which other batsman made a century?

6   Which former Australian Test spinner resigned as Sri Lanka's national coach in 1998?

7   Which two batsmen opened the Australian innings 62 times together?

8   Who hit a ball from New Zealand's Daniel Vettori 130 yards onto the roof of the Lillee-Marsh stand at Perth?

9   Who scored four successive Test ducks in Sri Lanka in 1992?

10 Name the 6'6 batsman, regarded as more of a one-day specialist, who scored two centuries in his eight Tests.

11 Name the medium pacer who took 160 wickets in 40 Tests and was dismissed only once on the 1948 tour.

12 Whose declaration stopped him setting a new highest innings score for Australia?

13 Who was the last man out when Australia lost to the West Indies by 1 run in 1993?

14 Which great leg-spinner took 5-14 and 3-19 to dismiss New Zealand for 42 and 54 in his last Test?

15 Name the outstanding left-arm seamer who took 186 Test wickets at only 20.53 each.

TEST • AUSTRALIA

1   Which talented strokemaker scored 71 not out in his first Test (1958) and 74 not out in his last (1965)?

2   Name the one-day 'specialist' who made 54 not out in his only Test innings, against Sri Lanka in 1995.

3   Who retired from Test cricket in 1996 after scoring 7,422 runs in 107 Tests?

4   About whom was it said: 'You might be the greatest player Victoria has produced, but you'll retire without a friend in the game'?

5   Who retired hurt twice in the same Test innings after injuries inflicted by West Indies fast bowler Andy Roberts?

6   Who took 0-110 in his first Test (bowling with a broken foot) before being recalled to traumatise England in 1974-75?

7   Whose first 90 overs in Test cricket brought him only one wicket at a cost of 335?

8   Who made 21 Test centuries and 16 Test ducks?

9   Which aptly-named wicketkeeper was Australia's No.1 immediately after the Second World War?

10   Name the outstanding wicketkeeper who made 187 Test dismissals from 1957 to 1966.

11   Name the two seamers who helped win the 1972-73 series in the Caribbean after Dennis Lillee's back injury.

12   Name the medium pacer who swapped the record for most Test wickets with Fred Spofforth several times in the 1880s.

13   Who made 86 and took 5-28 to win a Test in Cape Town in 1994.

14   Which pace bowler captained Australia only once, in his 54th Test?

15   Who took 31 wickets, a record for Australia against India, in the 1991-92 series?

TEST • SOUTH AFRICA

1 Who has played in most Tests for South Africa?
2 Who has scored most runs?
3 Who has scored most centuries?
4 Who has the highest individual innings?
5 Who has taken most wickets?
6 Who has the best bowling figures in an innings?
7 Who has the best bowling figures in a match?
8 Who took most wickets in a series?
9 Which fielder has taken most catches?
10 Which wicketkeeper has made most dismissals?
11 Who has captained South Africa most times?
12 Who was South Africa's oldest Test player?
13 Who was the youngest?
14 Who had the longest Test career?
15 Who scored a century for both Australia and South Africa against England, each time in his first Test against them?

1 Hansie Cronje (57). 2 Bruce Mitchell (3,471). 3 Dudley Nourse (9). 4 Daryll Cullinan (275*).
5 Allan Donald (260). 6 Hugh Tayfield (9-113). 7 Hugh Tayfield (13-165). 8 Hugh Tayfield (37).
9 Bruce Mitchell (56). 10 Dave Richardson (152). 11 Hansie Cronje (41). 12 AW 'Dave' Nourse
(46 years 206 days). 13 Paul Adams (18 years 340 days). 14 AW 'Dave' Nourse (21 years 313 days).
[John Traicos 23 years 40 days for South Africa and Zimbabwe]. 15 Kepler Wessels (1982 and 1994).

Quiz 2
TEST • SOUTH AFRICA

1 Who were South Africa's last opponents before they were banned from Test cricket in 1970?

2 Who was their captain in that series?

3 Who were their first opponents when the ban was lifted in 1992?

4 Who was their captain in that match?

5 Which South African captain threw a stump through the door of the umpires' room after a Test against Australia?

6 Name either of the two batsmen who shared a record partnership of 341 in 1964.

7 Which great opening batsman scored 508 runs at 72.57 in his only Test series in 1969-70?

8 Which other batsman averaged over 50 in his only Test series in 1969-70?

9 Who in 1947 equalled a record by scoring six consecutive Test fifties?

10 Who scored a century in each of four consecutive Test innings separated by the Second World War?

11 Whose entire Test career was made up of 45 consecutive Tests from 1902 to 1924?

12 South Africa have won only one Test series 5-0, as recently as 1998-99. Who were their opponents?

13 South Africa and Zimbabwe have played each other only once at Test level, in 1995. Which South African scored a century in that match?

14 And which took eleven wickets, including 8-71 in the second innings?

15 Who reached fifty in 31 balls against Sri Lanka in 1998?

TEST • SOUTH AFRICA

1   Who scored South Africa's first double century since their return to Test cricket?

2   Wicketkeeper Adam Boucher took 26 wickets in the 1998 series in England, equalling whose national record?

3   Name South Africa's first non-white player, who made his Test debut at the age of 40 in 1992.

4   Who took 21 wickets in his only Test series at the age of in 40 in 1951?

5   Which aptly-named opening batsman took nine hours to score a Test century in 1958?

6   Who was the first South African to do the Test double of 1,000 runs and 100 wickets?

7   Who was the first South African wicketkeeper to do the Test double of 1,000 runs and 100 dismissals?

8   Who reached the Test landmarks of 1,000 runs and 100 wickets in the same match in 1998?

9   Who in 1999 achieved his boyhood dream of scoring a hundred against the West Indies on his home ground?

10 Which country dismissed South Africa for 30 in both 1896 and 1924?

11 Who in 1965 scored his third Test hundred before the age of 21?

12 Which wicketkeeper made a king pair against Pakistan in 1995?

13 Which spinner took a record 36 wickets in the 1909-10 series against England ?

14 Which spinner took a record 37 wickets in the 1956-57 series against England ?

15 Which brilliant fielder scored his maiden Test century against Sri Lanka in 1993-94?

1 Gary Kirsten. 2 John Waite. 3 Omar Henry. 4 Geoff Chubb. 5 Jackie McGlew. 6 Trevor Goddard. 7 John Waite. 8 Shaun Pollock. 9 Jacques Kallis (in Cape Town). 10 England. 11 Graeme Pollock. 12 Dave Richardson. 13 Bert Vogler. 14 Hugh Tayfield. 15 Jonty Rhodes.

Quiz 4
TEST • SOUTH AFRICA

1 Name the only pair of half-brothers to open a Test innings.

2 The longest Test match of all time was staged at Durban in 1939. How many days did it last?

3 Which South African played a Test on his home ground Edgbaston in 1998?

4 Who was the first South African fast bowler to take 100 Test wickets?

5 Who was his equally hostile partner who took 58 Test wickets?

6 Who shared opening stands of 119 and 171 with Bruce Mitchell against England in 1929?

7 Who shared a record opening stand of 260 with Bruce Mitchell against England in 1931?

8 Who shared a stand of 319 with Dudley Nourse against England in 1947?

9 Which fast bowler helped destroy Australia in 1970 and had a son who played Test cricket?

10 Which South African captain had his elbow broken by Fred Trueman in a Test?

11 How was John McIllwain Moore Commaille generally known?

12 Who in 1970 took a wicket with his last ball in Test cricket?

13 Who was South Africa's first ever Test captain?

14 Who scored 294 runs and took 26 wickets in the 1966-67 series against Australia?

15 Name the off-spinner who sometimes bowled in a leg iron because of War wounds.

Sorry mate Fred xx

TEST • SOUTH AFRICA

1   Name the wicketkeeper who didn't concede a bye in a total of 559-9 in 1938-39.

2   Who scored 182, his first Test century, and equalled a Test record with 6 dismissals in an innings of the same match?

3   Which wicketkeeper made 9 dismissals in a Test in 1992?

4   Name the 6'5 pace bowler who took 8-53 against New Zealand in 1961-62.

5   Name the fast-medium bowler who took 11 wickets on his Test debut in 1962.

6   When South Africa ended a run of 28 Tests without a win in 1951, who were their opponents?

7   Who shared a stand of 341 with Graeme Pollock against Australia in 1964?

8   Whose world record of 72 Test innings without a duck ended in 1932?

9   Who scored a hundred before lunch against England in 1929?

10 Name the Greek leg-spinner who took 9 wickets in one series and scored 122 not out in another.

11 Name the 19-year-old left-hander who scored a century against Australia in 1964.

12 Who scored 732 runs against Australia in 1910-11, the South African record for any series?

13 Name the fast-bowling all-rounder whose 26 wickets at only 13.58 helped destroy Australia 4-0 in 1969-70.

14 Who carried his bat through an innings against England in 1910?

15 Who made exactly 100 while carrying his bat against Pakistan in 1997?

TEST • SOUTH AFRICA

1   Who averaged 60.83 with the bat in his 23 Tests?

2   Who averaged 53.81 with the bat in his 34 Tests?

3   Name the great cover fielder of the 1960s who averaged 49.08 with the bat in his 21 Tests.

4   Who in 1998 became the first black South African to play Test cricket?

5   Whose bowling action has been described as resembling 'a frog in a blender'?

6   Which all-rounder once burst into the Australian changing room brandishing a rifle?

7   Which 37-year-old scored his maiden Test century in a world record stand of 195 for the 9th wicket in 1998?

8   Who in 1998 took a wicket with his last ball in Test cricket?

9   Whose Test career lasted from 1912 to 1932?

10   Who played in every one of South Africa's Test matches from 1929 to 1949?

11   Which postwar batsman had a Test career which began in 1930?

12   Who took 8-64 to win a Test against India in 1996?

13   Who reached his only Test hundred with a six off Tony Lock?

14   Who was known as 'Toey' for his habit of stubbing his toe before bowling?

15   Name South Africa's captain, now a Test match referee, when they won the 1965 series in England.

TEST • SOUTH AFRICA

1   Who took 5-74 in South Africa's first Test in England for 29 years?

2   Name the father and son who were both over 40 when they played for South Africa?

3   Which fast bowler took 36 Test wickets from 1948 to 1951 while being suspected of throwing?

4   Who flattened John Edrich with a bouncer in the Lord's Test of 1965?

5   Whose 41 Test wickets from 1967 to 1970 cost only 15.02 apiece?

6   Which Test bowler's surname was an item of footwear?

7   By what name is South Africa's Test team known?

8   What do the following have in common? Hansie Cronje, Andrew Hudson, Jonty Rhodes, Fanie de Villiers, Kepler Wessels.

9   South Africa first played Australia in 1902. No South African batsmen made a hundred in his first Test against Australia until 1963. Who scored it?

10 Who scored 120 at Edgbaston and 120 at Lord's in 1924?

11 Name the wicketkeeper-batsman who helped South Africa win the 1935 series in England but died soon after it.

12 Who took 6-43 to help beat Australia by 5 runs in 1994?

13 Who took 6-81 to help beat Pakistan by 324 runs in 1995?

14 Which captain of South Africa was born in Yorkshire?

15 Against Zimbabwe in 1995, which pace bowler fell over three times while bowling in his first Test for two years?

Quiz 1

TEST • WEST INDIES

1 Who has played in most Tests for the West Indies?
2 Who has scored most runs?
3 Who has scored the most centuries?
4 Who has the highest individual innings?
5 Who has taken most wickets?
6 Who has the best bowling figures in an innings?
7 Who has the best bowling figures in a match?
8 Who took most wickets in a series?
9 Which fielder has taken most catches?
10 Which wicketkeeper has made most dismissals?
11 Who has captained West Indies most times?
12 Who was the West Indies' oldest Test player?
13 Who was the youngest?
14 Who had the longest Test career?
15 Who completed the West Indies' first Test hat-trick, in 1959?

1 Viv Richards (121). 2 Viv Richards (8,540). 3 Garry Sobers (26). 4 Brian Lara (375).
5 Courtney Walsh (397). 6 Jack Noreiga (9-95). 7 Michael Holding (14-149).
8 Malcolm Marshall (35). 9 Viv Richards (122). 10 Jeff Dujon (272). 11 Clive Lloyd (74).
12 George Headley (44 years 236 days). 13 Derek Sealy (17 years 122 days).
14 George Headley (24 years 10 days). 15 Wes Hall.

TEST • WEST INDIES

1 Who completed a Test hat-trick in 1961?

2 Who completed the only Test hat-trick to involve both opposition innings?

3 Who scored the West Indies' first century in Tests?

4 Who scored the West Indies' first double century in Tests?

5 Which England bowler dismissed Brian Lara when he scored his world record 375 in 1994?

6 Which opening batsman was hit by an unripe guava during the 2nd Test in India in 1994?

7 Name the famous 'three Ws.'

8 In 1984 the West Indies set a record for any country by winning how many Tests in a row?

9 Who took 7-53 at Headingley in 1984 despite a fractured left thumb encased in plaster?

10 Who captained the West Indies in exactly 50 Tests?

11 Name the wicketkeeper who captained the West Indies in their first ever Test, in 1928.

12 Who was the first black player to captain the West Indies?

13 Who was the first black player to captain the West Indies on a regular basis?

14 Name the two batsmen who shared a record Test partnership of 446 in 1958.

15 Which captain won all five tosses against India in 1948-49?

1 Lance Gibbs. 2 Courtney Walsh. 3 Clifford Roach. 4 Clifford Roach. 5 Andy Caddick.
6 Phil Simmons. 7 Clyde Walcott, Everton Weekes and Frank Worrell. 8 11.
9 Malcolm Marshall. 10 Viv Richards. 11 Karl Nunes. 12 George Headley. 13 Frank Worrell.
14 Conrad Hunte and Garry Sobers. 15 John Goddard.

TEST • WEST INDIES

1 Which country drew all five Tests in the Caribbean in 1971-72 despite losing the toss every time?

2 Before Australia's 2-1 win in 1994-95, who were the last country to win a series against the West Indies, back in 1979-80?

3 Who didn't turn up at Buckingham Palace to collect his OBE in 1994?

4 The trophy contested by the West Indies and Australia is named after which famous player?

5 Who in 1972 became the only batsman to score a century in each innings of his Test debut?

6 Who in 1948 achieved the unique distinction of scoring a century in his only Test innings?

7 Which left-hander scored an unbeaten century on his Test debut in 1975?

8 Which right-hander scored a century on his Test debut in 1978?

9 Whose 1,710 Test runs in 1976 are the record for a calendar year?

10 Who took a career-best 5-17 in one Test and scored a double century in another, both against New Zealand in 1996?

11 Who scored a double century in only 232 balls to pull off an unlikely win at Lord's in 1984?

12 What were the first names of the spinners who won the 1950 series in England, 'those two little pals of mine' Ramadhin and Valentine?

13 In which year did the West Indies last lose a Test series against England?

14 How many consecutive series have the West Indies won against England?

15 Name the promising all-rounder who died in a car crash in 1959.

1 New Zealand. 2 New Zealand. 3 Viv Richards. 4 Frank Worrell. 5 Lawrence Rowe.
6 Andy Ganteaume. 7 Leonard Baichan. 8 Basil Williams. 9 Viv Richards. 10 Jimmy Adams.
11 Gordon Greenidge. 12 Sonny and Alf. 13 1969. 14 15 OG 'Collie' Smith.

TEST • WEST INDIES

1   Who played in 85 consecutive Tests, a world record at the time and still the best for the West Indies, from 1955 to 1972?

2   Which opening batsman played in 72 consecutive Tests from 1979 to 1988?

3   Name the 17-year-old who made his Test debut against England in 1954.

4   Which country beat the West Indies 5-1 in 1975-76 to decide the unofficial world title?

5   Name either of the fast bowlers who took 27 wickets each in the 1985-86 series against England.

6   Name the batsman whose first scoring stroke in Test cricket was a six against England in 1986.

7   Who in 1984 became the first bowler to take 8 wickets in an innings against the West Indies in England?

8   Which wicketkeeper took 9 catches in one Test against Australia in 1981?

9   How many Test centuries did Clive Lloyd score on his home ground Old Trafford?

10 Who missed the 1998-99 series in South Africa after cutting himself with an airline knife during the flight?

11 Which West Indies batsman has a Test average of 51.32, the highest in the current squad?

12 Name the two fast bowlers who gave England 'Bodyline' captain Douglas Jardine a taste of his own medicine.

13 Name the opening bowler who took 5-46 on his Test debut in 1962 but won only one more cap, six years later.

14 Who bowled a record 774 balls in a single Test in 1957?

15 Name the controversial fast bowler who took 32 wickets in the 1963 series in England.

TEST • WEST INDIES

1 Who was the first West Indian wicketkeeper to do the Test double of 1,000 runs and 100 dismissals?

2 Name the wicketkeeper who didn't concede a bye in a total of 619 in 1969.

3 Name the wicketkeeper who made 9 dismissals in a Test in 1995.

4 Who hit a century in 80 balls against Pakistan in 1997?

5 Name the spin bowler who took 33 wickets in his debut series against England in 1950.

6 Name the fast bowler who took 33 wickets in his debut series against Pakistan in 1976-77.

7 Name the fast bowler who took 25 wickets in his debut series against Pakistan in 1976-77.

8 Name the great batsman who played against England in 1906 but had to wait until 1928 to make his official Test debut just before his 40th birthday.

9 Name either of the batsmen who put on a record 347 for the 7th wicket against Australia in 1955.

10 Who shared a stand of 338 with Everton Weekes against England in 1954?

11 Who shared a stand of 399 with Gary Sobers against England in 1960?

12 Who shared a stand of 303 with Viv Richards against England in 1976?

13 Who shared a stand of 308 with Viv Richards against Australia in 1984 – and later succeeded him as West Indies' captain?

14 Which captain's real christian names were Franz Copeland Murray?

15 Whose middle name is St Aubrun?

QUIZ 6
TEST • WEST INDIES

1 Whose middle names were Mortimore Maglinne?

2 Whose middle names are Dudley Ashton St John?

3 Whose middle names are Elcon Lynwall?

4 Whose full christian names are Hilary Angelo?

5 Which Test fast bowler was named after another?

6 Which Test cricketer was named after a great England batsman?

7 Which batsman's surname was the Roman god of wine?

8 Which batsman's middle name is a sign of the zodiac?

9 Which fast bowler was known as 'Big Bird'?

10 Which fast bowler was known as 'Whispering Death'?

11 Who was the last East Indian before Shivnarine Chanderpaul in 1994 to play Test cricket?

12 Lance Pierre and Lance Gibbs both bowled in Test matches. What is 'Lance' short for?

13 Whose innings of 134 constituted 63.50% of a West Indies total of 211 in 1976?

14 Who in 1939 equalled a record by scoring six consecutive Test fifties?

15 Who in 1933 followed his only Test century with a duck in the second innings?

TEST • WEST INDIES

1 Who made a century and a duck in two different Tests, in 1968 and 1971?

2 Who made a century and a duck in two different Tests in the 1980s?

3 Whose century against Australia in 1961 was the only one of his first-class career?

4 Which bespectacled batsman scored 99 against England on his Test debut in 1948?

5 Who scored 100 not out in his first Test innings, against New Zealand in 1972?

6 Which country didn't enforce the follow-on against the West Indies despite a first-innings lead of 563?

7 Who scored 827 runs in the 1954-55 series against Australia?

8 Who scored 824 runs in the 1957-58 series against Pakistan?

9 Who scored 829 runs in the 1976 series against England?

10 Who scored 722 runs in the 1966 series against England despite ending it with a duck?

11 Who averaged 60.83 with the bat in his 22 Tests?

12 Who averaged 58.61 with the bat in his 48 Tests?

13 Who averaged 57.78 with the bat in his 93 Tests?

14 Who averaged 56.68 with the bat in his 44 Tests?

15 Who averaged 50.23 with the bat in his 121 Tests?

TEST • WEST INDIES

1   Who was given out 'handled the ball' against India in 1983?
2   Which country did the West Indies twice 'blackwash' 5-0 in the 1980s?
3   Which captain declared when the West Indies were 51-6 (and lost the match) against England in 1935?
4   Which country did the West Indies beat by an innings and 336 runs away from home in 1959?
5   Which country scored 849 in an innings against the West Indies?
6   Which all-rounder completed his only Test century with a six off the last ball of a Test in 1980?
7   Who in 1998 became the first Guyanese batsman since Clive Lloyd in 1973 to score a Test century in Georgetown?
8   Whose Test career lasted 18 years to the day, from 1958 to 1976?
9   Who captained the West Indies when they lost a Test series for the first time in 15 years?
10 Who captained the West Indies when they lost all three Tests in Pakistan?
11 Which country made 619 and won by 382 after Garry Sobers put them in to bat?
12 Which fast bowler bowled unchanged for over three hours in the Lord's Test of 1963?
13 Who scored a record 13 centuries against the West Indies?
14 Which opening batsman turned his maiden Test century into a double, scoring 208 in 11 hours in 1996?
15 Which opening batsman scored his maiden Test century in 1996, reaching it with a four and a six?

TEST • NEW ZEALAND

1   Who has played in most Tests for New Zealand?
2   Who has scored most Test runs?
3   Who has scored most centuries?
4   Who has the highest individual innings?
5   Who has taken most wickets?
6   Who has the best bowling figures in an innings?
7   Who has the best bowling figures in a match?
8   Who took most wickets in a series?
9   Which fielder has taken most catches?
10 Which wicketkeeper has made most dismissals?
11 Who has captained New Zealand most times?
12 Who was New Zealand's oldest Test player?
13 Who was the youngest?
14 Who had the longest Test career?
15 Who completed a hat-trick on his Test debut in 1976?

1 Richard Hadlee (86). 2 Martin Crowe (5,444). 3 Martin Crowe (17). 4 Martin Crowe (299).
5 Richard Hadlee (431). 6 Richard Hadlee (9-52). 7 Richard Hadlee (15-123).
8 Richard Hadlee (33). 9 Martin Crowe (71). 10 Ian Smith (176). 11 John R Reid (34).
12 Jack Alabaster (41 years 247 days). 13 Daniel Vettori (18 years 10 days).
14 Bert Sutcliffe (18 years 72). 15 Peter Petherick.

TEST • NEW ZEALAND

1   Who made his Test debut in 1994 after playing in 55 one-day internationals?

2   Who scored New Zealand's first Test century?

3   Who was the first New Zealander to score 5,000 runs in Test cricket?

4   Name the two batsmen who shared a record stand of 467 in 1991.

5   Which country did New Zealand beat at home for the first time in 1985?

6   New Zealand have played England in 78 Tests. How many have they won?

7   In which year did New Zealand win a Test against England for the first time?

8   In which year did New Zealand win a Test in England for the first time?

9   In which year did New Zealand win a series against England for the first time?

10 In which year did New Zealand win a series in England for the first time?

11 Who scored 259 in nearly 12 hours against the West Indies in 1972?

12 Which father and two sons played Test cricket for New Zealand?

13 Name either of the batsmen who put on a record 151 for the last wicket in 1973.

14 Who in 1994 became the first player to score a fifty and take ten wickets in a Test at Lord's?

15 When New Zealand beat India in December 1998, who achieved his best Test figures of 7-65?

1 Gavin Larsen. 2 Stu Dempster. 3 John Wright. 4 Andrew Jones and Martin Crowe.
5 Pakistan. 6 4 7 1978 8 1983 9 1983-84. 10 1986 11 Glenn Turner. 12 Walter Hadlee father of
Dayle and Richard. 13 Brian Hastings and Richard Collinge. 14 Dion Nash. 15 Simon Doull.

Quiz 3

TEST • NEW ZEALAND

1 What is the lowest innings total in Test cricket, set by New Zealand against England in 1955?

2 Who was the only player to reach double figures in that innings?

3 Who captained New Zealand for the last time in that match?

4 Name the 18-year-old whose first-class career lasted only 16 days, long enough to play in two Tests against England in 1933.

5 Who was the youngest batsman (22 years 63 days) to carry his bat in a Test innings?

6 Who celebrated his first match as captain by scoring the slowest Test century by a New Zealander?

7 Name the respected pace bowler who dismissed Len Hutton for 0 and 1 when both made their Test debuts in 1937.

8 Which spinner took 7-87 in a losing cause against Pakistan in 1984?

9 Who was the first spinner to take 10 wickets in a Test for New Zealand?

10 Name his cousin, an 18-year-old pace bowler who dismissed Graham Gooch with his third ball in Test cricket.

INTENSIVE CARE

11 Name the seam bowler, making his Test debut, who almost died after being knocked out by a bouncer in 1975.

12 Which country were dismissed by New Zealand for less than 100 in each innings in 1984?

13 Who was dismissed after scoring 99 off 81 balls against England in 1984?

14 Which all-rounder was run out for 99, his highest Test score, against England in 1992?

15 Name the wicketkeeper who made 96 Test dismissals before dying of cancer at the age of 29.

1 26 2 Bert Sutcliffe. 3 Geoff Rabone. 4 Doug Freeman. 5 Glenn Turner. 6 Jeff Crowe.
7 Jack Cowie. 8 Stephen Boock. 9 John Bracewell. 10 Brendon Bracewell.
11 Ewen Chatfield. 12 England. 13 Richard Hadlee. 14 Dipak Patel. 15 Ken Wadsworth.

Quiz 4

TEST • NEW ZEALAND

1   Name the wicketkeeper who made a record 8 dismissals in a Test in 1983.

2   Name the two Maoris in the squad for the 1994 series in England.

3   Whose appearance against Sri Lanka in 1983 was his first Test for six years?

4   Which opening batsman scored 161 in eight hours as New Zealand beat Australia for only the second time?

5   Who was the first bowler to take 100 Test wickets for New Zealand?

6   Whose Test career was made up of 58 consecutive Tests from 1949 to 1965?

7   Which left-hander scored a great batch of runs (i.e. a century) on his Test debut in 1988?

8   Name the bespectacled 19-year-old who took his 50th Test wicket in 1998.

9   Which wicketkeeper played for the West Indies against New Zealand and for New Zealand against the West Indies?

10 Who captained New Zealand in their inaugural Test in 1930?

11 Who scored a hundred and took five wickets in an innings against India in 1965?

12 Who was the first New Zealander to do the Test double of 1,000 runs and 100 wickets?

13 Who was the first New Zealander to do the Test double of 2,000 runs and 200 wickets?

14 Name the wicketkeeper who didn't concede a bye in a total of 616-5 in 1989.

15 Which ginger-haired opener shared a record partnership of 387 with Glenn Turner in 1972?

1 Warren Lees. 2 Heath Davis and Adam Parore. 3 Glenn Turner. 4 Bruce Edgar.
5 Dick Motz in 1969. 6 John Reid. 7 Mark Greatbatch. 8 Daniel Vettori.
9 Simpson/Sammy/Guillen. 10 Tom Lowry. 11 Bruce Taylor. 12 Richard Hadlee.
13 Richard Hadlee. 14 Ian Smith. 15 Terry Jarvis.

QUIZ 5

TEST • NEW ZEALAND

1 Whose Test career ended in 1983 with a run of 72 innings without a duck?

2 Which opening bowler made 5 ducks in the 1961-62 series against South Africa?

3 Who took more than 7 hours to score 102 against India in 1955?

4 Who scored 62.89 % (100) of a New Zealand innings of 159 against England in 1963?

5 What was Martin Crowe referring to when he said 'It's a bit like climbing Everest and pulling a hamstring in the last stride'?

6 Name the two batsmen who both made 120, their maiden Test hundreds, to help beat Pakistan in 1994..

7 Which 19-year-old was run out for 99, his highest Test score, against South Africa in 1954?

8 Whose 111 against Pakistan in 1955 was his maiden first-class hundred?

9 Whose 105 against India in 1965 was his maiden first-class hundred?

10 Whose 152 against Pakistan in 1976 was his maiden first-class hundred?

11 Who scored a century in his first Test innings, against England in 1930?

12 Who were New Zealand playing in 1983 when they won two consecutive Tests for the first time?

13 Who averaged 563.00 in a two-match series against New Zealand?

14 Who in 1990 took a wicket with his last ball in Test cricket?

15 Name the bowler who was recalled to the Test side in 1998 after a gap of over 7 years.

14 Richard Hadlee. 15 Mark Priest.
10 Warren Lees. 11 John Mills. 12 Sri Lanka. 13 Wally Hammond in 1932-33.
6 Bryan Young and Shane Thomson. 7 John Beck. 8 Noel McGregor. 9 Bruce Taylor.
1 Glenn Turner. 2 Dick Motz. 3 John Guy. 4 John R Reid. 5 His record 299 against Sri Lanka.

Quiz 6

TEST • NEW ZEALAND

1 Which wicketkeeper was captain in all his 12 Tests?

2 Name the New Zealand captain who made a pair against Australia in 1997.

3 Who hit hundreds in consecutive Tests of the 1995-96 series in the West Indies?

4 Who was the first New Zealander to score a Test double century?

5 Name the brothers who captained New Zealand.

6 Which father and son have both taken 100 Test wickets for New Zealand?

7 Who made 173 against India in 1990, the highest Test score by a Number 9 batsman?

8 Who admitted to tampering with the ball after taking 7-52 against Pakistan in 1990?

9 Who in 1985 was run out without facing a ball to complete a pair on his Test debut?

10 Who captained New Zealand when they won a Test against England for the first time?

11 Name the New Zealand captain who batted for nearly 10 hours to score 107 and 68 against South Africa in 1953 (no-one else scored more than 32).

12 New Zealand's captain in their first eight Tests after the War played in glasses. Name him.

13 Name the former Warwickshire batsman who shared an opening stand of 214 against Zimbabwe in 1996.

14 Which former English county cricketer made a pair, lbw each time, against England in 1997?

15 Who hit his maiden Test hundred against Zimbabwe in 1996?

Quiz 1
TEST • INDIA

1 Who has played in most Tests for India?

2 Who has scored most Test runs?

3 Who has scored most centuries?

4 Who has the highest individual innings?

5 Who has taken most wickets?

6 Who has the best bowling figures in an innings?

7 Who has the best bowling figures in a match?

8 Who took most wickets in a series?

9 Which fielder has taken most catches?

10 Which wicketkeeper has made most dismissals?

11 Who has captained India most times?

12 Who was India's oldest Test player?

13 Who was the youngest?

14 Who had the longest Test career?

15 Which leg-spinner took 242 wickets as well as being dismissed for a duck 23 times in Test cricket?

---

1 Kapil Dev (131). 2 Sunil Gavaskar (10,122). 3 Sunil Gavaskar (34). 4 Sunil Gavaskar (236 not out). 5 Kapil Dev (434). 6 Anil Kumble (10-74). 7 Narendra Hirwani (16-136). 8 Bhagwat Chandrasekhar (35). 9 Sunil Gavaskar (108). 10 Syed Kirmani (198). 11 Sunil Gavaskar (47). 12 MH 'Vinoo' Mankad (41 years 305 days). 13 Sachin Tendulkar (16 years 205 days). 14 'Lala' Amarnath (19 years 00 days). 15 Bhagwat Chandrasekhar.

TEST • INDIA

1   Who bowled Graham Gooch to end his innings of 333 in 1990?

2   Name the wicketkeeper who dropped Gooch when he'd made 36 in his innings of 333 in 1990.

3   Name either of the two batsmen who shared an Indian record partnership of 413 in 1956.

4   What was the surname of the father and two sons who played Test cricket for India?

5   Who captained India in 40 Tests despite losing the sight in one eye?

6   Name the two batsmen who put on 344 against the West Indies in 1978-79, the highest unbroken stand in Test cricket.

7   Which England bowler was banned for one Test after barging Sunil Gavaskar to the ground in 1971?

8   Name the off-spinner, now a Test umpire, who captained India in the 1979 series in England.

9   India were the first country to lose two Test series 5-0. Name either of their opponents.

10   Who in 1985 became the only batsman to score a hundred in each of his first three Tests?

11   When India finally ended their run of 31 Tests without a win in 1984, whom did they beat?

12   When Sunil Gavaskar played in his 88th consecutive Test in 1984, he took the world record from his brother-in-law. Name him.

13   The earliest date for reaching 1,000 Test runs in a calendar year is 3 May. By which Indian batsman in 1983?

14   Name the wicketkeeper who set a record by completing five stumpings in a Test innings in 1988.

15   Who made a century and a duck in each of two Tests against England, in 1952 and 1964?

1 Manoj Prabhakar. 2 Kiran More. 3 Vinoo Mankad and Pankaj Roy. 4 Lala Amarnath father of Mohinder and Surinder. 5 The Nawab of Pataudi jnr. 6 Sunil Gavaskar and Dilip Vengsarkar. 7 John Snow. 8 Srinivasaraghavan Venkataraghavan (Venkat for short). 9 England 1959, West Indies 1961-62. 10 Mohammad Azharuddin. 11 England. 12 Gundappa Viswanath. 13 Mohinder Amarnath. 14 Kiran More. 15 Vijay Manjrekar.

TEST • INDIA

1   Who scored India's slowest Test century: exactly 500 minutes in 1992.

2   Who took more than ten hours to score 201 against Pakistan in 1983, at the time the slowest double century in first-class cricket?

3   Who had just completed a Test century when his hand was broken by a ball from Winston Davis?

4   Which cavalier opening batsman scored 22 in an over on his way to a hundred against Australia in 1986?

5   Whom did Kapil Dev replace as India's highest Test wicket taker in 1985?

6   Which 17-year-old Test spinner had the names of three Hindu deities in his surname?

7   Who in 1996 averaged 105.00 with the bat and topped the batting and bowling averages in his debut Test series?

8   Which Indian captain was hospitalised by a bouncer from Charlie Griffith in 1962?

9   Who were the first country to come from behind to win a series in India?

10 Name the batsman who was called up in an emergency to play against Pakistan in 1983, missing the first day of the match.

11 The first Test in which no-balls and wides were credited to the bowler's analyses took place in 1983. Who were India's opponents?

12 Which all-rounder was promoted to open the innings in 1983 and scored his first Test century?

13 Name the 17-year-old left-arm spinner who made his debut in 1982.

14 Name the 18-year-old who took a wicket in his first over in Test cricket in 1984.

15 Which batsman was concussed by a ball from Malcolm Marshall in 1983?

Quiz 4
TEST • INDIA

1   Which wicketkeeper retired with heat exhaustion against Sri Lanka in 1982?

2   Who scored his 5,000th Test run in the Golden Jubilee Match against England in 1980?

3   Which country once took India's first four wickets without conceding a run?

4   Kumar Sri Ranjitsinhji, His Highness Jam Sahib of Nawanagar, played Test cricket for England. What was his name shortened to?

5   Sir Gajapatairaj Vijaya Ananda, the Maharajkumar of Vizianagram was India's controversial captain on the 1936 tour of England. What was his name shortened to?

6   Rameshchandra Gangaram Nadkarni once conceded only 278 runs in 212 overs against England. How was he better known?

7   Pahelam Ratanji Umrigar scored 3,631 runs for India, a record at the time. What was his name shortened to?

8   Who was India's first ever Test captain?

9   Who was India's captain when they recorded their first Test win?

10 When India played their first Test (1932) and achieved their first Test victory (1952), who were their opponents each time?

11 Who was the first Indian to do the Test double of 1,000 runs and 100 wickets?

12 Who was the first Indian wicketkeeper to do the Test double of 1,000 runs and 100 dismissals?

13 Name the wicketkeeper who didn't concede a bye in a total of 652 in 1983.

14 Whose 100th Test was Sachin Tendulkar's first?

15 Name the specialist close fielder who took 6 catches in a Test in 1971.

1 Syed Kirmani. 2 Gundappa Viswanath. 3 England. 4 Ranji. 5 Vizzy. 6 Bapu.
7 Polly. 8 Kankaiya (CK) Nayudu. 9 Vijay Hazare. 10 England. 11 Vinoo Mankad.
12 Syed Kirmani. 13 Syed Kirmani. 14 Kapil Dev. 15 Eknath Solkar.

QUIZ 5
TEST • INDIA

1 Name the Test debutant who equalled two world records by taking 5 catches in an innings and 7 in a match in 1977.

2 Who equalled a world record by taking 5 catches in an innings in 1989?

3 Who equalled a world record by taking 5 catches in an innings in 1992?

4 Which all-rounder took a record 34 wickets in the 1951-52 series against England?

5 Which leg-spinner took a record 34 wickets in the 1955-56 series against New Zealand?

6 Which leg-spinner took a record 35 wickets in the 1972-73 series against England?

7 Which all-rounder made 5 ducks in the 1983-84 series against the West Indies?

8 Who scored fifty in only 29 minutes against England in 1964?

9 Who scored fifty in only 30 balls, the fastest in all Test cricket, as well as two others in 33?

10 Who scored a Test century in only 74 balls in 1986?

11 Who in 1960 became the first player to bat on every day of a Test match?

12 Who batted on every day of a Test match in 1984-85?

13 Who batted throughout an entire day's play with Gundappa Viswanath against England in 1982?

14 Who made a century and a duck in a Test against the West Indies in 1989?

15 Which left-hander was the first Indian batsman to score a century in his first Test innings?

TEST • INDIA

1   Who scored a century in each innings against Australia in 1948?

2   Who averaged 51.12 with the bat in his 125 Tests?

3   Who were the opposition when 1,093 runs were scored for the loss of only 10 wickets in 1955?

4   Which country did India beat for the first time in 1978?

5   Which country won in Calcutta for the first time in six attempts in 1977?

6   Which negligible batsman scored 50 not out against New Zealand in November 1976?

7   Which 35-year-old conceded only 48 runs in 49 overs against the West Indies despite suffering from fibrositis?

8   Name the 5'4 pace bowler who took 74 Test wickets from 1959 to 1968.

9   In which year did India last win a series away from home?

10 Name the 35-year-old Trinidad-born all-rounder who made his Test debut in 1998.

11 Who in 1998 took his 100th catch in Test cricket?

12 Who saved a follow-on in 1990 by hitting a record four consecutive sixes?

13 Who in 1952 stumped four batsmen in his only Test?

14 India played their first Test in England in 1932. When they first won a Test there, it was enough to win the series. In which year?

15 Which captain won all five tosses against England in 1963-64?

15 The Nawab of Pataudi jnr.

11 Mohammad Azharuddin. 12 Kapil Dev. 13 Rajindernath. 14 1971

7 Polly Umrigar. 8 Ramakant 'Tiny' Desai. 9 1986 (in England). 10 Robin Singh.

1 Vijay Hazare. 2 Sunil Gavaskar. 3 New Zealand. 4 Australia. 5 England. 6 Bishan Bedi.

Quiz 7
TEST · INDIA

1 Which leading batsman went home in a huff before the 1996 Tests in England?

2 When Sourav Ganguly made a hundred in his maiden Test innings, at Lord's in 1996, which other new cap was out for 95?

3 Who captained India in the 1989-90 series, their last against Pakistan until 1998-99?

4 Whose best bowling figures are 8-86 against Pakistan in 1999?

5 Who took 8 wickets in each innings on his Test debut in 1988?

6 Who in 1995 took 6-59 in 31 overs in his first Test for five years?

7 Who were the first country to lose all three Tests of a series in India?

8 Who scored 560 runs, including a century and five half-centuries, in the 1948-49 series against the West Indies?

9 Who captained India in England when they won in 1971 and lost in 1974?

10 Name three Test cricketers whose surnames were professions.

11 Which 1990s batsman averaged 113.29 in his first seven Tests?

12 Who set a record for an overseas batsman by scoring a century in each of his three Tests at Lord's?

13 Name the wicketkeeper whose maiden Test century helped beat Australia in 1996.

14 Which country dismissed India for 100 and 66 in 1996 to win by 328 runs?

15 Who dismissed Denis Compton with his first ball in postwar Test cricket?

TEST • PAKISTAN

1 Who has played in most Tests for Pakistan?

2 Who has scored most runs?

3 Who has scored most centuries?

4 Who has the highest individual innings?

5 Who has taken most wickets?

6 Who has the best bowling figures in an innings?

7 Who has the best bowling figures in a match?

8 Who took most wickets in a series?

9 Which fielder has taken most catches?

10 Which wicketkeeper has made most dismissals?

11 Who has captained Pakistan most times?

12 Who was Pakistan's oldest Test player?

13 Who had the longest Test career?

14 In 1998 Australia's Mark Taylor played in his 99th Test. So did one of the Pakistani batsmen, who made a pair. Name him.

15 Who made his Test debut in 1998 after playing in 66 one-day internationals (despite allegedly being only 18!)?

Quiz 2
TEST • PAKISTAN

1 Name the two bowlers who bowled unchanged through a Test innings in 1956.

2 Name the two bowlers who bowled unchanged through a Test innings in 1994.

3 Who was facing the last ball when Ian Healy missed a stumping off Shane Warne that would have won Australia the 1994 series?

4 Name either of the two batsmen who shared a Pakistani record partnership of 451 in 1983.

5 Who took a wicket with his first ball in Test cricket at the age of 17?

6 Name two of the four Mohammad brothers who played Test cricket for Pakistan.

7 Who was the first batsman to be dismissed for 199 in a Test innings?

8 Which current batsman scored 100 not out on his Test debut in 1982 at the age of 18.

9 Which current fast bowler made his Test debut at the age of 18 in 1985?

10 Which current fast bowler made his Test debut in 1989 on the day before his 18th birthday?

11 Whose Test career lasted from 1959 to 1979?

12 Whose Test career lasted from 1964 to 1983?

13 Who had a run of 63 wickets in eight Tests in 1996?

14 Name either of the brothers who played against England in 1983-84.

15 Who was banned from bowling by the umpires after sending down too many bouncers in a Test in 1976?

1 Fazal Mahmood and Khan Mohammad. 2 Wasim Akram and Waqar Younis.
3 Inzamam ul-Haq. 4 Javed Miandad and Mudassar Nazar. 5 Intikhab Alam.
6 Hanif, Mushtaq, Sadiq and Wazir. 7 Mudassar Nazar. 8 Salim Malik. 9 Wasim Akram.
10 Waqar Younis. 11 Mushtaq Mohammad. 12 Majid Khan. 13 Mushtaq Ahmed.
14 Ramiz and Wasim Raja. 15 Imran Khan.

TEST • PAKISTAN

1   Who took over behind the stumps in 1980 to allow Taslim Arif to take his only Test wicket?

2   Hanif Mohammad's 337 against the West Indies in 1958 was the longest innings in first-class cricket. How many hours did it last?

3   Who twice took more than 7 hours to score a Test century?

4   Who batted for nearly 7 hours to score 189, adding 154 with his brother, against the West Indies?

5   Whose century against England in 1977 took more than 9 hours, the slowest in all Test cricket?

6   Name the two batsmen whose 190 against England in 1967 was once the record 9th-wicket partnership in all Test cricket.

7   Who was the first Pakistani batsman to score 5,000 Test runs?

8   When Ian Botham passed 5,000 Test runs at the Oval in 1987, who passed 6,000?

9   Who were Pakistan's opponents when only 95 runs were scored in a full day's play in 1956?

10 Who was the first Pakistani to do the Test double of 1,000 runs and 100 wickets?

11 Who was the second?

12 Who was the first Pakistani wicketkeeper to do the Test double of 1,000 runs and 100 dismissals?

13 Name the wicketkeeper playing his first Test for two years who hit a maiden Test century in 1993.

14 Who was given out 'handled the ball' against Australia in 1982?

15 Which opening batsman scored a double century at Lord's in 1982?

TEST • PAKISTAN

1   Which opening batsman scored a double century at Old Trafford in his first Test series?

2   When Greg Chappell, Dennis Lillee and Rod Marsh announced their retirement from Test cricket in 1984, which long-serving Pakistani did the same?

3   Who partnered Javed Miandad in a stand of 397 in 1985?

4   Name the opening bowler who broke Rod Marsh's cheekbone in 1983.

5   Whom did Zaheer Abbas overtake as Pakistan's leading run-scorer in Tests?

6   Against which country did Imran Khan score a century and take ten wickets in the same Test?

7   Who emulated Geoff Boycott by scoring his hundredth first-class hundred during a Test match?

8   Who were Pakistan's opponents when both teams scored 500 in their only innings of the 2nd Test in 1984-85?

9   Against which country did Pakistan give away a record 13 wides in an innings?

10 Against which country in 1982 did Imran Khan achieve his Test best figures of 8-58 in an innings and 14 wickets in the match?

11 Name the batsman, the son of a famous father, who scored the slowest 150 in Test cricket.

12 Which spinner was controversially hit in the mouth by a Bob Willis bouncer at Edgbaston in 1978?

13 What was significant about Nasim-ul-Ghani's maiden first-class century, at Lord's in 1962?

14 Which 19-year-old was the youngest bowler to take 50 Test wickets?

15 Which wicketkeeper made 9 dismissals in a Test in 1994?

TEST • PAKISTAN

1   Which bowler sent down 512 balls in a Test innings in 1958?

2   Name either of the batsmen who shared a partnership of 350 against New Zealand in 1972-73.

3   Who scored a hundred before lunch against New Zealand in 1976?

4   Who made a century and a duck in two different Tests in the 1950s?

5   Who made a century and a duck in two different Tests in the 1970s?

6   Who was 17 when he became the youngest player to hit a Test century?

7   Who was 19 when he became the youngest player to hit a Test double century?

8   Which No.11 helped Inzamam-ul-Haq put on 57 to beat Australia by one wicket in 1994?

9   Who in 1964 became the first Pakistani to score a century in his debut Test innings?

10 In which city did Pakistan play their inaugural Test in 1952?

11 Name either of the two players who claimed they were mugged in Johannesburg, causing the postponement of the 1st Test in 1998.

12 Name the all-rounder who scored three centuries against South Africa in the winter of 1997-98.

13 Name the 17-year-old opening bowler who won his first cap in 1998.

14 Who made a pair on his Test debut in 1990?

15 Name the wicketkeeper who in 1998 made a pair in his first Test as captain.

TEST • PAKISTAN

1   Who set a record by making his Test debut in 1998 after playing in 66 one-day internationals?

2   Name the pace bowlers who put on 191 with the bat to save the Adelaide Test in 1990.

3   Name either of the batsmen whose stand of 323 effectively won the 1997 series against the West Indies.

4   Who was dropped as captain after Pakistan collapsed for 92 to lose the 1997 series against South Africa?

5   Who made Test double centuries in England in 1971 and 1974?

6   Who helped Wasim Akram put on a record 313 against Zimbabwe in 1996?

7   Name the 19-year-old who scored a duck and a century on his Test debut in 1996.

8   Who was the first Pakistan captain to score a Test century?

9   Who took 6-16 to dismiss the West Indies for 53 in 1986?

10 Which country dismissed Pakistan for 62, their lowest ever total?

11 Who referred to Pakistani pace bowler Asif Masood as Massif Arsood?

12 Which famous batsman kept wicket in Pakistan's inaugural Test?

13 Who scored 201 to secure Pakistan's first win in New Zealand?

14 Name the brothers who scored hundreds in the same innings against New Zealand.

13 Mushtaq Mohammad. 14 Sadiq and Mushtaq Mohammad.
9 Abdul Qadir. 10 Australia. 11 Brian Johnston. 12 Hanif Mohammad.
4 Saeed Anwar. 5 Zaheer Abbas. 6 Saqlain Mushtaq. 7 Mohammad Wasim. 8 Javed Burki.
1 Shahid Afridi. 2 Imran Khan and Wasim Akram. 3 Aamir Sohail and Inzamam-ul-Haq.

Quiz 7
TEST • PAKISTAN

1   Who took 6 wickets in each innings to give Pakistan their first ever win in Australia?

2   Which player topped Pakistan's Test batting and bowling averages in the Caribbean in 1976-77?

3   Which country dismissed Pakistan for 106 to win a three-match series 3-0?

4   During the 1976-77 series in the West Indies, who retired hurt in each of two successive Tests?

5   Who scored 557 runs at 92.83 in the three Tests against Australia in 1993?

6   Name either of the batsmen who made a maiden Test hundred in the 1993-94 series in New Zealand.

7   Which fast bowler, appropriately enough, married a dentist?

8   Who took 10 wickets in a Test for the first time in 1995?

9   Who scored a century in his first Test and again in his 100th?

10 Name the pace bowler who didn't play in a Test between 1987 and 1994.

11 Who took 7-52 and 4-78 to set up Pakistan's first win in New Zealand?

12 Who played in his only Test at the age of 16?

13 Who played in his only Test at the age of 14?

14 Who was described as 'the Alec Bedser of Pakistan'?

15 Who carried his bat for 124 during his only Test series?

IT WAS ME WHO TOOK THE 10 WICKETS IN '95 ME!

---

1 Imran Khan. 2 Wasim Raja. 3 Australia. 4 Sadiq Mohammad. 5 Salim Malik.
6 Saeed Anwar and Basit Ali. 7 Waqar Younis. 8 Mushtaq Ahmed. 9 Javed Miandad.
10 Mohsin Kamal. 11 Intikhab Alam. 12 Khalid Hassan. 13 Hasan Raza. 14 Fazal Mahmood.
15 Nazar Mohammad.

Quiz 1
TEST • SRI LANKA

1 Who has played in most Tests for Sri Lanka?
2 Who has scored most runs?
3 Who has scored most centuries?
4 Who has the highest individual innings?
5 Who has taken most wickets?
6 Who has the best bowling figures in an innings?
7 Who has the best bowling figures in a match?
8 Who took most wickets in a series?
9 Which fielder has taken most catches?
10 Which wicketkeeper has made most dismissals?
11 Who has captained Sri Lanka most times?
12 Who was Sri Lanka's oldest Test player?
13 Who was the youngest?
14 Who had the longest Test career?
15 Who were Sri Lanka's first opponents in Test cricket?

1 Arjuna Ranatunga (82). 2 Aravinda De Silva (5,152). 3 Aravinda De Silva (17). 4 Sanath Jayasuriya (340). 5 Muttiah Muralitharan (203). 6 Muttiah Muralitharan (9-65). 7 Muttiah Muralitharan (16-220). 8 Rumesh Ratnayake (20). 9 Roshan Mahanama (56). 10 Romesh Kaluwitharana (58). 11 Arjuna Ranatunga (55). 12 Somachandra De Silva (42 years 78 days). 13 Sanjeeva Weerasinghe (17 years 189 days). 14 Arjuna Ranatunga (17 years 11 days). 15 England.

TEST • SRI LANKA

1 Who were Sri Lanka's first opponents in a Test away from home?

2 When Sri Lanka won a Test and a series for the first time, who were their opponents?

3 When Sri Lanka played their 50th Test match, their opponents were playing their 300th. Who were they?

4 Which country's win over Sri Lanka in 1988 was their first in 18 Tests?

5 Against which country did Sri Lanka score their world record total of 952-6 in 1997?

6 Name the two batsmen who put on 576 in 1997, the highest partnership in all Test cricket.

7 Who scored 111 and 94 in a Test against England in 1984?

8 Name the 19-year-old pace bowler who took 7-116 in an innings on his Test debut in 1994.

9 Who was hobbling on crutches just before bowling 45 overs against England in 1984?

10 Who scored a century in seven hours to save a Test against Zimbabwe in 1994?

11 Who took 8-83 in a losing cause against Pakistan in 1985?

12 Muttiah Muralitharan's 16 wickets against England in 1998 were a record for a Test at which ground?

13 Which current international player scored a fifty in Sri Lanka's first ever Test, against England in February 1982?

14 Whose only wicket cost 294 runs, making him the most expensive bowler in Test history?

15 Which wicketkeeper set a record by scoring a century and making nine dismissals in the same Test.

1 Pakistan. 2 India. 3 West Indies. 4 England. 5 India. 6 Sanath Jayasuriya and Roshan Mahanama. 7 Duleep Mendis. 8 Ravindra Pushpakumara. 9 Somachandra De Silva. 10 Arjuna Ranatunga. 11 Ravi Ratnayeke. 12 The Oval. 13 Arjuna Ranatunga. 14 Roger Wijesuriya. 15 Amal Silva.

TEST • SRI LANKA

1   Who was the first Sri Lankan bowler to take 50 Test wickets?

2   Who was the first Sri Lankan bowler to take 100 Test wickets?

3   Two batsmen scored their first Test centuries against India in 1985-86. Arjuna Ranatunga was one. Who was the other?

4   Who in 1984 scored Sri Lanka's first hundred in a home Test?

5   Which brothers opened the innings against New Zealand in 1982?

6   In 1998 Sri Lanka scored their highest innings total away from home: 591. On which ground?

7   Who captained Sri Lanka in 18 consecutive Tests in the 1980s?

8   Which former Test batsman took over as national coach in 1998?

9   Name the wicketkeeper who twice took 9 catches in a Test match.

10 Name the wicketkeeper who scored 132 not out from 158 balls in his debut Test innings in 1992.

11 Who wore new contact lenses while scoring 137 against Australia in 1992?

12 Whose double century helped win a Test against Zimbabwe in 1997-98?

13 Who returned to Test cricket after a gap of four years and helped win the 1997-98 series against Zimbabwe?

14 Who took 13 wickets at only 7.69 each in two Tests against Zimbabwe in 1996?

15 Name the wicketkeeper who had his arm broken by Courtney Walsh in 1997.

TEST • SRI LANKA

1 Who scored his maiden Test century in his 28th Test, against Zimbabwe in 1994?

2 Who joined the tour party in Australia when Muttiah Muralitharan was no-balled for throwing in 1995?

3 Who took five catches in an innings against Australia in 1996?

4 Who was the only Tamil in the team that played Australia in 1992?

5 Who had Test averages of 104.66 in Australia in 1989-90 and 98.60 in New Zealand the following year?

6 Which top-order batsman averaged 01.50 in the 1991-92 series in Pakistan?

7 Which batsman's first name is Pinnaduwage?

8 Which Sri Lankan was Kapil Dev's 432nd Test victim, a new record?

9 Who took 5 wickets in an innings for the first time on the way to becoming the first Sri Lankan to take 10 in a Test?

10 Which England nightwatchman scored 98 on his Test debut against Sri Lanka in 1988?

11 Which Indian batsman took over two hours to score 9 runs against Sri Lanka in 1994?

12 Name the wicketkeeper who took 7 catches and scored 91 on his Test debut in 1995.

13 Who took over behind the stumps and took a catch to dismiss Salim Malik in 1986?

14 Which Indian batsman has scored a record five Test centuries against Sri Lanka?

15 Which Indian spinner took 6-12 in 17.5 overs to dismiss Sri Lanka for 82 in 1990?

1 Hashan Tillekeratne. 2 Ruwan Kalpage. 3 Ravindra Pushpakumara.
4 Muttiah Muralitharan. 5 Aravinda De Silva. 6 Aravinda De Silva. 7 Arjuna Ranatunga.
8 Hashan Tillekeratne. 9 Chaminda Vaas. 10 Jack Russell. 11 Rajesh Chauhan.
12 Chamara Dunusinghe. 13 Aravinda De Silva. 14 Mohammad Azharuddin.
15 Venkatapathy Raju

TEST • ZIMBABWE

1 Which two players have appeared in all of Zimbabwe's 33 Tests so far?
2 Who has scored most Test runs for Zimbabwe?
3 Who is in second place on the list?
4 Who have scored most centuries?
5 Who has the highest individual innings?
6 The previous highest was only 121. Who set it?
7 Who has taken most wickets?
8 Who has the best bowling figures in an innings?
9 Who has the best bowling figures in a match?
10 Who took most wickets in a series?
11 Which fielder has taken most catches?
12 Which wicketkeeper has made most dismissals?
13 Who has captained Zimbabwe most times?
14 Who was Zimbabwe's oldest Test player?
15 Who was the youngest?

1 Alistair Campbell and Andy Flower. 2 Andy Flower (2,090). 3 His brother Grant (2,061).
4 Andy Flower and Grant Flower (5). 5 Dave Houghton (266). 6 Houghton himself.
7 Heath Streak (106). 8 Heath Streak (6-90). 9 Adam Huckle (11-255). 10 Heath Streak (22).
11 Alistair Campbell (33). 12 Andy Flower (78). 13 Alistair Campbell (17). 14 John Traicos
(45 years 304 days). 15 Henry Olonga (18 years 212 days).

Quiz 2
TEST • ZIMBABWE

1 Who had the longest Test career?

2 Who in October 1992 were Zimbabwe's first opponents at Test level?

3 Who was the first man since 1877 to score a century in his country's inaugural Test?

4 Who took Zimbabwe's first wicket in Test cricket?

5 Against which country did Zimbabwe achieve their first win, in 1995?

6 Against which country did Zimbabwe achieve their first away win, in 1998?

7 Who captained them in that 1998 match?

8 Who were the opposition when only 1,000 spectators watched each day of the 3rd Test at Harare in 1994?

9 Name the two Zimbabwean Test players whose christian name is Heath.

10 By which name is current Test player Mpumelelo Mbangwa usually known?

11 Name the rugby international who made his Test cricket debut aged 36.

12 Who scored more runs than any batsman on either side in the 1993 series against Pakistan?

13 Who made a pair against Pakistan in 1993?

14 Who scored a double century against Pakistan in 1995?

15 Which country dismissed Zimbabwe for 145 and 127 to achieve their first ever innings victory in a Test?

TEST • ZIMBABWE

1   Name the left-arm seamer who took 5-42 to dismiss Pakistan for 147 in 1993?

2   Who took 6 wickets for 63 runs in Zimbabwe's win over Pakistan in 1998?

3   Who sent down 50 overs in his first bowl for Zimbabwe in Test cricket?

4   Who took 5-70 in Zimbabwe's win over India in 1998?

5   Who marked his Test debut by taking Sachin Tendulkar's wicket twice?

6   Who said, after a Test defeat in Sri Lanka, 'I feel like the umpires raped us'?

7   Name the 37-year-old left-hander who returned to Test cricket with a fifty against Sri Lanka in 1996.

8   Who said 'We flippin' murdered them' after a draw with Zimbabwe?

9   Who helped Grant Flower put on a record 156 for the first wicket against New Zealand in 1997?

10   Who in 1993 became the first Zimbabwean to carry his bat through a Test innings?

11   Which bowler conceded only 54 runs in 58 overs in a Test in 1994?

12   Who took 27 wickets in the three-Test series against Zimbabwe in 1993?

13   Who took 22 wickets at only 13.54 in the three-Test series against Pakistan in 1995?

14   Which country staged a fielding practice session after beating Zimbabwe within four days?

15   Who took almost six hours to score 73 against England in 1996?

TEST • ZIMBABWE

1   Who was the first Test player born in Egypt?
2   Which Zimbabwean made his Test debut for England in 1991?
3   Which Zimbabwean Test player is a big game hunter by profession?
4   Which Zimbabwean Test player is an opera singer?
5   Which bowler played for Zimbabwe in the 1980s but in only one Test, at the age of 33, in 1995?
6   Who took three wickets in four balls against Sri Lanka in 1996?
7   Who scored a century in his first Test innings for England and later coached Zimbabwe?
8   Dave Houghton was the first Zimbabwean to score 1,000 Test runs. Who was the second, in the very next match?
9   Only two batsmen have scored two Test centuries each against Zimbabwe. For which country?
10 Who took 27 wickets in only three Tests against Zimbabwe in 1993?
11 Which Zimbabwean has bowled only one ball in Test cricket?
12 Who made his Test debut at the age of 35?
13 Who made his Test debut at the age of 37?
14 Who made his Test debut at the age of 45?
15 Who missed his maiden Test century after spending 15 minutes on 99?

TEST • POT LUCK

The 1,000th Test match took place between Pakistan and New Zealand at Hyderabad in 1984.

The 1,000th man to play Test cricket was Australia's Len Maddocks in 1954.

The 2,000th man to play Test cricket was Sherwin Campbell of the West Indies in 1995.

The first century in Test cricket was scored by Charlie Bannerman of Australia in 1877.

The 100th century in Test cricket was scored by Jack Sharp of England in 1909.

The 500th century in Test cricket was scored by Neil Harvey of Australia in 1950.

The 1,000th century in Test cricket was scored by Ian Chappell of Australia in 1968.

The 1,500th century in Test cricket was scored by his brother Greg in 1982.

The 2,000th century in Test cricket was scored by Roshan Mahanama of Sri Lanka in 1993.

The first batsman to twice score a hundred in each innings of a Test was England's Herbert Sutcliffe in 1925 and 1929.

The first batsman to score 1,000 Test runs in his debut calendar year was Mark Taylor in Australia in 1989.

The only batsman to score 1,000 Test runs in a calendar year before the First World War was Australia's Clem Hill in 1902.

The highest number of Test wickets taken in a calendar year was 85 by Dennis Lillee in 1981.

The first side to score 100 and 200 in a Test innings were Australia in 1877.

The first side to score 300 and 400 in a Test innings were England in 1880.

TEST • POT LUCK

The first side to score 400 in each innings of a Test match were Australia in 1924.

The first side to score 500 in a Test innings were Australia in 1884

The first side to score 600 in a Test innings were Australia in 1925.

The first side to score 700 and 800 in a Test innings were England in 1930

The first side to score 900 in a Test innings were England in 1938.

The current highest score is 952-6 by Sri Lanka against India in 1997.

Australia are the only country to have scored 700 in a Test innings three times.

The first six in a Test match (without the aid of overthrows) was hit by Australia's Joe Darling against England in 1898.

Of the players who didn't score a run in Test cricket, only England pace bowler Arthur Mold played as many as three innings.

The result and margin of victory in the very first Test match (Melbourne 1877) were the same as those in the Centenary Test (Melbourne 1977), Australia winning by 45 runs.

In the 1st Test of the 1990-91 series, both New Zealand and the Sri Lanka set new records for their highest team and individual score. Martin Crowe 299 out of 671-4, Aravinda De Silva 267 out of 497.

No bowler has reached 100 Test wickets without taking 5 in an innings. The closest were Phil Edmonds of England (125) and India's Ravi Shastri (151) who did it only twice.

The first batsman to be dismissed for 99 on his Test debut was Australia's Arthur Chipperfield at Trent Bridge in 1934. He was 99 not out at lunch!

TEST • POT LUCK

In January 1982, Lynton Taylor, managing director of one of Kerry Packer's companies, announced that he doubted whether Test cricket could be saved!

The first captain to put the opposition in to bat was Australia's Percy McDonnell in 1887. England were dismissed for 45, their lowest ever score – but won the match!

The highest score by a player in his last Test as captain was Ian Chappell's 192 against England in 1975.

The first time four batsmen were out in the nineties in the same Test was in 1992 (New Zealand v England): Robin Smith 96, Allan Lamb 93, Dipak Patel and John Wright both 99.

The second time four batsmen were out in the nineties in the same Test was in 1995 (England v West Indies): Graeme Hick 96, Jack Russell 91, Richie Richardson 93, Mike Atherton 95.

The only time three batsmen from the same side have been out in the nineties in the same Test was in 1935 (West Indies v England): Derek Sealy 92, Learie Constantine 90, George Headley 93.

Dermot Reeve (England 1992) was the only Test cricketer born in Hong Kong.

The fewest balls bowled in a completed Test was 872 when Australia thrashed New Zealand in 1945-46.

The earliest date of birth for any Test cricketer was 16 November 1827 (England's James Southerton).

In 1994 New Zealand's Martin Crowe became the first player to appear on the winning side against all the other eight countries.

TEST • POT LUCK

The first century partnership in Test cricket was between WG Grace and Alfred 'Bunny' Lucas in 1880.

The first double century partnership in Test cricket was between Billy Murdoch and HJH 'Tup' Scott in 1884.

The oldest ever Test player was Wilfred Rhodes, the second-oldest WG Grace. Rhodes' first Test was Grace's last.

Wilfred Rhodes had the longest ever Test career: 30 years 315 days from 1899 to 1930.

Wilfred Rhodes played Test cricket alongside Fred Tate (1902) and his son Maurice (1926).

The first triple century partnership in Test cricket was between Jack Hobbs and Wilfred Rhodes in 1912.

The first quadruple century partnership in Test cricket was between Don Bradman and Bill Ponsford in 1934.

The only quintuple century partnership in Test cricket was between Sanath Jayasuriya and Roshan Mahanama in 1997.

The first batsmen to bat throughout a full day's play in a Test were Jack Hobbs and Herbert Sutcliffe in 1925.

The first bowler to take 5 wickets in a Test innings was Australia's Billy Midwinter in 1877.

The first bowler to take 6 and 7 wickets in a Test innings was Australia's Tom Kendall in 1877.

The first bowler to take 8 wickets in a Test innings was England's George Lohmann in 1887.

The first bowler to take 9 wickets in a Test innings was George Lohmann in 1896.

The first bowler to take 10 wickets in a Test innings was Jim Laker in 1956.

The first bowler to take 10 wickets in a Test match was Australia's Fred Spofforth, who took 13 in 1879.

TEST • POT LUCK

The first bowler to take 14 wickets in a Test match was Fred Spofforth in 1882.

The first bowler to take 15 wickets in a Test match was England's Johnny Briggs in 1889.

The first bowler to take 16 and 17 wickets in a Test match was England's Sydney Barnes in 1913.

The only bowler to take 18 and 19 wickets in a Test match was England's Jim Laker in 1956.

The only bowler to take 14 wickets in a Test match twice was Sydney Barnes in 1913 and 1914 (both times in the same series)

When the famous England bowler Alfred Shaw died, he was buried a pitch length from the grave of his Notts and England team mate Arthur Shrewsbury. Twenty-seven yards, in fact (Shaw always took a five-yard run-up).

The only two Test cricketers to play Davis Cup tennis were Cota Ramaswami of India and West Indies wicketkeeper Ralph Legall.

All-rounder Chris Lewis had his head shaved at the start of the 1993-94 tour of the West Indies – and missed the first match with sunstroke!

The first player to score 100 runs and take 10 wickets in the same Test was Australia's Alan Davidson in 1960.

The second player to score a century and take 10 wickets in the same Test was Ian Botham in 1980.

The first player to make a double century and take five wickets in an innings of the same Test was Denis Atkinson for the West Indies in 1955.

Ian Botham was the only player to score a century and take 5 wickets in an innings of the same Test more than twice. He did it five times.

TEST • POT LUCK

Ian Botham achieved the double Test of 1,000 runs and 100 wickets in the quickest time, his 21st Test.

Curtly Ambrose achieved the double Test of 1,000 runs and 100 wickets in the slowest time, his 69th Test.

When Australia lost 'Botham's Test' at Headingley in 1981, and to South Africa by 5 runs in 1994, they were all out for 111, the dreaded 'Nelson' (representing the three stumps).

England and South Africa lost five wickets between them on 111 at Lord's in 1955.

Earlier in 1955, England had dismissed Australia for 111 twice in the same series.

England took South Africa's last three wickets on 111 at Durban in 1913.

The first batsman to be dismissed for 111 in a Test was AW 'Dave' Nourse of South Africa in 1921.

The first batsman to be dismissed for a double Nelson 222 was India's Gundappa Viswanath in 1982.

The only batsman to be dismissed for a triple Nelson 333 was Graham Gooch in 1990.

The West Indies reached 444-4 at Trent Bridge in 1966 – but didn't lose a wicket.

The first country to score 500 in a Test innings and lose was Australia against England in 1894.

The first batsman to hit two centuries in the same Test series was Australia's Joe Darling in 1897-98.

The first batsman to score 500 runs in a Test series was Australia's Joe Darling in 1897-98.

The first left-hander to score a Test century was Australia's Joe Darling in 1897-98.

The first left-hander to score a century on his Test debut was John Mills of New Zealand in 1930.

TEST • POT LUCK

Bob Taylor played in most Tests (30) after his 40th birthday,

Jack Hobbs scored most Test runs (2,440) after his 40th birthday.

Clarrie Grimmett took most Test wickets (96) after his 40th birthday.

Sydney Barnes averaged only 10.93 per Test wicket after his 40th birthday.

Herbert Sutcliffe (England) and Everton Weekes (West Indies) set a Test record by reaching 1,000 Test runs in only 12 innings.

The first brothers to play Test cricket were Charlie (1877) and Alec (1879) Bannerman of Australia.

The first pair of brothers to open a Test innings were Edward and WG Grace against Australia in 1880.

Rockley Wilson played in his only Test match (1921) almost 22 years after his brother Clem's last.

The first 30 Test matches (1877-1888) were all between England and Australia.

Outstanding batsmen who made a duck in their first Test innings include Graham Gooch, Len Hutton, Herbie Taylor, Victor Trumper and Gundappa Viswanath.

England wicketkeeper Alfred Lyttleton removed the pads to take 4 wickets against Australia in 1884. He later became an MP.

England all-rounder Dick Pougher had the names of New Zealand wicketkeeper Artie Dick in his own name: Arthur Dick Pougher.

Leading batsmen Denis Compton and Vijay Manjrekar both played Test cricket after having a kneecap removed.

TEST • POT LUCK

Greg and Ian Chappell made a total of 12,455 Test runs and 38 Test centuries, a record for brothers, outscoring the four Mohammad brothers of Pakistan.

Sunil Gavaskar and Gundappa Viswanath made a total of 16,202 Test runs, a record for brothers-in-law.

Joe Hardstaff's 205 not out against India in 1946 was the first Test century after the War.

The first time five runs were awarded in a Test match for a ball hitting a helmet on the ground was in the Centenary Test of 1980, David Gower picking up the unexpected bonus.

The only country to win a series after being 2-0 down was Australia against England in 1936-37.

The England-Australia Test at Edgbaston in 1989 produced the first known example of seven byes from a single ball.

The highest innings total by a side losing less than half its wickets was the West Indies' 790-3 against Pakistan in 1958.

In his 100th Test, at Karachi in 1989, Kapil Dev was attacked by a Muslim spectator who also ripped Kris Srikkanth's shirt.

The first two bowlers to take 9 wickets in a Test innings, George Lohmann in 1896 and Sydney Barnes in 1913, both did it in Johannesburg.

The first time both captain scored centuries in the same Test was in 1913: Herbie Taylor (South Africa) and Johnny Douglas (England).

The oldest Test captain was WG Grace, aged 50 years 320 days in 1899.

The youngest Test captain was the Nawab of Pataudi junior, aged 21 years 77 days in 1962.

The first batsman to share in 50 century partnerships in Tests was India's Sunil Gavaskar.

TEST • POT LUCK

Joe Solomon (West Indies) and Dilip Vengsarkar (India) were out hit wicket in Tests when their hats fell on their stumps.

Australia's Allan Border played in more Test innings than any other batsman: 265.

The first fielder to take 100 Test catches was Wally Hammond, who reached the landmark by dismissing an equally great batsman, George Headley, in 1939.

A record five batsmen scored centuries in one innings for Australia against the West Indies in 1955: Colin McDonald 127, Neil Harvey 204, Keith Miller 109 , Ron Archer 128 and Richie Benaud 121.

Australian fast bowler Ernie Jones, who once sent a bouncer through WG Grace's beard, was the first bowler to be no-balled for throwing in a Test, against England in 1898.

The first wicketkeeper to captain a Test team was Billy Murdoch of Australia in 1882.

Don Bradman's Test debut in 1928 ended in defeat by 675 runs.

The first batsman to score two not-out fifties in the same Test was George 'Jackie' Grant of the West Indies in 1930.

The only batsman to score two not-out hundreds in the same Test was Aravinda De Silva of Sri Lanka in 1997.

South Africa's Jimmy Sinclair was the only batsman to score over half his side's total in two completed innings of a Test match, hitting 106 and 4 (110) out of 177 and 35 (212) in 1899.

South Africa's Percy Sherwell took 9 stumpings in 1910-11, the record for any Test series. He was captain in all his 13 Tests.

The first wicketkeeper to make 6 dismissals in a Test innings was Wally Grout of Australia in 1957.

The first wicketkeeper to make 7 dismissals in a Test innings was Wasim Bari of Pakistan in 1979.

TEST • POT LUCK

The first wicketkeeper to make 8 dismissals in a Test match was Jim (JJ) Kelly of Australia in 1902.

The first wicketkeeper to make 9 dismissals in a Test match was Gil Langley of Australia in 1956.

The first wicketkeeper to make 10 dismissals in a Test match was Bob Taylor of England in 1980.

The only wicketkeeper to make 11 dismissals in a Test match was 'Jack' Russell of England in 1995.

The first wicketkeeper to make 20 dismissals in a Test series was Herbert Strudwick of England, who made 21 in 1913-14.

The first wicketkeeper to make 22 dismissals in a Test series was John Waite of South Africa, who made 23 in 1953-54.

The first wicketkeeper to make 24 dismissals in a Test series was John Waite of South Africa, who made 26 in 1961-62.

The first wicketkeeper to make 27 dismissals in a Test series was Rod Marsh of Australia, who made 28 in 1982-83.

The first wicketkeeper to make 100 dismissals in a Test career was Bert Oldfield of Australia in 1934.

The first wicketkeeper to make 200 dismissals in a Test career was Godfrey Evans of England in 1957.

The first wicketkeeper to make 300 dismissals in a Test career was Rod Marsh of Australia in 1982.

The first fielder to take 5 catches in a Test innings was Vic Richardson of Australia in 1936.

The first fielder to take 6 catches in a Test match was Arthur Shrewsbury of England in 1888.

The first fielder to take 7 catches in a Test match was Greg Chappell of Australia in 1974.

TEST • POT LUCK

The only fielder to take 13 catches in a Test series more than once was Bobby Simpson of Australia in 1957-58 and 1960-61.

India and Pakistan are the only countries to have held each other to a 0-0 draw in a five-Test series three times.

Of the ten youngest Test players, eight have come from Pakistan, the other two from India.

Of the ten oldest Test players, six have come from England.

Warwick Armstrong captained Australia in a record 10 Tests without ever being on the losing side (1920-21): 8 wins and 2 draws.

Ian Botham captained England in a record 12 Tests without ever being on the winning side (1980-81): 8 draws and 4 defeats.

Only one Test partnership of over 400 has involved three different players. In 1982, Dilip Vengsarkar retired hurt after putting on 99 with Gundappa Viswanath, who added a further 316 with Yashpal Sharma.

George Lohmann was the only bowler to take 8 wickets in a Test innings four times.

Kapil Dev is the only player to take part in 50 consecutive Tests more than once, 66 (1978-84) and 65 (1985-94).

Kapil Dev bowled most balls in Test cricket (27,740), conceded most runs (12,867) and took most wickets (434).

Impressionist Rory Bremner had his hand broken by a ball from New Zealand Test bowler Chris Cairns in a pro-celebrity match.

TEST • ASHES

The captains in the 1905 series were the Honourable Stanley Jackson and the Honourable Joe Darling. Jackson was later knighted.

The captains in the 1905 series, Stanley Jackson and Joe Darling, were born on the same day: 21 November 1870.

Bill Woodfull captained Australia in 25 Tests. In both 1930 and 1934 they regained the Ashes on his birthday.

Bill Woodfull was the first Australian captain to regain the Ashes in England. The second, Allan Border, did it in 1989, coincidentally in a Test which included his birthday.

The third match of the 1946-47 series was the first drawn Test in Australia since 1881-82.

The 1997 Lord's Test ended Australia's run of 18 Tests without a draw.

The oldest player to appear in an Ashes Test was Bert Ironmonger, who was 50 years old in 1933. He was nicknamed 'Dainty' because he wasn't.

The first bowler to take a wicket with his first ball in Test cricket was Arthur Coningham (1894) who later reacted to being no-balled by throwing the ball at the England captain.

Billy Murdoch (1884) and Affie Jarvis (1885) came on as substitute fielders and took catches for England.

In 1912 England's Joe Vine came on as substitute fielder and took a catch for Australia.

The first substitute to keep wicket in a Test match (and take a catch) was Arthur Jones of England in the last Test of the 1905 Ashes series.

Since 1896, no team has lost the Old Trafford Test and finished the summer holding the Ashes.

TEST • ASHES

The most Test runs between dismissals were scored by Steve Waugh against England in 1989: 393, including his first two Test centuries.

In the 5th Test against England in 1998-99 Steve Waugh set a new world record by being dismissed in the 90s for the 9th time in Test matches.

Darren Gough, who became a father on the night before the first Test of the 1994-95 series, christened his son Liam plus the first names of the batsmen he dismissed on the first day: David (Boon) and Michael (Bevan).

England selectors have had some strange reasons for picking players, none more so than in 1901-02. Suffering from what appeared to be the first stages of TB, Charlie McGahey was taken to Australia for his health!

When Wally Hammond scored his imperious 240 at Lord's in 1938, he was dropped by Arthur Chipperfield, who broke his finger in the process, took no further part in the match, and wasn't capped again.

Hugh Trumble took 141 Test wickets from 1890 to 1904, a world record at the time and all of them against England. His 45 catches in Tests were also a world record.

In the 1968 series Colin Cowdrey scored his 7,000th Test run, set a world record for most Test catches, and became the first player to play in 100 Tests.

Albert Trott played for both England and Australia, was the first bowler to take 8 wickets in an innings on his Test debut (1895), and was the only batsman to hit a ball over the pavilion at Lord's.

Pace bowler Martin McCague was a controversial choice for England's tour of Australia in 1994-95. Taunted as a 'traitor' (he learned his cricket in Australia), he conceded 96 in the only innings he bowled, was out for a duck, suffered a stress fracture, and hasn't been capped since!

TEST • ASHES

At Melbourne in 1877, Australian opener Charlie Bannerman faced the first ball in Test cricket, scored the first run, the first fifty and the first century. His 165 constituted 67.34% of Australia's innings (245), a world record that still stands.

Max Walker took so long stopping a ball from going for four during the 1975 series that the batsman ran five.

Fred Spofforth's 94 Test wickets, a world record at the time, were all taken in his 18 matches against England, at a cost of only 18.42 each. He took 5 in an innings 7 times.

Peter May's 113 in 1958-59 was the first century by an England captain in Australia since Archie MacLaren in 1901.

Steve Waugh was Angus Fraser's first Test wicket, clean bowled in 1989. They were still playing against each other in 1998-99.

Against Australia in 1905, Stanley Jackson headed the batting and bowling averages and was the first captain to win every toss in a five-Test series. England won 2-0.

Monty Noble won all five tosses against England in 1909. Australia won 2-1.

Lindsay Hassett won all five tosses against England in 1953. Australia lost 1-0.

Charlie Turner and Jack (JJ) Ferris bowled unchanged through two Test innings, against England in 1887 and 1888.

Johnny Briggs and George Lohmann bowled unchanged through two Test innings, against Australia in 1886 and 1892.

Archie Jackson scored 164 on his Test debut in the 1928-29 series and died at the age of 23 on the day Australia lost the Ashes in 1933.

Dennis Amiss, Derek Underwood and Geoff Arnold all made a pair in the 5th Test of the 1974-75 series.

TEST • ASHES

In the 1st Test of the 1894-95 series, Australia needed only 64 to win on the last day – but a hung-over Bobby Peel was held under a cold shower and took 6-67 before lunch to win the match by 10 runs.

Bobby Peel made a pair during the 1895 series, each time stumped by Affie Jarvis off Charlie Turner.

Australian captain Joe Darling made a pair during the 1902 series, each time caught by Len Braund off Sydney Barnes.

In the Old Trafford Test of 1956, left-hander Ken Mackay made a pair, each time caught by Alan Oakman off Jim Laker.

In the Old Trafford Test of 1956, left-hander Neil Harvey made a pair in barely two hours.

While Jim Laker was taking all 10 wickets in an innings in 1956, Tony Lock's figures were 55-30-69-0.

Seven centuries were scored at Trent Bridge in 1938, a record for a single Test.

The first Test to be finished within two days was the famous Oval match of 1882, when the Ashes were born.

The widest margin of victory in any Test was England's innings and 579 runs at the Oval in 1938.

The widest margin of victory by a runs margin in any Test was England's 675 runs at Brisbane in 1928.

At Melbourne in 1925, England became the first side not to lose a wicket in a full day's play in a Test match.

Don Bradman was the only batsman to score 2,000 runs against England both home and away.

In the 5th Test of the 1997 series, Adam and Ben Hollioake bowled in tandem during a partnership between the Waugh twins. They were the first brothers to bowl in the same Test innings for England.

Australia's three main pace bowlers all recorded their best Test figures in the 1997 series in England: Glenn McGrath 8-38, Mike Kasprowicz 7-36, Jason Gillespie 7-37.

TEST • ASHES

The only country to win a Test series from 2-0 down were Australia in 1936-37.

The 1970-71 series was the only one to feature a '7th Test,' added on when the 3rd was abandoned.

The first pair to put on a hundred for the last wicket in a Test were Reggie Duff and Warwick Armstrong, who added 120 against England in 1901-02.

At Trent Bridge in 1948, England slow left-armer Jack Young bowled 11 consecutive maidens, a Test record at the time, conceding only 79 runs from 60 overs.

Hedley Verity took 14 wickets in a day in the 1934 Lord's Test despite driving over a black cat on the way to the ground.

In 1997 Australia's Greg Blewett became the first batsman to score a century in each of his first three Ashes Tests.

In the 1st Test of the 1997 series, Mike Atherton equalled a record by captaining England for the 41st time and scored his 5,000 Test run.

In the same game, Nasser Hussain (207) and Graham Thorpe (138) both improved their highest Test scores in a record partnership of 288.

At Sydney in 1895, England were dismissed twice in a single day, for 65 and 72, losing by an innings and 147.

A record 27 wickets fell during the second day of the 1st Test of the 1888 series, including a record 18 before lunch.

In the decisive 4th Test of the 1961 series, one captain (Richie Benaud) bowled the other (Peter May) round his legs for a second-ball duck.

In the 4th Test of the 1946-47 series, Arthur Morris and Denis Compton both hit a hundred in each innings, the first time this had happened in a Test match.

TEST • ASHES

In his only two Tests, both in the 1950-51 series, England seamer John Warr had bowling figures of 0-142, 0-63 and 1-76 and batting scores of 4, 0, 0, 0.

In the 4th Test of the 1882-83 series, at Sydney, each of the four innings was played on a different wicket.

On his Test debut, at the Oval in 1977, Mick Malone took 5-63 in 47 overs and made 46, his highest first-class score. Then he joined Packer and didn't play in another Test.

Jack Sharp's century against Australia in 1909 was the 100th in Test cricket.

The captains in the 1956 series were both sons-in-law of other Test cricketers: Peter May (Harold Gilligan) and Ian Johnson (Roy Park). Gilligan's brother Arthur also captained England.

Alec Stewart's 8 dismissals at Old Trafford in 1997 are a record for an England wicketkeeper against Australia.

Before the 1989 series in England, Steve Waugh hadn't made a century in his first 26 Tests. He has now scored 17, seven against England.

The Waugh twins played their 50th Test together at Headingley in 1997.

Ian Healy's 300th catch in Test cricket, at Headingley in 1997, was also his 100th against England.

At Melbourne in 1959, Norm O'Neill was caught by Colin Cowdrey off Fred Trueman for a duck. Four years later he was caught in the same fielding position by the same fielder off the same bowler for the same score on the same ground!

For the first time in any Test, three bowlers took seven wickets in an innings at the Oval in 1997: Glenn McGrath 7-76, Mike Kasprowicz 7-36, Phil Tufnell 7-66.

Australia won an Ashes series for an unprecedented 5th consecutive time in 1997 and added to the record in 1998-99.

TEST • ASHES

England's dramatic win at the Oval in 1997 prompted the BBC's Match of the Day to nominate Mike Atherton as its Man of the Day.

Cyril Walters captained England in only one Test, the first of the 1934 series, in which he overbowled leg-spinner Tommy Mitchell 'because he was a chosen member of the team.'

In England's second innings of the 2nd Test in 1894-95, all eleven batsmen reached double figures, the first time it had happened in a Test match.

In the 4th Test of the 1928-29 series, all four innings reached 300. England won by 12 runs.

Graham Thorpe had to miss the final Test of the 1993 series when his thumb was broken in the nets by 17-year-old Peter Dickinson, who played for Thorpe's own club.

England's victory at the Oval in 1993 ended a record run of 18 matches against Australia without a win.

Mike Atherton's 553 runs in 1993 were the record for an Ashes series by a batsman who didn't score a century.

Terry Alderman (42) and Dennis Lillee (39) took 81 wickets in the 1981 series.

Shane Warne (34) and Tim May (21) took 55 wickets in the 1993 series, surpassing the record for a pair of Australian spinners in England set by Grimmett and O'Reilly (53) in 1934.

Between 1928 and 1938 Australia beat England only once without the help of a century by Don Bradman.

England's innings of 61 in 1902 lasted only 94 balls, the fewest they've faced in any Test innings.

The 1979-80 series featured one of the most famous scorecard entries: Lillee caught Willey bowled Dilley.

TEST • ASHES

Andrew Stoddart's 173 in 1894-95 was the highest score by an England captain in Australia until Mike Denness hit 188 in 1975.

When England were 770-6 against Australia in 1938, the next man in, wicketkeeper Arthur Wood making his Test debut, said 'Aye, I'm at my best in a crisis!' He scored 53.

The 1958-59 series was the first to be shown on Australian TV.

In the 1928-29 series, 'Stork' Hendry scored a Test hundred despite having his drink spiked with whisky by England's Douglas Jardine!

When Maurice Tate took 38 wickets in the 1924-25 series to break Arthur Mailey's Ashes record of 36, his 37th victim was Mailey himself.

Two England fast bowlers who won Ashes series in Australia, Harold Larwood (1932-33) and Frank Tyson (1954-55), later emigrated there.

On the day Graham Gooch was born in 1954, two England batsmen made ducks against Australia. On Gooch's 40th birthday, he was playing against Australia when they reached 613-4 by the end of the second day.

Australian batsmen scored 10 centuries in the series of 1920-21, 1946-47 and 1993. England scored 8 in 1938 and 1985.

Gubby Allen was born in Australia, had an uncle (Reg Allen) who played for Australia, and captained England against Australia in 1936-37.

After Mike Atherton had lost the toss for the fifth time in a row against Australia in 1997, Richie Benaud referred to him as 'Not a lucky tosser.'

In 1955, Trevor Bailey allowed himself to be bowled to give veteran Ray Lindwall his 100th wicket against England. Four years later Lindwall ended Bailey's Test career by dismissing him for a duck in each innings!

Bob Wyatt was England's captain the last time they beat Australia at Lord's, in 1934.

Against England in 1884, Percy McDonnell became the first

TEST • ASHES

batsman to score a century in each of two consecutive Test innings.

The actual Ashes, in their urn, were the ashes of a bail burned by Australian women at the end of the 1882-83 series.

The most illustrious Test hat-trick probably belonged to Jack T Hearne in 1899: Clem Hill, Syd Gregory and Monty Noble.

Syd Gregory set virtually unbeatable records by playing in 52 Ashes Tests (1890-1912) and making 8 tours of England.

Syd Gregory was the son of Ned Gregory and nephew of Dave Gregory, who both played in the very first Test match (1877), and cousin of Jack Gregory!

Jack Gregory's all-round performance in the 1920-21 series was one of the greats: 23 wickets, a batting average of 73.67, a record 15 catches.

Australian batsman Rick Darling nearly died when he was hit by a ball from Bob Willis in 1979 and his chewing gum became lodged in his throat. Prompt action by John Emburey saved him.

At Brisbane in 1936, Bert Oldfield took three catches in the first innings and made three stumpings in the second.

It's said that during the 1920-21 Ashes series a Mrs Park dropped her knitting, bent down to pick it up, and therefore missed her husband's entire international career as a batsman! Roy Park was bowled by the only ball he received in Test cricket.

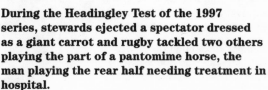

During the Headingley Test of the 1997 series, stewards ejected a spectator dressed as a giant carrot and rugby tackled two others playing the part of a pantomime horse, the man playing the rear half needing treatment in hospital.

TEST • ENGLAND

Jack Sharp (1903-09) played football as well as cricket for England. He scored a goal in his first international match and a century in his last.

Leslie Gay (1893-94) was the only player to keep goal and wicket for England.

Harry Makepeace, who also played football for England, scored his maiden Test century at the age of 39 in 1921.

Albert 'Monkey' Hornby captained England at both cricket (1882-84) and rugby.

Gregor MacGregor played cricket for England (1890-93) and rugby for Scotland (1890-96) while still a Cambridge undergraduate.

Reggie Spooner scored his only Test century in his last international year (1912) and played rugby for England against Wales in 1903.

Maurice Turnbull played cricket for England and helped Wales beat England at rugby in 1933.

George Vernon went in at No.11 in his only Test (1882-83) even though he didn't bowl. He was capped five times by England at rugby.

John Arnold won only one England cap at both football (1933) and cricket (1931). He missed chances at Hampden Park and made a duck in his first Test innings.

Against New Zealand in 1958, the England batting was opened by a football international (Arthur Milton) and a rugby international (MJK Smith).

The famous Somerset all-rounder Sammy Woods played for both England and Australia at cricket (1888-96) and for England at rugby (1890-95).

TEST • ENGLAND

Chris Old, who played cricket for England (1972-81), was the brother of Alan Old, who played rugby for England (1972-78).

Jack MacBryan, who won an Olympic gold medal for hockey, didn't bat or bowl in his only Test (1924), which was almost completely washed out.

The first three England teams to go into a Test match without a recognised spinner all lost, against Australia in 1932-33 and 1954 and New Zealand in 1984.

In 1986 John Emburey became the first slow bowler to take five wickets in an innings in the Caribbean since doing it himself in 1981.

Before a Test in 1987, John Emburey recommended that England play only one spinner on the Headingley wicket. His captain Mike Gatting agreed – and left Emburey out!

Percy Chapman, one of England's most successful captains, scored his only Test hundred in 1930, an innings that ended when he swallowed a bluebottle!

Fred Trueman once referred to his Yorkshire team mate Jimmy Binks as 'the greatest uncapped wicketkeeper who ever played cricket.' Binks was capped twice by England in 1964.

The England team who played the West Indies in April 1930 had an average age of 37 years 198 days. Two players were over 50, three others over 40.

When Andy Sandham scored 325 against the West Indies in 1930, he was using Freddie Calthorpe's bat and wearing Patsy Hendren's boots!

Teddy Wynyard, who played in his first Test in 1896 and his second ten years later, captained the Old Carthusians in the 1881 FA Cup final, scoring the first goal in a 3-0 win.

TEST • ENGLAND

Father and son Frank and George Mann both captained England against South Africa.

Father and son Colin and Chris Cowdrey both captained England against the West Indies.

When Chris Cowdrey dismissed Kapil Dev with his fourth ball in Test cricket, his father Colin, listening on the radio, was so astonished that he drove the wrong way down a one-way street.

When Dean Headley won his first cap in 1997, it was the first time three generations of the same family had appeared in Test cricket. His father Ron (1973) and famous grandfather George (1930-54) played for the West Indies.

Jim Parks and his son Jim Parks jnr both played for England. Jim junior's son Bobby kept wicket for England as a replacement.

Bernard Bosanquet, generally regarded as the inventor of the googly, was the father of the well-known ITV newsreader Reginald Bosanquet.

Because of confusion over their initials, Test batsman Fred Fane and his father both read their own obituaries.

Chris Old's best Test figures (7-50 in 1978) included four wickets in five balls, the third of which was a no-ball.

Ossie Wheatley was the chairman of selectors who vetoed the re-appointment of Mike Gatting as England captain in 1989. As Ian Botham said, 'Most of the players wouldn't have known Ossie Wheatley from Ossie Ardiles.'

Future England captain Mike Denness came on as a substitute fielder for the Rest of the World in 1970 and helped Eddie Barlow take a hat-trick against England.

In 1984, Tony Pigott postponed his wedding to win his only cap – but needn't have bothered. The ceremony was scheduled for the fourth day of the Test, which England lost in three!

Pace bowler Norman Cowans, whose 6-77 helped to win the Melbourne Test in 1982, was England's 500th Test cricketer.

TEST • ENGLAND

Against Pakistan in 1982, Bob Willis became the first specialist fast bowler to play 100 Test innings.

Bob Willis finished his Test career with a record 55 not-out innings.

The tallest England captains were Tony Greig (6'7) and Bob Willis (6'6)

Bob Willis took over as England captain against New Zealand in March 1978 when Geoff Boycott's eye was scratched by a contact lens.

In India's Golden Jubilee match in 1980, Geoff Boycott carried on with his innings despite being given out by the umpire. No-one was unduly surprised.

Against Australia in 1968, Colin Cowdrey celebrated becoming the first player to play 100 Tests by scoring a century in the first innings.

Graham Gooch's duck at Lord's in 1996 was his first in 60 Test innings.

Graham Gooch scored his first 1,000 Test runs without making a century.

Graham Gooch didn't score a Test century until his 36th innings (1980), then went on to make 20 in total.

Mike Gatting scored his first Test century (1984) in his 54th Test innings.

Mark Ramprakash scored his first Test century (1998) in his 38th innings.

Graham Gooch shared eight century opening stands against the West Indies, with eight different partners.

England three times won a Test while losing only two wickets, beating South Africa in 1924, New Zealand in 1958 and India in 1974.

Ted Dexter gave up the England captaincy in 1964 to contest the General Election. He lost in Cardiff South-East to future Prime Minister Jim Callaghan.

TEST • ENGLAND

The 1998 series against South Africa was the first England have won after being one down with two to play.

Top-order batsmen who were dismissed by the first ball they faced in Test cricket include Ernest Tyldesley (1921), Bob Wyatt (1927) and Les Ames (1929)

Respected medium-pacer Derek Shackleton, who had to wait 11 years for his fourth England cap, was virtually blind in one eye.

When England were dismissed for 71 and 126 by the West Indies at Old Trafford in 1976, their top scorer was Extras (19 and 25).

When England were dismissed for 227 by Pakistan at Lord's in 1982, their top scorer was Extras (46).

JR Webber's planned biography of WG Grace is expected to run to 1,500,000 words, twice the length of War And Peace.

John McLaren played in only one Test, in 1912, making 0 not out in each innings.

England's youngest Test captain was Monty Bowden. aged 23 years 144 days in 1889.

England captain JWHT Douglas sometimes scored so slowly that his initials were translated as Johnny Won't Hit Today.

George Lohmann set world record bowling figures in consecutive Tests against South Africa in 1896: 8-7 and 9-28.

Geoff Arnold set a record by twice taking a wicket with the first ball of a Test match: Sunil Gavaskar in 1974 and John Morrison of New Zealand in 1975.

Against Australia in 1947, Godfrey Evans set a record by taking 97 minutes to score his first run.

Ian Botham hit 24 runs from an over by Derek Stirling (New Zealand) in 1986 after being hit for 24 in an over by Andy Roberts (West Indies) in 1981.

TEST • ENGLAND

Only two sides have won a Test match after following on, England beating Australia in 1894 and 1981.

Mickey Stewart was an England player in the 1960s and an England manager in the 1990s, when one of his players was his son Alec.

In 1961-62, England played a Test in Pakistan then five in India then went back to Pakistan to play two more.

Charles Palmer was England's tour manager when he played his only Test, in Barbados in 1954, making a duck in the second innings.

Opening batsman Charlie 'Jack' Russell scored a century in each innings against South Africa in 1923. The last three innings of his Test career were 96, 140 and 111.

The first England batsman to carry his bat through a Test innings was little Bobby Abel against Australia in 1892.

The first England batsman to twice carry his bat through a Test innings was Len Hutton in 1950 and 1951.

The only batsman to score 99 while carrying his bat was Geoff Boycott against Australia in 1979.

Future England captain Pelham 'Plum' Warner scored a century while carrying his bat on his Test debut in 1899.

Wilf Barber bowled only two balls in Test cricket, taking a wicket with the second, against South Africa in 1935.

Graham Gooch was the only batsman to score a triple century and a century in the same Test, against India in 1990.

The first substitute to make a Test stumping was Neville Tufnell against South Africa in 1910.

The first batsman given out obstructing the field was Len Hutton against South Africa in 1951.

TEST • ENGLAND

England equalled a Test record by losing 8 consecutive Tests in 1920 and 1921.

England set a Test record by scoring 503 runs in a day against South Africa in 1924.

The number of balls in an over in Test matches in England has varied as follows: 4 from 1880 to 1888), 5 from 1890 to 1899, 6 from 1902 to 1938, 8 in 1939, 6 again from 1946 to the present day.

Angus Fraser's 8-53 in 1998 surpassed his own 8-75 as the best bowling figures by an England bowler against the West Indies.

In his 50th Test as captain, at Georgetown in 1998, Mike Atherton made 0 and 1, dismissed by Curtly Ambrose each time. England lost by 242 runs.

Ian Botham was issued with a writ for £100,000 from his solicitors following his unsuccessful libel action against Imran Khan in 1996.

Playing in his only Test in 1933, 37-year-old Charles 'Father' Marriott took 5-37 and 6-59, the best match figures on debut for England this century.

While the West Indies were scoring 324 and 223 at Lord's in 1995, England didn't bowl a no-ball or a wide.

Patsy Hendren played in two series in the West Indies after his 40th birthday.

Alf Gover, who bowled for England before and after the last War, is the oldest surviving Test cricketer (b.1908) but has no birthday in 1999: he was born on February 29th.

Pace bowler Ken Farnes missed out on a Test hat-trick in 1938 when Denis Compton dropped a catch off the third ball.

Pace bowler John Price missed out on a possible Test hat-trick in 1971 when Pakistan's last man fell ill.

Against Zimbabwe in 1996, Mike Atherton broke Peter May's record by captaining England for the 36th consecutive time.

TEST • ENGLAND

Alec Stewart was the world's leading run maker in Tests in 1998, with 793.

More than 80 players have won only one Test cap for England. None scored more runs than Norman Oldfield, who made 80 and 19 against the West Indies in 1939.

WW 'Dodger' Whysall, who played in four Tests in the 1920s, died of septicaemia after falling (dodging someone?) on a dance floor.

The England team in the 1st Test of the 1992-93 series in India was made up of players from 11 different counties.

Peter Smith arrived at the Oval to play against the West Indies in 1933 only to find that the invitation was a hoax. He finally made his Test debut 13 years later.

Between Peter Smith in 1947 and Graham Gooch in 1975, no cricketer with a moustache played Test cricket for England!

The first day of the Trent Bridge of 1957 was Peter Richardson's 26th birthday, which he celebrated by scoring 126 in a partnership of 266 with Tom Graveney.

Tom Graveney made 258, his highest first-class score, against the West Indies in 1957. In 1966 he returned to Test cricket with 459 runs at 76.50 against the same opposition.

Ken Barrington's 10th Test century was his first in England.

Ken Barrington was the first England batsman to score centuries on all six English Test grounds and against six other countries.

After Ken Barrington had scored 137 against New Zealand in 1965, he was dropped for scoring too slowly. When he came back later in the same series, he made 163!

OVAL CRICKET GROUND

TEST • ENGLAND

After Geoff Boycott had made his highest Test score, 246 not out against India in 1967, he was dropped for scoring too slowly, even though England won by 6 wickets.

Soon after his only Test, in 1880, WG Grace's brother Fred became the first Test cricketer to die, aged only 29.

England captain George Mann made Test history against New Zealand in 1949 by declaring on the first day.

Paul Kinneir (1911), Rockley Wilson (1921) and Harry Lee (1931) all played in their only Test after their 40th birthday..

England used four different captains against the West Indies in 1988 – Mike Gatting, John Emburey, Chris Cowdrey, Graham Gooch – and lost the series 4-0.

Four England captains, past and present, played in the 1977 Centenary Match: Mike Brearley, Tony Greig, Keith Fletcher and Bob Willis.

Archie MacLaren (1897) and Allan Lamb (1990) both scored a century in their first Test as England captain.

Archie MacLaren captained England in a record 22 Tests against Australia, losing 11. England lost all five series in which he was captain.

Among regular bowlers, far and away the most economical in Test cricket was Billy Attewell (1884-93) who conceded only 21.96 runs per 100 balls.

Among regular bowlers, the best strike rate belongs to George Lohmann (1886-96) who averaged a wicket every 34.11 balls.

Devon Malcolm was the first player to play against six different countries in six consecutive Tests.

Test players Colin Blythe, Johnny Briggs and Tony Greig were epileptics. Briggs died in an asylum.

TEST • ENGLAND

Johnny Briggs took 8-11 (all bowled) in a Test innings in 1889. He was one of the very few players to achieve a hat-trick and score a century in Tests.

When Johnny Briggs took 15 wickets in a Test in 1889, the only other England wicket taker was Arnold Fothergill, who took 3.

Neil Foster bowled in his first Test, against New Zealand in 1983, with two metal plates in his back.

The 1987-88 series in New Zealand included the first Test to end on February 29th.

Sandford Spence Schultz, who made his only Test appearance in 1879, changed his name to Storey at the time of the First World War.

The oldest wicketkeeper in any Test was Frank Woolley, who deputised for Les Ames at the age 47 years 87 days in 1934.

The oldest first-choice wicketkeeper in any Test was Herbert Strudwick in 1926, aged 46 years 202 days.

Nick Cook took 32 wickets in his first four Tests (1983-84), breaking a record set by Tom Richardson in 1895.

Kenny Palmer, later a Test umpire, played for England as an emergency replacement against South Africa in 1965. His bowling figures in his only Test were 1-189.

The first Test captain to put the opposition in to bat was Andrew Stoddart, against Australia in 1895, in the 45th Test to date. England were dismissed for 65 and 72 and lost by an innings and 147.

Mike Atherton has taken only two Test wickets, five years apart, but they were good ones: Dilip Vengsarkar and Wasim Akram.

The first teenager to play Test cricket for England was Denis Compton, aged 19 years 83 days in 1937.

TEST • ENGLAND

TV and radio commentator Jonathan Agnew took only four Test wickets (1984-85) at a cost of 93.25 each.

In 1998, Phil Tufnell played his 33rd Test and became the 33rd England player to take 100 Test wickets.

Nasser Hussain's 106 in Antigua in 1998 maintained his record of scoring more hundreds than fifties in Test cricket.

Joe Hardstaff and Jim Parks had sons with the same christian names who also played Test cricket for England.

The entire first-class careers of Charles Coventry and Basil Grieve began and ended with England's two Tests in South Africa in 1889.

In the 2nd Test of that series, Joseph McMaster made a duck in his only first-class innings.

The last player to be capped by England without playing for a first-class county was David Townsend, who opened the batting against the West Indies in 1934-35.

Wally Hammond was the first batsman to score double centuries in successive Test innings and the only one to do it twice: 251 and 200 against Australia in 1928-29, and 227 and 336 not out against New Zealand in 1933.

Robin Smith's century against Sri Lanka in 1993 was his 8th in Test cricket but first outside England.

Chris Broad's six Test centuries were all scored abroad.

In his Test and first-class career, pace bowler Bill Bowes took more wickets than he made runs: 1,638 to 1,529 and 68 to 28.

Ian Botham was refused entry into the USA in 1998 because of his drug conviction in 1985.

The England eleven who played in the 1st Test against Australia in 1902 all scored first-class centuries.

Albert Trott and Schofield Haigh bowled unchanged throughout an innings in 1899, taking 4-19 and 6-11 respectively to dismiss South Africa for 35.

TEST • ENGLAND

Sydney Barnes and Frank Foster bowled unchanged throughout a South African innings in 1912. taking 5-16 and 5-25 respectively. They took 9 wickets in the second innings.

Sydney Barnes bowled unchanged throughout both of South Africa's innings at the Oval in 1912, taking 5-28 and 8-29.

Sydney Barnes' 49 wickets in 1913-14 are the record for any series – but it could have been more. He refused to play in the 5th Test because accommodation wasn't provided for his wife and son.

At Old Trafford in 1936, England scored 571-8 in only 375 minutes. Six Indian bowlers conceded more than 60 runs each.

Aubrey Smith, later a Hollywood actor, was the only player to captain England in his only Test, against South Africa in 1889.

England were dismissed for 99 by the 1994 South Africans, their lowest total at Lord's since 1888.

Phil DeFreitas bowled 30 no-balls in the 1st Test against New Zealand in 1994.

George Street played only one Test, as a replacement against South Africa in 1923. He kept wicket, opened the batting, and died less than two years later.

Andy Lloyd's helmet, dented by Malcolm Marshall in 1984, is now in the museum at Edgbaston!

Tim Robinson scored 160 in his second Test (1984) and retired with contact lens trouble in his third.

John Selby was apparently dropped from the England team for 'misbehaving' with team mate William Scotton's wife.

Norman Mitchell-Innes played his only Test innings, in 1935, while in his second year at university.

TEST • ENGLAND

Fast bowler Tom Richardson was a real workhorse, averaging 33 overs per Test innings and over 6 wickets a match. In one Test he bowled a remarkable 68 five-ball overs in the first innings and 42.3 in the second.

Les Ames made 8 dismissals in one Test against the West Indies and hit his highest Test score (149) against them in another.

Against Pakistan in 1967, substitute Alan Bull (who never played first-class cricket) took a catch to dismiss Asif Iqbal.

The first Test in which an extra day was added because of rain was between New Zealand and England in 1947.

The England selectors did well to persevere with Bill Edrich. He averaged 40.00 in his 39 Tests (1938-55) but only 8.00 in his first 11 innings.

The England selectors did well to persevere with Dennis Amiss. He averaged 46.30 in his 50 Tests (1966-77) but only 18.31 in his first 12.

Charles Studd, who played for England in the 1880s, later became a missionary in Africa and China.

The only player to play in three Tests without batting was Fred Root in 1926.

England's 644-5 in the Timeless Test in Durban in 1939 is the highest fourth-innings total in first-class cricket.

Eddie Paynter scored four centuries and averaged 59.23 in Tests despite having lost two fingers in an accident.

Only four players batted against South Africa at Lord's in 1924. They made a double hundred, two hundreds and a fifty as England declared at 531-2 and won by an innings.

Against Pakistan in 1996, Simon Brown and Alan Mullally became the first pair of left-arm seamers to play in the same England team since before the First World War.

TEST • ENGLAND

The first English batsman to score a Test century away from home was George Ulyett in 1882, who also took 7-36 to beat Australia in 1884.

The first pair of batsmen to bat throughout a full day's play in a Test were Jack Hobbs and Herbert Sutcliffe, against Australia in 1925.

Hobbs and Sutcliffe were also the first pair to bat throughout an entire Test (!), against Australia in 1926 when only 50 minutes' play was possible because of rain.

England's win in their first Test of 1992 made them the first side to win three consecutive matches against three different countries: West Indies, Sri Lanka and New Zealand.

Phil Tufnell's 7-47 improved the best figures for an England bowler in a Test in New Zealand, beating Fred Trueman's 7-75 in 1963.

Colin Cowdrey scored centuries in Jamaica and Trinidad in both the 1959-60 and 1967-68 series.

Dominic Cork's 7-43 against the West Indies in 1995 were the best figures by a bowler making his England debut. Jack (JJ) Ferris took 7-37 in 1892 but had previously played for Australia.

The first England player to make a pair in a Lord's Test was Johnny Wardle in 1956.

In a first-class career of 316 matches, Harry Wood's only century was made in a Test match against South Africa in 1892.

Alec Stewart's unbeaten 101 against Zimbabwe in 1996 was his 9th Test century and his first as a wicketkeeper.

Mike Brearley's Test batting average was 22.88. In his 66 Test innings, he failed to score a century.

No leg-spinner played Test cricket for England between Robin Hobbs in 1971 and Ian Salisbury in 1992.

TEST • ENGLAND

The first England left-hander to score a hundred on his Test debut was Graham Thorpe, as recently as 1993.

Walter Lees took 26 wickets at 17.96 in his only Test series, against South Africa in 1905-06.

England wicketkeeper Herbert Strudwick took three catches as a substitute in a Test innings in 1904.

Trevor Bailey typically took well over 7 hours to score 68 in a Test innings in 1958.

Wally Hammond's 905 runs in 1928-29 are still the record for an England batsman in a Test series.

Seam bowler Paul Allott made 52 not out, his maiden first-class fifty, on his Test debut in 1981.

Famous Yorkshire bowlers George Hirst and Wilfred Rhodes dismissed Australia for 36 in 33 overs in 1902.

George Hirst and Wilfred Rhodes put on 15 runs for the last wicket ('we'll get 'em in singles') to win a Test against Australia in 1902.

WG Grace's 9 wins as captain over Australia were a record before Mike Brearley.

Denis Compton scored 5,807 Test runs at an average of 50.06 in all Tests but only 53 at 7.57 in the 1950-51 series against Australia.

When England were all out for their lowest ever score, 45 in 1887, their top score of 17 was made by seam bowler George Lohmann.

Frank Woolley made 95 and 93 in the same Test in 1921.

England lost only 5 wickets in beating India by an innings in 1979, all of them taken by Kapil Dev.

Ian Botham scored only one 50 in his twelve Tests as England captain.

During the 1980-81 series in the Caribbean, the rest day of the 1st Test was taken early to avoid clashing with a steel band festival.

TEST • ENGLAND

The smallest England players were both known as 'Tich': leg-spinner Percy Freeman was 5'2, wicketkeeper Walter Cornford barely over five feet.

England players who played Test cricket in glasses include Geoff Boycott, Bill Bowes, Jack Crawford, Paul Gibb, Charles Palmer and MJK Smith.

England players who became vicars include Tom Killick, Vernon Royle and David Sheppard. And one of Doug Wright's names was Parson!

The following were all middle names of England cricketers: Crisp, Firebrace, Gibbons, Ledger.

After problems regarding his involvement in a rebel tour to South Africa, Robin Jackman took a wicket with his fifth ball in Test cricket.

In Kingston in 1981, Robin Jackman finished an over started by Graham Dilley, whose boots needed repairing.

Against Pakistan in 1984, Graham Dilley was no-balled six times in his first over.

Against Pakistan in 1982, Robin Jackman, David Gower and Allan Lamb were all out for 0 after eating duck the night before!

Roland Butcher was born close to the Kensington Oval in Barbados and made his Test debut there in 1981. He was the first black West Indian to play for England.

In Bombay in 1981, England restricted India to 179 and 227 but still lost by 138 runs after making 166 and 102.

When Ian Botham achieved the Test double of 2,000 runs and 200 wickets, he did it in the fewest matches (42), the shortest time (4 years) and at the youngest age yet (26).

TEST • ENGLAND

Derek Underwood once took the wickets of India's No.1 and No.11 batsmen in the same over.

After breaking Garry Sobers' aggregate record of Test runs, Geoff Boycott was sent home early from the 1981-82 tour of India.

Geoff Boycott's time at the crease in Test matches added up to over 450 hours, the equivalent of fifteen 24-hour days.

England's game in Calcutta in 1982 was watched by 394,000 spectators, a record for any cricket match.

In the 5th Test of the 1981-82 series in India, England used ten bowlers in the second innings (Paul Allott was injured) while Graham Gooch kept wicket for 12 overs.

In terms of balls faced, England's fastest double century was Ian Botham's 208 off 226 deliveries against India in 1982.

Against Australia in 1982, Chris Tavaré set a record by not scoring a run off 89 consecutive balls.

Against Pakistan in 1982, Chris Tavaré set a record by not scoring for an hour, twice, in the same innings.

When Graeme Fowler and Chris Tavaré scored centuries against New Zealand in 1983, they were the first England openers to do so in the same innings since 1960.

William Gunn and his nephews George and John all played Test cricket.

George Gunn, who was in Australia for his health in 1907-08, was called up for the 1st Test and scored 119 and 74 on his England debut.

George Gunn had a gap of almost 18 years in his Test career (1912-30), apparently because he didn't reply to a letter from the England selectors!

Billy Gunn played football and cricket for England and played and umpired in the same Test match (1887).

TEST • ENGLAND

Robin Smith's brother Chris was lbw to the first ball he faced in Test cricket (1983) and took 264 balls to score his first Test fifty, both times against New Zealand.

England's defeat by the West Indies at Lord's in 1984 was their first after a declaration in their second innings since 1948.

England's defeat by the West Indies at Headingley in 1984 marked the first time they'd lost the first three Tests of a home series since 1921.

Graham Gooch celebrated his 41st birthday in 1994 by becoming the first batsman to score 2,000 runs on any Test ground (Lord's).

Charles (CB) Fry played cricket and football for England as well as equalling the world record for the long jump in 1893.

Denis Compton won an FA Cup winner's medal with Arsenal in 1950.

In 1984-85 England became the first country to win a series in India after going 1-0 down.

England won six lbw decisions in one innings against the West Indies in 1986 – but still lost by 10 wickets.

England were gifted 94 extras by the West Indies in 1986 – but still lost by 240 runs.

When England lost their 6th successive match, in 1986, they changed captains – and lost their 7th.

The first time both sides were dismissed for identical scores in the first innings of a Test was in 1910, when South Africa and England both made 199.

England and India were both dismissed for 390 in their first innings at Edgbaston in 1986.

England used four wicketkeepers in one Test in 1986: Bill Athey, substitutes Bob Taylor and Bobby Parks, and Bruce French.

TEST • ENGLAND

David Gower was called for deliberately throwing the last ball of a Test in 1986 when New Zealand were certain to win.

Against New Zealand in 1986, with the first ball of his return to international cricket after suspension, Ian Botham equalled the world record for most Test wickets.

Rain at Lord's in 1987 stopped England from fielding in a home Test for the first time since 1931.

England fielded an unchanged team throughout the five-Test series against Australia in 1884-85.

England used 25 players against Australia in 1909, and lost the series 2-1.

England used a record 30 players against Australia in 1921, and lost the series 3-0.

England used 23 players against the West Indies in 1988, and lost the series 4-0.

The 1965 Edgbaston Test against New Zealand was played in such cold weather that two of the drinks intervals involved hot drinks!

At Headingley in 1947, pace bowler Ken Cranston ended South Africa's second innings by taking four wickets in six balls.

Wally Hammond and Stan Worthington were both bowled by Mahomed Nissar of India in 1936, but not before they'd each scored a century and shared a record stand of 266.

At Lord's in 1935, Les Ames and Herbert Sutcliffe both batted with a runner against South Africa, who won a Test in England for the first time. Sutcliffe wasn't capped again.

TEST • ENGLAND

Wally Hammond finished two Tests with a six, in Australia in 1933 and the West Indies in 1935.

Gubby Allen bowled three wides and four no-balls in one over against Australia in 1934.

The partnership of 246 by Les Ames and Gubby Allen against New Zealand in 1931 was the highest for the 8th wicket in Tests until 1996.

England's opening bowlers in a Test against the West Indies in 1948, Gubby Allen and Harold Butler, had an average age of 40.

England's opening batsmen in a Test against the West Indies in 1976, Brian Close and John Edrich, had an average age of 42.

Wicketkeeper Lieut.-Col. Ron Stanyforth went off injured against South Africa in 1928 and wasn't capped again. He captained England in all his four Tests.

Great batsman Wally Hammond also took 83 Test wickets, including 5-36, his best figures, on his Test debut in 1927.

The opening stand of 179 between Mike Atherton and Mark Butcher against South Africa in 1998 was the highest by any country in the 34 Tests held at Edgbaston.

When England bowled out Australia for 81 and 70 in 1888, the match was over before lunch on the second day.

When England bowled out South Africa for 95 and 93 in 1912, the match was over before lunch on the second day.

David Denton's only century in eleven Tests (1910) was made at a run a minute.

George Simpson-Hayward, the last lob bowler to take wickets in Test cricket, took 8 of them on his Test debut in 1910.

Wilfred Rhodes took 15 wickets in one Test in 1904 – despite having eight catches dropped off his bowling!

Reginald 'Tip' Foster's 287 in 1903, the highest in Test cricket till then, is still the highest by a batsman making his Test debut.

TEST • ENGLAND

During his innings of 287 in 1903, Reginald 'Tip' Foster became the first batsman to share three century partnerships in the same Test innings.

Only 9 players have set the highest individual score in a Test. Only one, Reginald 'Tip' Foster, didn't live to see his record broken.

No declarations were allowed in Test cricket until 1889.

Tim O'Brien made three ducks in Oxford v Cambridge matches, another in his debut Test innings, another in his Test comeback, and three in his eight Test innings, in which he averaged 7.37.

By the time he captained England in 1896, Tim O'Brien had become Sir Timothy Carew O'Brien, Third Baronet.

One of the victims of the first Test hat-trick, by Fred Spofforth in 1879, was Francis Alexander McKinnon, the 35th McKinnon of McKinnon.

The Hon. Ivo Francis Walter Bligh captained England and became the 8th Lord Darnley.

England's first ever Test captain in the Caribbean was the Hon. Frederick Somerset Gough Calthorpe.

Kumar Sri Ranjitsinhji, His Highness the Jam Sahib of Nawanagar scored Test centuries for England, as did his nephew Kumar Sri Duleepsinhji.

Of England's first ever Test eleven (1877), five were born in Yorkshire and three in Sussex.

Pat Pocock played Test cricket with Colin Cowdrey (1968-69) and his son Chris (1984-85).

Test all-rounder Charlie Absolom died when a crane dumped a cargo of sugar on him in Trinidad.

Dick Barlow was a famous defensive batsman but his best Test performance was with the ball: 7-44 against Australia in 1886. He was later a Test umpire.

TEST • ENGLAND

The 'Major' in Test all-rounder Major Booth's name was his christian name, not a military rank. When he died in the First World War, he was Second Lieutenant Major Booth!

Brian Close captained England in seven Tests (1966-67), winning six and drawing the other.

Graham Roope was batting at the other end when both John Edrich and Geoff Boycott (in a Test) made their hundredth hundreds.

All three Grace brothers (Edward, Fred and WG) made ducks in Test cricket.

Fred Grace had no luck. Overshadowed by his famous brother WG, he made a pair in his only Test and died soon after it at the age of 29.

Arthur Hill had a short but successful Test career (1896): four wickets for only eight runs in 40 balls; a century; a batting average of 62.75.

Andy Sandham's 325 against the West Indies in 1930 was the first triple century in a Test and represented more than a third of his entire Test output.

When he hit the first triple century in Test history, Andy Sandham was playing in his last Test at the age of 39.

The surname of England captain 'Shrimp' Leveson-Gower was pronounced 'Loosen-Gore.'

Bill Lockwood, a famous pace bowler, took 43 Test wickets at only 20.55 each – after narrowly escaping a shark attack.

Frank Milligan played in two Tests in South Africa and died there the following year during the siege of Mafeking.

TEST • ENGLAND

Both of Lionel Palairet's Test matches involved close finishes, England losing by three runs and winning by one wicket against Australia 1902.

Wally Hammond (1947) and Len Hutton (1955) hit England's top score in their final Test innings, both against New Zealand at the end of tours Down Under.

Len Hutton was picked as captain for all five Tests against South Africa in 1955 but dropped out with lumbago and didn't play for England again.

England won the only Triangular Tournament held in one country (1912), winning four and drawing two of their six Tests.

Against South Africa in 1907, all-rounders Len Braund and Gilbert Jessop put on 145 at the remarkable rate of two runs a minute.

When England won a Test by 288 runs in 1896, their highest individual score was only 43 – but South Africa were dismissed for 93 and 30.

Keith Fletcher took over 7 hours and 329 balls to score a century at the Oval in 1974, the slowest Test century made in England .

Sydney Barnes averaged exactly 7 wickets per match (189 in 27), the highest average for any bowler who took over 100 in Tests.

England's lowest innings total against Pakistan is the same home and away: 130 in 1954 and 1987.

Jack Sharpe scored 44 runs and took 11 wickets for England from 1890 to 1892, despite being blind in one eye.

England's total of 416-4 against New Zealand in 1931 was enough to squeeze in three individual hundreds, by Sutcliffe (117), Duleepsinhji (109) and Hammond (100 not out).

TEST • AUSTRALIA

Don Bradman and Richie Benaud captained Australia in a total of eleven Test series, losing none.

Richie Benaud put the opposition in to bat three times in Test matches, winning all three.

Don Bradman is the only pre-war Test captain still alive.

Three of Australia's all-time greats, Greg Chappell, Dennis Lillee and Rod Marsh, played their first and last Tests in the same series: 1971 and 1983-84.

Rod Marsh took a record 95 Test catches off Dennis Lillee's bowling. Uncannily, he made exactly the same number of dismissals as Lillee took wickets: 355.

Greg Chappell scored a century in both his first and last Test innings: 1970 and 1984.

In 1969, Doug Walters became the first batsman to score a double century and a century in the same Test.

When Ian Healy had to fly home from the tour of Pakistan in 1994 after breaking his thumb, his replacement Phil Emery played in his only Test – and had to go off with a badly bruised thumb!

Walter Giffen, brother of the famous George, scored 2, 0, 1, 3, 3 and 2 in his only three Tests, figures which might have been a better if he hadn't lost the tops of two fingers in 1886.

'Fast bowlers are quick,' said former Australia captain Ian Chappell. 'Just watch this. Admittedly it's in slow motion.'

Australia produced the only great-grandfather and great-grandson to play Test cricket: Billy Cooper (1881-84) and Paul Sheahan (1967-74).

When Allan Border averaged 74.42 in the 1983-84 series in the Caribbean, the next best was Wayne Phillips' 25.80.

TEST • AUSTRALIA

Allan Border surprised everyone, including himself, by taking 11-96 in a Test in 1989, the best match analysis by an Australian captain. He also scored Australia's slowest Test fifty.

In 1985 Allan Border became Australia's first left-handed captain since Joe Darling eighty years earlier.

In 1957 Ian Craig became Australia's youngest ever captain: 22 years 194 days.

Two players called Wayne Phillips played Test cricket for Australia, one in the 1980s, the other in 1992.

The 1st Test of the 1983-84 series against Pakistan was the first in Australia in which no-balls and wides were added to the bowlers' analyses.

When Australia played Sri Lanka for the first time, in 1983, five of their first six batsmen were left-handed.

In Australia's 3rd Test against the West Indies in 1981-82, Greg Chappell broke a finger, Kim Hughes broke a toe, Dennis Lillee strained his groin, and Rod Marsh was hit on the head in his record 80th Test!

Against India in 1979, Geoff Dymock took 7-67 and 12 wickets in the match, his best Test figures, and dismissed every batsman at least once.

David Boon's 7,422 Test runs included only one six.

Between 1881 and 1947, all Test matches in Australia were played to a finish, i.e. there were no draws.

When Brian Taber made 8 dismissals against South Africa in 1966, it was not only the first Test he played in but the first he'd ever attended.

The only bowler to twice concede 300 runs in a Test was Arthur Mailey, against England in 1921 and 1924.

Fred Spofforth's 14-90 in 1882 were the best Test figures by an Australian until Bob Massie's 16-137 in 1972.

TEST • AUSTRALIA

In 1901-02 Clem Hill became the first batsman to be dismissed for 99 in a Test and the only one to be dismissed in the nineties in three consecutive Test innings.

Australia won the 1977-78 series against India on the 42nd birthday of their captain Bobby Simpson.

As well as his 309 in a day in 1930, Don Bradman scored 200 Test runs in a day six times.

The only batsman to score two separate Test fifties on the same day was Monty Noble against England in 1899. He was not out each time.

Jack Moroney made a century in each innings against South Africa in 1950 and a duck in each innings against England in 1950.

The Chappell brothers Ian and Greg provided the only example of two batsmen scoring centuries in each innings of the same Test, against New Zealand in 1974.

Don Bradman's Test record of a centuries in 6 consecutive Tests (1937-38) might have been even better: he couldn't bat in the 7th and scored centuries in the 8th and 9th.

At Lord's in 1890, Jack Barrett was promoted to opener in the second innings and became the first Australian to carry his bat through a Test innings.

Bill Brown scored 206 in carrying his bat at Lord's in 1938.

The first batsman from any country to carry his bat twice was Bill Woodfull in 1928 (when Australia batted two short) and 1933.

Australia were the first country to lose 7 Tests in a row, from 1885 to 1888.

Australia were involved in both Test matches which ended in a tie, against the West Indies in 1960 and India in 1986.

Syd Gregory, who played for Australia from 1890 to 1912, was born at the Sydney Cricket Ground, where his father was a groundsman.

TEST • AUSTRALIA

The best Test match figures by a player on the losing side were Merv Hughes' 13-217 against the West Indies in 1988.

Darren Lehmann was 12th man for Australia in 1989-90 but didn't play in a Test match until 1998.

Charlie Turner took 5-41 and 4-52 against England in 1887, but Australia still lost by 71 runs.

Charlie Turner took 5-44 and 7-43 against England in 1888, but Australia still lost by 126 runs.

When Mark Taylor took his 40th catch off Shane Warne in Tests (1997) he set a new record for a fielder off any one bowler.

George Coulthard umpired a Test match (1879) before playing in one (1882).

Patrick George McShane played in his first Test (1885) after umpiring the previous one.

Otto Nothling was the only player to be capped by Australia at cricket (1928) and rugby (1921-23).

Michael Slater's 219 against Sri Lanka in 1995 was Australia's 500th Test century.

Mark Waugh's first ten Test centuries were all made at different venues, including six in Australia.

Against the West Indies in 1995, the Waugh twins shared a partnership of 231 during which each scored his 8th Test century.

The five leading Test run makers in 1993 were all Australian, headed by David Boon (1,241) and Mark Taylor (1,106). Boon scored his 5,000th and 6,000th runs in Test cricket.

Shane Warne (72) and Merv Hughes (57) were the world's leading wicket takers in Tests in 1993.

Shane Warne (68) and Glenn McGrath (63) were the world's leading wicket takers in Tests in 1997.

TEST • AUSTRALIA

Two Australian bowlers made striking Test debuts at Melbourne in 1960-61, Frank Misson taking a wicket with his second delivery and Johnny Martin taking three in four balls.

Howell finished off South Africa in 1902 by taking the last three wickets in four balls.

Clarrie Grimmett took 44 wickets in his last series, in South Africa in 1935-36, including 13 in his final Test. On the way, he became the first bowler to take 200 Test wickets.

The Test at Sydney in 1947 was the first in Australia to be totally ruined by rain, which wiped out all but 10 hours of play.

SHANE WARNE WINS THE DERBY. A horse of that name won the Pakistan Derby in 1996.

The biter bit. Glenn McGrath was dismissed by the first ball he faced in Test cricket, bowled by New Zealand seamer Murphy Su'a in 1993.

In one Test in 1992-93, off-spinner Tim May had the remarkable figures of 5-9, made 42 not out, and celebrated his 31st birthday.

Pace bowler Mike Kasprowicz had to wait till his third Test, in 1997, to take his first Test wicket.

Don Bradman's lowest average in any Test series, the 1932-33 Bodyline rubber, was pretty good by most people's standards: 56.57.

The first black player to play Test cricket for Australia was Sam Morris, who won a single cap in 1885.

Australia scored a record 12 centuries in the 1954-55 series against the West Indies.

Australia didn't win a series against the West Indies between 1976 and 1995.

Five Australians scored centuries in one Test innings in 1955 – this after Les Favell had made 0 and Arthur Morris 7, leaving Australia 7 for two wickets!

TEST • AUSTRALIA

Three days after his father died, Ian Healy became the first wicketkeeper to appear in 100 Tests.

Lindsay Kline's hat-trick against South Africa in 1958 was made up of the last three wickets of the match, which Australia won by an innings.

No wonder Australia lost 4-0 to South Africa in 1969-70: they dropped 30 catches in the four matches!

Don Bradman scored a hundred in each innings against India in 1948. In the next Test of the series, Vijay Hazare scored a hundred in each innings for India.

Steve Waugh won the 1995 series in the Caribbean by scoring 200 at No.5 – while staying in hotel room 5-200.

In his first Test as captain (1964) Bobby Simpson put South Africa in to bat and hit the winning runs.

In Johannesburg in March 1994, Mark Taylor didn't bring Shane Warne on till the 49th over in the first innings and the 44th in the second. Australia lost by 197 runs.

In the three Tests of the 1993-94 series in South Africa Shane Warne bowled 190.5 overs, an average of 38 per innings.

Allan Border scored 27 Test hundreds but none between 1988 and 1992, a gap of 61 innings.

The first Australian to be given out after a look at a video replay was Ian Healy, run out against New Zealand in 1993.

Before the 1969-70 series in South Africa, Australian captain called Ian Chappell 'the best batsman in the world.' Chappell made three ducks in the series, in which he averaged 11.50.

TEST • AUSTRALIA

Australia's leading bowlers of the late 1990s, Glenn McGrath and Shane Warne, both reached 100 Test wickets in 23 Tests.

As former Test batsman Peter Burge began to put on weight, he was known as 'the fastest growing sport in Australia.'

Opening batsmen Michael Slater and Mark Taylor both took their first Test wickets in the same innings in 1994.

Pace bowler Graham McKenzie took 246 Test wickets but only one in the 1969-70 series in South Africa at a cost of 333 runs.

Simon O'Donnell played in 87 one-day internationals but only six Tests for Australia.

Merv Harvey, Neil's brother, opened the innings in his only Test, against England in 1947.

John Benaud, Richie's brother, was dropped despite scoring 142 against Pakistan in 1973.

Steve Waugh was voted Man of the Series in three consecutive rubbers against South Africa.

In his first series abroad, in the West Indies in 1990-91, Steve Waugh's brother Mark topped the batting and bowling averages.

Eric Freeman's first scoring stroke in Test cricket (against India in 1968) was a six. He then took two wickets in his first 10 balls.

Australia's series win in 1996-97 was their first in South Africa since 1957-58.

Craig McDermott took almost half of his first-class wickets (677) in Test matches (291).

The partnership of 385 between Greg Blewett and Steve Waugh in 1997 was the highest for any wicket in a Test in South Africa.

The first Australian captain to win consecutive series against the West Indies was Mark Taylor in 1994-95 and 1996-97.

TEST • AUSTRALIA

Don Bradman's 974 runs against England in 1930 are still the world record for any Test series.

Lindsay Hassett declared when Australia were 32-7 at Brisbane in 1950 – and won the match.

Paul Reiffel headed Australia's bowling averages against England in 1993 and the batting in 1997.

Off-spinner Ashley Mallett dismissed Colin Cowdrey in his first over in Test cricket.

Even for someone nicknamed Rowdy because he wasn't, Ashley Mallett once batted remarkably soporifically, having taken sleeping tablets instead of salt pills.

David Hookes celebrated his first cap by equalling a Test record with five successive fours off Tony Greig in the Centenary Test of 1977.

Doug Walters scored 15 Test centuries but none in four visits to England.

Terry Jenner, later Shane Warne's personal coach, was hit on the head when he ducked into a short ball by John Snow in 1971.

Jack (JJ) Ferris took five wickets in an innings four times for Australia and twice in his only Test for England.

'Jack' Badcock scored a Test hundred in 1937 but averaged only 4.57 in eight Test innings the following year.

Hard to know why Australia kept picking Jack Badcock when his scores in the 1938 series in England were 9, 5, 0, 0, 4, 5 not out, 0 and 9!

When Australia were dismissed for their lowest ever Test score, 36 in 1902, Victor Trumper scored exactly half their runs.

Victor Trumper top-scored in four consecutive Test innings in 1904.

TEST • AUSTRALIA

When Australia were all out for 42 against England in 1888, only Tom Garrett reached double figures, and even he managed only 10.

Of Australia's first ever Test eleven (1877), four were born in England, one in Ireland, and another in India!

Wicketkeeper Gil Langley missed the Old Trafford Test of 1956 after damaging his hand by sleeping on it.

The full christian names of off-spinner Gerry Hazlitt were Gervys Rignold.

Ken Burn was chosen as a wicketkeeper for the 1890 tour of England. It was only when he was on the ship that his team mates realised he'd never kept wicket in his life! He played as a batsman in two Tests.

Australia's captain Warwick Armstrong accidentally (and illegally) bowled consecutive overs in a Test in 1921.

When temperamental fast bowler Arthur Coningham tried to divorce his wife for adultery with a Catholic priest! he took a revolver into the courtroom.

In his last match before his first retirement from international cricket, Bobby Simpson achieved his best Test bowling figures: 5-59 against India in 1968.

In the same match that he set a new record by captaining Australia for the 31st time (1977), Bobby Simpson took his 100th catch in Test cricket.

In one Test in 1991, Allan Border scored his 9,000th Test run, the West Indies' Desmond Haynes scored his 6,000th, and Craig McDermott took his 100th Test wicket.

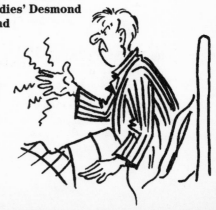

In 1991 Australia dismissed the West Indies for 149, their lowest total at home for 18 years – and still lost by 343 runs.

TEST • AUSTRALIA

Non-striker Ian Redpath was run out without a warning while backing up by West Indies fast bowler Charlie Griffith in a Test in 1969.

Wally Grout celebrated his Test debut in 1957 by becoming the first wicketkeeper to take six catches in a Test innings.

In the 1954-55 series in the West Indies, Australia scored 700 in one innings, 600 in two more, and 500 in another. Not surprisingly, they didn't lose a Test while winning three.

Australia's innings of 199-8 was enough to win a Test in 1946 by an innings and 103 (!). New Zealand were all out for 42 and 54.

Australia's innings of 382 was enough to win a Test in 1947 by an innings and 226. India were all out for 58 and 98.

Australia's first innings of 75 was enough to a Test in 1950 (!). South Africa didn't enforce the follow-on, were caught on a spinners' wicket, and lost by 5 wickets.

Australia's first innings of 520 wasn't enough to win a Test in 1953. South Africa won by 6 wickets to square the series.

In three consecutive Tests in South Africa in 1935-36, Jack Fingleton made a century, Clarrie Grimmett took 10 wickets, and Australia won by an innings.

Against the West Indies in 1931, Don Bradman was dropped when he'd made 4 and went on to score 223.

In his first innings against South Africa in 1931-32, Don Bradman was dropped when he'd made 11 and 15 and went on to score 226 – then 112, 2, 167 and 299 not out!

Don Bradman was absent hurt against South Africa in 1932 – and in both innings against England in 1938, when Jack Fingleton joined him on the sidelines.

Australia scored 494 runs in a day against South Africa in 1910.

TEST • SOUTH AFRICA

South Africa's first win, in their 12th Test (1906), was by the smallest margin (one wicket). The last pair put on 48 to win the match.

Having had to wait till he was 39 before winning his first cap, Jimmy Cook was dismissed by the first ball he faced in Test cricket, caught by Sachin Tendulkar off Kapil Dev in 1992.

Wicketkeeper Dave Richardson made a pair against Pakistan in 1995. In the previous match, he'd scored his only Test century!

When Jimmy Matthews achieved the unique feat of a hat-trick in each innings of a Test match, against South Africa in 1912, his third victim each time was Tommy Ward, who made a king pair in his first Test!

Tabs Taberer once won a bet by throwing a cricket ball 100 yards while standing in a bathtub.

Colin Wesley made a king pair against England in 1960, dismissed by Brian Statham each time.

Although George Bissett had bowled him for a single in 1928, England opener Percy Holmes was confident before the next Test: 'I can play bloody Bissett with a broom handle.' Bissett dismissed him for a duck in each innings!

In 1896, Joe Willoughby of South Africa and George Lohmann of England dismissed each other for 0 in each innings.

Eiulf Peter 'Buster' Nupen took 11 wickets in a Test in 1930. Not bad for someone with only one eye. He'd lost the other as a young man while knocking two hammers together. Don't ask.

South Africa fielded an unchanged team throughout the five matches against England in 1905-06, winning a Test and a series for the first time.

TEST • SOUTH AFRICA

The 1998 series was the first in England to show the speed of each delivery on a screen. It was no shock that the fastest ball (93 mph) was bowled by Allan Donald.

In South Africa's 50th Test against England (1998) Allan Donald took his 50th wicket of the year and his 50th against England.

On his Test debut in 1939, wicketkeeper Ronnie Grieveson took four catches off Norman Gordon. Grieveson's death in 1998 left Gordon as South Africa's oldest surviving Test cricketer.

Arthur Ochse, who made his debut on the day after his 19th birthday in 1889, was South Africa's youngest Test cricketer before Paul Adams in 1995.

Jimmy Sinclair hit six sixes in his rapid-fire 104 against Australia in 1902.

Jimmy Sinclair, who scored South Africa's first three Test centuries (1899-1902), was also capped at rugby, scoring the try that helped the Springboks win a series for the first time (1903).

Frank Mitchell was capped by both England and South Africa at cricket (1899-1912) and England at rugby (1895-96). He was captain in his last international in each sport.

JH 'Biddy' Anderson played in one Test for South Africa and three times at rugby (1903), the first rugby series ever won by the Springboks.

'Kim' Elgie appeared in three cricket Tests for South Africa and kicked five points when Scotland ended their record run of 17 successive rugby defeats by beating Wales in 1955.

Tony Harris scored 60 in his first Test innings (1947) but was better known as a brilliant rugby fly-half, helping South Africa to win the famous 1937 series in New Zealand.

Percy Twentyman Jones made a pair in his only Test (1902) but scored a try in the first rugby match won by South Africa.

TEST • SOUTH AFRICA

William Milton, who appeared in South Africa's first three Tests (1889-92), had previously played for England at rugby, as did two of his sons.

HG 'Tuppy' Owen-Smith averaged exactly 42 in Test cricket, scoring a century in 1929 against England, whom he represented at rugby.

Albert Powell won a single cap at both rugby (1896) and cricket (1899).

Alf Richards was bowled for a duck in his last Test innings (1896) and won three caps at rugby, in which he was a controversial international referee.

Googly bowler Reggie Schwarz played in 20 Tests (1906-12) and played rugby for England, who lost all three matches without scoring a try.

Clive van Ryneveld captained South Africa in the 1956-57 series with England, for whom he'd played superbly at rugby, scoring two tries against Scotland in his last international.

WS 'Buster' Farrer played tennis at Wimbledon before making his Test debut in 1962.

Percy Sherwell was South African tennis champion in 1904. Lionel 'Doodles' Tapscott also played tennis for South Africa.

Wicketkeeper captain Percy Sherwell batted at Number 11 against England in the 1905-06 series and scored a century while opening the batting against England in 1907.

Philip and Reggie Hands played in the same Test for South Africa in 1914. Reggie was also capped by England at rugby.

Philip Hands won the DSO and Military Cross in World War I, during which his brother Reggie died. Test batsman Pieter Van der Bijl also won the Military Cross in World War I.

TEST • SOUTH AFRICA

The 10-day Test against England in 1939 was the only one in which two bowlers sent down more than 700 balls each: Norman Gordon and Chud Langton.

Percy 'Plum' Lewis made a pair in his only Test, against England in 1913, each time caught by Frank Woolley off Sydney Barnes.

Against Australia in 1921, opening batsman Jack Zulch was bowled by a ball from Ted McDonald that broke a piece off his bat on the way. He was given out hit wicket.

A record 9 batsmen were bowled in one South African innings against England in 1889. The odd man out was run out.

A record 23 batsmen were bowled in one Test between South Africa and England in 1896.

All eleven South African batsmen reached double figures in an innings against England in 1906.

The first Test in which extras provided the highest score in an innings was between England and South Africa in 1912: 17 out of 58.

A record 20 players bowled in the 3rd Test between England and South Africa in 1964-65.

South Africa's series win in Sri Lanka in 1993 was their first away from home since 1965.

South Africa set a record by losing their first 8 Tests, from 1889 to 1899.

South Africa were the only side to be dismissed for under 50 in each innings of a Test match: 47 and 43 by England in 1889.

When they were dismissed for 47 and 43 by England in 1889, seven of the South African players made ducks but none made a pair.

TEST • SOUTH AFRICA

Against Sri Lanka in 1998, opener Gerry Liebenburg was out to the first ball he received in Test cricket – then was dropped off his first ball in the second innings!

Murray Bisset was South Africa's youngest Test captain, aged 22 years 306 days in 1899. He then had to wait 10 years for his next cap.

The 2nd Test against India in 1996-97 was the first in which South Africa scored four centuries, including two by Gary Kirsten.

South Africa's captain Hubert Deane was known as 'Nummy' because his hand was numbed when he lost a finger joint as a boy.

Paul Winslow once hit his Test team mate Hugh Tayfield for two consecutive sixes, both caught by the same spectator.

South Africa won each of the four Tests against Australia in 1969-70 by a wider margin than the last: 179 runs, an innings and 129, 307 runs, 323 runs.

South Africa improved on that by beating Sri Lanka by an innings and 208 in 1993. Their first match in England since 1965, at Lord's in 1994, brought their biggest win by a runs margin: 356.

Left-armer William 'Gobo' Ashley took 7-95 in the only Test innings in which he bowled, against England in 1889. But South Africa were dismissed for 47 and 43.

Brothers Alec and George Hearne and their cousin Jack all played for England in Cape Town in 1892. A third brother Frank was playing for South Africa, as did his son, another George, in 1922-23. Jack W Hearne, who also played for England, was a distant cousin!

Twice in the 1902-03 series against Australia, a player captained South Africa in his only Test: Henry 'Tabs' Taberer and JH 'Biddy' Anderson.

TEST • SOUTH AFRICA

In the last Test of the 1957-58 home series against Australia, fast bowler Neil Adcock allegedly averaged four bouncers an over. He took only three wickets as South Africa lost by 8 wickets.

At Trent Bridge in 1965, the Pollock brothers set up South Africa's last win in England before 1994, Graeme scoring 125, Peter taking 5 wickets in each innings.

Current Test batsman Adam Bacher is the nephew of Ali Bacher, who captained South Africa in 1970.

In the 1938-39 series against England, South Africa's first innings consisted of 5 fifties and 5 ducks.

Herbie Wade captained South Africa in every one of his ten Tests (1935-36).

In one Test in 1957, Hugh Tayfield sent down 137 consecutive balls without conceding a run, a record in all first-class cricket.

In the Test after that, Tayfield bowled throughout the last day, delivering 35 eight-ball overs in almost five hours.

If Gary Kirsten had held a catch at short leg in 1995, Mike Atherton would have been the only batsman to be dismissed for 99 in a Test three times.

Leading Test all-rounder Trevor Goddard became a vicar, fast bowler Peter Pollock a lay preacher.

The following all made a pair in their only Test match: Clarence Wimble (1892), Percy Twentyman Jones (1902), Percy 'Plum' Lewis (1913), Cec Dixon (1914), John Du Preez (1967).

South Africa used no fewer than six seam bowlers in the 3rd Test of the 1966-67 series against Australia.

During the 1888-89 tour Charles Finlason angered the England players with his comments as a journalist. They had their revenge by dismissing him for 0 and 6 in his only Test.

In 1932, South Africa dismissed Australia for 153 – but still lost by an innings! All out for 36 and 45, their aggregate of 81 is the lowest by any side losing all 20 wickets in a Test.

TEST • SOUTH AFRICA

South Africa have been playing Test cricket since 1889, but not until 1992 did a South African batsmen score a hundred on his Test debut, Andrew Hudson making 163 in Barbados.

Anton Murray, who shared a record Test partnership of 246, was the youngest commissioned officer in South African military history: 17 in 1939.

When Bruce Mitchell scored 120 and 189 not out at the Oval in 1947 he became the first South African to score 300 runs in a Test.

The start of the 5th Test of the 1930-31 series was held up because no-one could find bails that fitted the stumps.

Against Sri Lanka in 1993, Kepler Wessels scored an unusual 6: five of the runs were overthrows from two fielding errors.

South Africa first played Australia at home in 1902 and first beat them at home in 1966.

South Africa's visit in 1955 was the first series in England to produce five definite results. South Africa lost three Tests with Jack Cheetham as captain and won two under Jackie McGlew.

South Africa's defeat in Johannesburg in 1997 was their first by an innings since 1964 and their worst against Australia since 1950.

In that 1997 match South Africa were all out for 130 despite having Test century makers coming in at Nos. 8 and 9.

Test wicketkeeper Tom Campbell was knocked unconscious when he fell out of a mail train, then died in an accident involving another mail train.

Bob Catterall's entire Test career consisted of 24 consecutive matches against England from 1922 to 1931.

In his only Test, against Australia in 1970, Paul Chevalier took a wicket with his 5th ball and made 0 and 0 not out.

THE ULTIMATE FACT AND QUIZ BOOK

TEST • SOUTH AFRICA

In 1957 Russell Endean became the first batsman to be given out 'handled the ball' in Test cricket. In 1951 he was involved when Len Hutton was given out for obstructing the field.

Ernest 'Barberton' Halliwell introduced the famous old wicketkeeping habit of putting a piece of raw steak in the gloves to protect the hands.

When England's George Mann caught Norman 'Tufty' Mann during the 1948-49 series, John Arlott won the race to call it 'Mann's inhumanity to Mann.'

Tufty Mann's first bowling spell in Test cricket, at Trent Bridge in 1947, consisted of 8 consecutive maidens to Denis Compton and Bill Edrich.

Compton and Edrich made hay against South Africa that summer, for Middlesex and England. In the Tests, they scored 1,305 runs at an average of 100.38. They even took 7 wickets in the 2nd Test.

England medium-pacer George Lohmann set all kinds of records in taking 35 wickets against South Africa in 1895-96. He later moved to South Africa for his health but died there at the age of 36.

No other Test cricketer had the same christian names as Sivert Vause Samuelson.

Two Test cricketers who were very game: Joe Partridge and Eric Quail Davies.

Major Robert Stewart's only Test was against an England team managed by Major Wharton.

Test batsman Robert Poore was ADC to England captain Lord Harris and later became a Brigadier-General.

TEST • SOUTH AFRICA

George Thornton (1902) had a mathematically perfect little Test career. One match, one run, one wicket, one catch!

Aubrey Faulkner scored South Africa's first double century: 204 against Australia in 1910-11.

Aubrey Faulkner was the only player to score 200 runs and take 8 wickets in the same Test.

Aubrey Faulkner had some of the best all-round figures in Test cricket: 1,754 runs at 40.79, 82 wickets at 26.58.

South Africa fielded four legspin/googly bowlers in the Headingley Test of 1907 (Faulkner, Schwarz, Vogler, White) but England slow left-armer Colin Blythe took 8-59 and 7-40 to win the match.

Bert Vogler's unbeaten 62 against England in 1906 was the highest score by a No.11 batsman in a Test until 1973.

SJ 'Tip' Snooke was the first South African to take 8 wickets in a Test innings (1906). His brother Stanley played in his only Test the following year.

South Africa first played Australia in 1902. Their first win was in 1911 and their second in 1952.

South Africa's victory at Trent Bridge in 1951 ended a run of 28 Tests without a win.

Against Australia in 1935, Dudley Nourse made a duck in the first innings and 231 in the second, a new highest score for South Africa!

Australia's Jack Gregory hit a century in only 70 minutes in 1921. At the other end of the scale, in the same Test, South Africa's Charlie Frank took nearly 9 hours to score 152.

South Africa used ten bowlers in an Australian innings of 578 in 1911 – and lost by 530 runs.

TEST • SOUTH AFRICA

HF Mosenthal took two catches as substitute fielder against England in 1896 and never appeared in another Test.

In a one-off Test in 1892, Frank Hearne made his debut for South Africa after playing for England, and Jack (JJ) Ferris and Billy Murdoch played their debuts for England after playing for Australia.

South Africa made 18 single-figure scores in a Test in 1889. They were bowled out for 47 and 43.

Six England batsmen had higher scores than South Africa's total of 30 at Edgbaston in 1924.

South Africa have been dismissed for under 50 in a Test innings a record seven times, the last against Australia (twice in the same Test) in 1932.

South Africa's lowest innings total in a home Test against Australia was 85, which they made twice in the 1902-03 series.

In his only Test (1914) Lindsay 'Len' Tuckett made 0 and 0 not out and took 0-45 and 0-24. His son Lindsay jnr played in nine Tests.

Needing 170 with two days left, South Africa lost their last 6 wickets for 9 runs to go one down in the 1996-97 series in India.

After scoring a hundred in the Lord's Test of 1994, South Africa's veteran opening batsman Peter Kirsten reeled off the injuries he'd received while scoring a century in the Lord's Test of 1994 – bruised fingers, head and chest, a sore calf muscle.'
'Cricket has been good to me,' he said.

TEST • WEST INDIES

While seam bowler Uton Dowe was taking 1-168 against Australia in 1973, the Jamaican crowd invented the eleventh commandment: 'Dowe shalt not bowl'!

In their 700th Test (1994), England became the first country to win a Test in Barbados since they did so themselves in 1935. The West Indies had been unbeaten there in 29 Tests, winning the previous twelve.

England's win in Barbados in 1994 was only their 5th in their last 50 against the West Indies.

In their 305th Test, against England in 1994, the West Indies established two firsts: a specialist bowler as captain (Courtney Walsh) and a Test team with no players from Barbados.

Keith Arthurton's 126 at Sabina Park in 1994 was the hundredth hundred made by the West Indies in Tests against England.

Against India in 1983, acting captain Viv Richards allowed an extra half-hour's play to let Kapil Dev complete a century.

Against England in 1935, George Carew was dismissed by the first ball he received in Test cricket. He didn't face another for 13 years, when he scored a century against the same country.

At the time of the 1954-55 series against Australia, former West Indies fast bowler Leslie Hylton had been convicted of murdering his wife. After John (JK) Holt had dropped two catches, the cry went up: 'Free Hylton, hang Holt!'

After the 1995 tour of England, Kenny Benjamin protested about being fined for breaching dress-code regulations. It wasn't his fault, he claimed, that he had to wear Ian Bishop's blazer, Junior Murray's shirt and Winston Benjamin's trousers!

TEST • WEST INDIES

In 1976 Test cricket had been in progress for 99 years when Lance Gibbs became the first bowler from outside England and Australia to set the world record for most Test wickets.

When Lance Gibbs and Garry Sobers bowled England out at Headingley in 1966, at one stage they were sending down 26 overs an hour.

Lance Gibbs had remarkable figures in an innings against India in 1962, taking 8 wickets while conceding only 38 runs in 53.3 overs, 37 of which were maidens.

In 1984, Viv Richards scored the first double century by a West Indies batsman in a Test in Australia, then had a hand in both of Allan Border's dismissals, as bowler and temporary wicketkeeper.

Australian captain Greg Chappell's 182 not out was the decisive score of the 1975-76 series – after he'd been dropped by Keith Boyce. As Wisden said, 'If ever a missed catch will go down in history as having lost a series...'

In the second Test of the 1984 series in England, Clive Lloyd passed 7,000 runs, Ian Botham and Gordon Greenidge 4,000 and Larry Gomes 2,000.

Three West Indian batsmen reached landmarks in the same Test against England in 1986: Viv Richards 6,000 runs, Gordon Greenidge 5,000, Larry Gomes 3,000.

West Indies' youngest captain was George 'Jackie' Grant on his Test debut: 23 years 217 days in 1930.

Both captains suffered injuries in the last match of the 1934-35 series against England: Bob Wyatt a broken jaw, 'Jackie' Grant an injured ankle.

Against India in 1983, Andy Roberts took his 200th Test wicket and made his highest first-class score (69).

Viv Richards scored a hundred in both his 50th and his 100th Tests, taking his 100th catch in the latter.

TEST • WEST INDIES

Against Australia in 1984, one of big Joel Garner's overs began with six consecutive no-balls and lasted ten minutes.

In the 2nd Test against England in 1984, the West Indies lost a second-innings wicket for the first time in seven Tests.

Derrick Parry's first and last moments in Test cricket were unhappy ones. In 1978 he was bowled by the first ball he faced, in 1980 his missed run-out cost the West Indies the last series they lost for 15 years!

Fast bowler Michael Holding scored almost a quarter of his Test runs in sixes: 204 out of 910.

At Old Trafford in 1933, it's said that the great George Headley slowed down to allow wicketkeeper Ivan Barrow the honour of becoming the first West Indian to score a Test century in England.

Courtney Walsh missed a Sunday League game to watch Jamaica lose 5-0 to Argentina in France 98.

Leg-spinner Willie Rodriguez made his Test debut in the 2nd Test against India in 1961-62. In the 1st Test, he'd come on as a substitute and taken three catches.

The highest number of runs conceded in a Test was 374 by Jamaican leg-spinner OC 'Tommy' Scott against England in 1929-30: 5-266 and 4-108.

In the 1980-81 series against Pakistan, fast bowler Seymour Clarke took three wickets in four balls and equalled a Test record by hitting three consecutive sixes.

Clive Lloyd set a world record by playing 58 innings before his first Test duck. He made only 4 ducks in his 175 Test innings.

A record 12 batsmen were given out lbw in each of two Tests played by the West Indies, against New Zealand in 1980 and England in 1984.

The West Indies set a record by drawing 10 consecutive Tests from 1971 to 1973.

TEST • WEST INDIES

A record 7 hundreds were scored in the 5th Test of the 1954-55 series against Australia.

A record 17 fifties were scored in the 4th Test of the 1968-69 series against Australia.

Test all-rounder Cyril 'Snuffy' Browne was the first black West Indian to be made an honorary life member of the MCC.

Ken Weekes, who scored a century against England in 1939, was the only Test cricketer born in the USA.

Eric Atkinson's first Test, against Pakistan in 1958, was the last for his brother Denis.

Gordon Greenidge and Desmond Haynes opened 148 innings together and shared 16 century partnerships, both Test records.

After going down to Australia in 1972-73, the West Indies didn't lose a home series until the same country beat them in 1994-95.

In 1995, wicketkeeper Courtney Browne dropped an easy catch off Steve Waugh, whose 200 effectively decided the series, the first the West Indies had lost since 1980.

Gordon Greenidge and Viv Richards had contrasting fortunes when they made their debuts in the same Test in 1974: Greenidge 93 and 107, Richards 4 and 3.

Brian Lara reached his first Test century against India (1997) with a four and a six.

Viv Richards' first Test innings on his home territory of Antigua, against England in 1981, was 114, of which 90 came in boundaries.

Viv Richards' last Test in Antigua (1991) brought him scores of 0 and 2. It was the only Test duck he made on his home ground.

Curtly Ambrose took his 300th Test wicket on his home ground in Antigua in 1988.

TEST • WEST INDIES

The Perth pitch was so bad in 1997 that Curtly Ambrose was run out when his bat became stuck in a hole!

When John (JK) Holt was given out lbw for 94 in his debut Test innings, against England in 1954, threats were made against umpire Perry Burke's family.

Against England in 1948, Ernest 'Foffie' Williams hit 28 off the first 6 balls he received (6,6,4,4,4,4) on his way to reaching fifty in half an hour.

King Dyal, Bridgetown's most flamboyant supporter (he went home to change his clothing at every interval), died in 1997 aged 96. His real first names were Redvers Dundonald.

John Goddard won all five tosses against India in 1948-49. The West Indies won 1-0.

Garry Sobers won all five tosses against England in 1966 (3-1) and New Zealand in 1971-72 (0-0).

The 1st Test of the 1997-98 series, in Kingston, was abandoned after 62 balls with England 17-3.

Alf Valentine and Sonny Ramadhin were picked for the 1950 tour of England despite having played only two first-class matches each. They took 59 wickets in the series.

Alf Valentine took 33 in the 1950 series in England, having just been given his first pair of NHS glasses!

The West Indies and England both scored 593 in the first innings in Antigua in 1994, the hosts losing five wickets, England all ten.

When Denis Atkinson and Clairmonte Depeiaza shared their record stand of 347 against Australia in 1955, each made his only Test century. Atkinson, the captain, also took 5-56.

The great three Ws – Walcott, Weekes and Worrell – scored a total of 12,113 Test runs at an average of 54.81.

TEST • WEST INDIES

Nelson Betancourt was captain in his only Test, against England in 1930, at the age of 40.

Archie Wiles made only one Test appearance, at Old Trafford in 1933, when he scored 0 and 2 at the age of 40.

The first Windward Islander to play Test cricket was 18-year-old Alphonso (Alfie) Roberts, who won his only cap in 1956.

The first Leeward Islander to play Test cricket was 19-year-old Elquemedo Willett in 1973.

The first Antiguan to play Test cricket was Andy Roberts in 1974.

The only West Indian to take 9 wickets in a Test innings was Jack Noreiga, a 34-old unknown in only his second Test, against India in 1971.

Test all-rounder Collis King was banned from playing in the North Wales League because he was too good. He once hit 283 in a single afternoon match.

The last match of the 1929-30 series against England set records (all subsequently broken) for the longest Test (9 days), highest team innings (849), individual innings (325) and match aggregate (1,815).

The 1st Test of the 1934-35 series was a very low-scoring affair: West Indies made 102 then declared at 51-6. England declared at 81-7 then made 75-4 and won by 6 wickets.

When Curtly Ambrose & Co dismissed England for 46 in 1994, only 39 runs came from the bat, a record low for any England innings.

The first time five bowlers conceded over 100 runs each in a Test innings was against Australia in 1955: Tom Dewdney, Frank King, Denis Atkinson, Collie Smith, Frank Worrell. Garry Sobers conceded 99!

England were so badly beaten in the Caribbean in 1985-86 that only one batsman (David Gower) averaged over 30 in the series.

TEST • WEST INDIES

As well as being the only opener to carry his bat three times in Tests, Desmond Haynes was also last man out in each innings against New Zealand in 1980.

Ian Botham was on the winning side only once in 20 Tests against the West Indies, in his last. His final innings against them, in 1991, was the only time they didn't take his wicket. He scored 4 not out.

In 1994 a pub in Northampton changed the painting on its sign from WG Grace to Brian Lara.

Clifford Roach (1930) and Bernard Julien (1973) scored their maiden first-class centuries in a Test match. Gerry Alexander (1961) scored his only first-class century in a Test match.

Bertie Clarke, who played Test cricket in 1939, was suspended from practising medicine after being found guilty of performing illegal operations in the 1970s.

The West Indies scored over 600 in each of two consecutive innings against India in 1948, but both Tests were drawn.

Against England in 1968, MC 'Joey' Carew conceded only 23 runs in 25 overs, including 16 consecutive maidens.

In his last Test, against New Zealand in 1987, Michael Holding took 0-99 and was out for a duck.

England recovered from 2-0 down to draw the 1953-54 series partly thanks to their captain Len Hutton who scored 677 runs at an average of 96.71.

The first two batsmen to make a century in each of their first two Test innings were both West Indians: Lawrence Rowe and Alvin Kallicharran, both in the same series in 1972.

The lowest total the West Indies have defended to win a Test was 120 against India, whom they dismissed for 81 in 1997. It was Brian Lara's first Test as captain.

In 1997, Shivnarine Chanderpaul turned his 14th Test fifty into his first Test hundred.

TEST • WEST INDIES

The best figures for a West Indian pace bowler on his Test debut were Franklyn Rose's 6-100 against India in 1997.

On Australia Day 1997, the West Indies dropped three catches, missed a stumping and took three wickets off no-balls. Australia won by an innings.

No England batsman made a century in the five-Test series against the West Indies in 1963.

No batsman on either side made a century in the 1986-87 series in Pakistan.

Carl Hooper was one of the victims of Dominic Cork's hat-tricks in first-class (1994) and Test (1995) cricket.

West Indies captain Gerry Alexander played left-back for Pegasus when they won the FA Amateur Cup in 1953.

The three players who scored most sixes in Test cricket were all West Indian: Viv Richards (84) Clive Lloyd (69) Gordon Greenidge (67). Carl Hooper scored his 50th six in Test cricket during the 1997-98 series against England.

When India set a record by scoring 406-4 to win a Test in 1976, West Indies used three spinners for the last time: Raphick Jumadeen, Imtiaz Ali and Albert Padmore.

Top-order batsman Basil Butcher had figures of 5-34 against England in 1968, the only wickets he took in Test cricket.

Robin Bynoe made his Test debut at the age of 18 in 1959, scored only a single, and wasn't capped again until 1966, when he scored two!

On his first day as a Test cricketer, in 1962, Jackie Hendriks broke a finger. In his next series, three years later, he was hospitalised by a ball from Graham McKenzie!

The Cameron brothers weren't the most successful in Test history. Jimmy's three wickets cost 92.66 each and John averaged 2.00 with the bat.

TEST • WEST INDIES

Roy Fredericks blistering innings of 169 at Perth in 1975 included a hundred before lunch scored off only 71 balls.

In one Test in 1948, England's two opening bowlers had an average age of 40, while West Indies seamer Berkeley Gaskin was ten days short of his 40th birthday.

The only West Indian bowler to take a wicket with his first ball in Test cricket was Tyrell Johnson against England in 1939.

37-year-old pace bowler Hines Johnson took 5-41 and 5-55 on his Test debut in 1948. His other christian names were Hophnie and Hobah.

When Wes Hall first toured England, in 1957, he hadn't taken a single first-class wicket.

Rohan Kanhai hit a double century against both India and Pakistan on the 1958-59 tour.

Rohan Kanhai's Test career was ended by a cartilage operation in 1974. His last 61 Tests were all consecutive.

Jamaican bowler Esmond Kentish's only two Tests were both against England, both in Kingston, six years apart.

In his second Test, in 1954, Kentish bowled to a ring of seven fielders on the leg side, took 5-49, and wasn't capped again!

Wicketkeeper Desmond Lewis wasn't capped again after averaging 86.33 in his only three Tests, against India in 1971.

The West Indies appointed four different captains in the four Tests against England in 1929-20, chosen by each of the regions.

Bruce Pairaudeau, who hit a hundred on his Test debut in 1953, had scored his maiden first-class century when he was only 16.

OC 'Tommy' Scott once finished off an Australian Test innings by taking 4 wickets in 9 balls without conceding a run. His son Alfred also played Test cricket.

TEST • WEST INDIES

Clyde Walcott once hit 12 centuries in 12 consecutive Tests, a West Indies record.

Clifford Roach scored the West Indies' first Test century (1930) and made a pair in his first Test in England (1933).

George Headley was born in Panama, the only West Indies captain born outside the West Indies.

The West Indies lost by an innings at Lord's in 1957 after dropping 12 catches in the match.

The West Indies lost the 1951-52 series in Australia after dropping any number of catches, including five in 20 minutes off Alf Valentine alone.

The West Indies lost the 1968-69 series in Australia after dropping a total of 35 catches. Their captain Garry Sobers called them the worst fielding side he'd ever seen.

Conrad Hunte broke his bat in hitting Fred Trueman for six in 1963.

Garry Sobers and Frank Worrell batted throughout a full day's play against England in 1960, then throughout the next, which was shortened by an hour.

The four batsmen who scored centuries in an innings against New Zealand in 1952 were nearly five: Allan Rae was bowled for 99.

In his 15 innings against India, Everton Weekes hit 7 hundreds and 4 fifties for a total of 1,495 runs at an average of 106.78.

The West Indies used an average of seven bowlers in each innings of the 1948-49 series in India.

Two Guyanese left-handers, Leonard Baichan and Clive Lloyd, put on 164 against Pakistan in 1975.

Michael Holding and Colin Croft took their 100th Test wickets in the same match, against England in 1981.

TEST • WEST INDIES

The West Indies fielded an unchanged team throughout the five-Test series against Australia in 1990-91, winning it 2-1.

In 1991 the West Indies won a Test against Australia in Guyana for the first time since 1965.

Gordon Greenidge made his highest Test score, 226, in his last series, against Australia in 1990-91. He celebrated his 40th birthday in his final Test.

Playing against Australia in 1931, Edward 'Barto' Bartlett couldn't bat in either innings after crushing his finger against his boot while attempting a catch.

Against India in 1952-53, Clyde Walcott was given out lbw for 98 – by his uncle Harold!

Against England in 1990 and Australia in 1991, the fourth day in the Jamaica Test was wiped out by the absence of proper equipment to deal with heavy rain.

TEST • NEW ZEALAND

Eric Tindill, who played rugby (1936) as well as cricket (1937-47) for New Zealand, also became an international rugby referee and a Test cricket umpire.

Milford 'Curly' Page, who captained New Zealand on the England tour of 1937, played rugby for the All Blacks in 1928.

Richard Hadlee took four wickets for five runs to beat Australia in 1982 then finished the match with a six.

Test fast bowler Heath Davis has one of the longest middle names in Test cricket: Te-Ihi-O-Te-Rangi (salutations to Rangi, god of the sky).

New Zealand's defeat by an innings and 222 runs by Australia in the second Test of 1993 was their heaviest ever – apart from the innings and 337 of their women's team against England in 1935.

Chris Kuggeleijn was dismissed by the first ball he faced in Test cricket but also took the catch that gave Richard Hadlee his 374th wicket, a new world record at the time.

Dayle Hadlee had a lot less success in Test cricket than his younger brother (71 wickets to Richard's 431) partly because he'd lost part of a toe when he ran over his own foot with a lawnmower!

Against Australia in 1995, Richard Hadlee took a catch off the bowling of Vaughan Brown, who thus took his only Test wicket. In doing so, Hadlee (9-52) lost the chance of taking all 10 wickets in the innings.

Richard Hadlee took five wickets in a Test innings 36 times, a record for any country.

Ken Rutherford's first seven Test innings, all in the West Indies in 1984-85, were 0, 0, 4, 0, 2, 1, 5. He later set a record by being dismissed for 0 in each of his three Tests at Lord's.

TEST • NEW ZEALAND

Ken Rutherford scored his maiden Test century in 1988 after averaging 11.20 in his first 13 Tests.

In 1984 wicketkeeper Ian Smith celebrated his first Test hundred by hitting the last two balls of the innings for six then taking a catch off the first ball of the England innings.

Bruce Edgar took over five hours to score 55 against Australia in 1982, the slowest first-class fifty in New Zealand.

At the end of his Test career (1965), John R Reid held the New Zealand records for most matches, matches as captain, runs, centuries and wickets. He also made a stumping in his second Test.

In beating England for the first time (1978) New Zealand dismissed them for 64, their lowest total since 1948.

In 1986, New Zealand won a series in England for the first time, at the 10th attempt.

New Zealand's series defeat against England in 1991-92 was their first at home since 1978-79. They lost only two Tests in that run.

The 1987-88 series against England was the only one to end without a single six being hit.

In less than a year from the start of 1997-98, New Zealand captain Stephen Fleming flew 91,306 miles on cricket duty.

Stephen Fleming equalled the Test record by taking five catches in an innings against Zimbabwe in 1997.

Don Cleverley's bowling didn't live up to his name in his only two Tests, played 14 years apart (1932-46): his bowling figures were 0-130.

The first New Zealander to score a century in his first Test was John Mills in 1930. The second was Bruce Taylor in 1965. They were both left-handed.

TEST • NEW ZEALAND

Against Australia in 1993, for only the second time in Test history, five bowlers conceded 100 runs each in the same innings: Danny Morrison, Chris Cairns, Simon Doull, Richard de Groen, Dipak Patel.

Matthew Henderson (1930) and Dennis Smith (1933) both took a wicket with their first ball in their only Test, both against England at Christchurch. It was Smith's only Test wicket.

Matt Poore, Ian Colquhoun and Johnny Hayes all made a pair in the 2nd Test against England in 1955.

Ian Colquhoun made a pair against England in 1955. In his only other Test, he'd made 0 and 1, and was therefore dismissed by the last three balls he faced in Test cricket.

Before eye trouble forced him to retire from cricket, Rodney Redmond equalled a record by hitting five successive fours on his way to making 107 and 56 in his only Test in 1973.

Glenn Turner was the youngest batsman to carry his bat through a Test innings: 22 years 63 days at Lord's in 1969.

Bev Congdon, a substitute behind the stumps, made a stumping against Pakistan in 1965.

Vic Pollard's century against England 1973 was his first in 56 innings in 30 Tests.

New Zealand set a record by not winning any of their first 44 Tests, from 1930 to 1956 when they beat the West Indies by 190 runs.

Richard Collinge scored 68 not out against Pakistan in 1973, the highest Test score by a Number 11 batsman.

On 21 March 1998, for the first time ever, four Test matches were going on simultaneously. The only country not in action were New Zealand.

TEST • NEW ZEALAND

When Matt Horne scored 133 against Australia in 1997, it was only the third time he'd opened a first-class innings, making a century each time.

Stephen Fleming took most Test catches by any fielder in 1997: 28.

Danny Morrison made 24 Test ducks but none in the 1989-90 series against India, when he made 1 not out, 1 not out and 0 not out!

Danny Morrison surprised everyone by helping Nathan Astle survive 266 balls to add an unbeaten 106 for the last wicket and draw a Test against England in 1997.

Radio New Zealand News: 'Danny Morrison's groin strain is a big headache.'

New Zealand couldn't pick Bruce Murray or Vic Pollard for the 2nd Test against England in 1970-71 because neither would play on a Sunday.

Daniel Vettori bowled 58 overs in an innings against Zimbabwe in 1997, 34 of them in a row on the first day, then hit his Test-best score of 90.

Daniel Vettori's first Test victim, Nasser Hussain in 1997, had also been his first first-class victim three weeks earlier.

Father and son Giff and Graham Vivian both made their Test debuts while they were still teenagers, in 1931 and 1965 respectively.

New Zealand's oldest Test debutant was Bert McGirr (38 years 101 days) in 1930.

In the home series of 1985-86, John F Reid faced the bowling of his cousin Bruce who was playing for Australia.

John F Reid shares the record of playing most Tests without facing England (19).

TEST • NEW ZEALAND

In his only Test, against South Africa in 1953, Eric Fisher dropped Jackie McGlew twice on his way to making 255 not out. New Zealand lost by an innings and 180.

John Wright's final Test innings, run out against Australia in 1993, was ended by the third umpire.

On his Test debut in 1996, leg-spinner Greg Loveridge marked his 21st birthday by breaking a knuckle, an injury which put him out for the rest of the season!

New Zealand's were so badly mauled in the 1993-94 series in Australia that none of their bowlers averaged under 50. The top seven Australian batsmen all averaged over 60.

Sachin Tendulkar and Ken Rutherford scored their 2,000th Test run in the same match in 1994. Rutherford was seven years older and had played in 13 more Tests.

Test opener Trevor Franklin was once given out off a ball that broke his arm. He also broke his leg in a collision with an airport baggage trolley.

No wonder England were able to declare at 567-8 at Trent Bridge in 1994: New Zealand's five bowlers had only taken 22 previous Test wickets between them.

Against Sri Lanka in 1990-91, Andrew Jones scored three successive hundreds, including two in the same Test, and finished with 513 runs, a New Zealand record for a home series.

Playing against England in 1959, wicketkeeper Eric Petrie was cut on the head by a ball from his own leg-spinner then became Fred Trueman's 100th Test victim.

In his first Test, against Pakistan in 1973, John Parker broke a bone in his hand and couldn't bat.

Murray Parker made his Test debut in his brother John's first Test as captain (1976).

TEST • NEW ZEALAND

During the 1996 series in England, a bouncer from Craig White knocked the silver fern badge off Martin Crowe's helmet.

When New Zealand lost the 2nd Test against Pakistan in 1976, the last ball was bowled by wicketkeeper Warren Lees.

Although only one Test was scheduled in England in 1931, two more were arranged when New Zealand declared at 469-9 and reduced England to 146-5.

In the India v New Zealand series of 1995-96, a bowler on each side was accused of throwing: Chetan Chauhan and Dion Nash.

Opening bowler Willie Watson claimed in a book that New Zealand players used a bottletop to rough up the ball against Pakistan in 1990. Mark Greatbatch was apparently in charge of 'scratching duties.'

Against England in 1992, John Wright became the first batsman since 1955 to be stumped for 99 in a Test.

When Phil Tufnell bowled 71 overs in 1992, he broke the record for the most in a first-class innings in New Zealand, previously 70 by Stephen Boock against Pakistan in 1989.

Test batsman Mark Greatbatch played the part of WG Grace in a feature film, but the film had to be reversed because Greatbatch was left-handed.

In the 1993-94 series in Australia, so many catches were dropped off the bowling of Danny Morrison that he finished with only three wickets at 140.66 each.

If Martin Crowe hadn't been out for 83 in Johannesburg in 1994 he would have become the only batsman to score a centuries against all the other eight Test-playing nations.

BAR

TEST • NEW ZEALAND

Jack Newman was the first player to reach Test level direct from country cricket. He was hit for three successive sixes by Wally Hammond in 1933 and later knighted.

In their centenary year (1995) New Zealand won one Test, drew two and lost five.

When New Zealand were all out for 97 at Trent Bridge in 1973, the highest score was made by their 20 extras.

Richard Hadlee's 151 not out against Sri Lanka in 1987 was his highest Test score and New Zealand's hundredth hundred.

Against the West Indies in 1986-87, John Wright batted for four hours in the first innings and nearly ten in the second, making 75 and 138.

Off-spinner Narotam 'Tom' Puna, who played in three Tests in 1966, was born in Bombay.

In the 1996-97 series against England, Stephen Fleming became New Zealand's youngest ever captain (23) and made his maiden Test hundred after scoring 10 fifties in his previous 22 Tests.

The last day of England's win in Wellington in 1997 was watched by less than 1,000 people, most of them English.

New Zealand's first Test was in 1930. Their first win was against the West Indies in 1956. Their first series win was against the West Indies in 1980.

Les Watt was 12th man in both Tests against England in 1951 and made his only Test appearance against the same country four years later, scoring 0 and 2.

Test cricketer Philip Horne played badminton for New Zealand in the 1986 Commonwealth Games.

Laurie Miller and Bert Sutcliffe were both on 0 when they were hospitalised by South African fast bowler Neil Adcock in 1953.

TEST • NEW ZEALAND

Cyril Alcott took 5 wickets for 3 runs against Somerset in 1927 but his 6 Test wickets cost 90.16 each.

Murray Webbe's four Test wickets cost 117.75 each. Billy Bell's two Test wickets cost 117.50 each. John Dunning's five Test wickets cost 98.60 each.

Paul Barton scored his only Test century, against South Africa in 1962, with a dislocated shoulder.

Pace bowler Bob Blair was one of the first players to make three pairs in Tests.

Len Butterfield and Charlie Rowe both made a pair in their only Test, the one-off match against Australia in 1946.

A century in each innings by Glenn Turner helped New Zealand beat Australia for the first time, in 1974.

George Cresswell, who took 6-168 in an England total of 482 in 1949, shot himself in 1966.

In 39 Tests, Graham Dowling made only three centuries, all against India. His 239 in 1968 was a New Zealand record at the time.

Two of Walter Hadlee's sons played Test cricket and another, Barry, took part in the World Cup.

Noel Harford scored 93 and 64 on his debut in 1955 but averaged only 5.54 in the rest of his Test career.

Noel Harford's younger brother Roy took seven catches, out of 12 wickets to fall, in his last Test.

All-rounder Denis Moloney died of war wounds while he was a prisoner at Alamein.

Frank Mooney's selection for the 1949 tour of England led to a strike among Dunedin dock workers campaigning for a different wicketkeeper.

TEST • NEW ZEALAND

Like 'Monkey' Hornby of England, Bruce Murray took a single Test wicket without conceding a run.

Brun Smith averaged 47.40 in Test cricket and was known as a quick scorer. He hit 96 in only two hours and 54 not out in 50 minutes during the 1949 series in England.

John Sparling made his only Test fifty on his 20th birthday, at Old Trafford in 1958.

Don Taylor won his first Test cap in 1947 then had to wait almost exactly nine years for his second.

When New Zealand took an innings lead over England for the first time (1949), captain Walter Hadlee ordered drinks all round (36 beers) in the press box.

When New Zealand were dismissed for 47 and 74 at Lord's in 1958, their highest partnership was their last, a monumental 18!

New Zealand were all out for under 100 in three successive Tests in that 1958 series. At Headingley they made 67 and 129 and England won while scoring only 267 and losing only two wickets.

England spinner Tony Lock had extraordinary figures in the 1958 series against New Zealand: 176 overs, 93 maidens, 254 runs, 34 wickets at an average of 7.47.

Terry Jarvis took two catches after coming on as a substitute fielder against England in 1965.

New Zealand's inaugural Test against Sri Lanka, in 1983, provided their first ever win inside three days. Their captain Geoff Howarth described the Christchurch wicket as unfit for any grade of cricket.

New Zealand's tour of Pakistan in 1996-97 was ravaged by injuries. Even their manager Earle Cooper had to fly home with a detached retina!

In 1956, New Zealand took 62.2 overs to complete an innings of 74 all out. They had their revenge later in the series by dismissing the West Indies for 77.

TEST • NEW ZEALAND

New Zealand's trip to the West Indies in 1971-72 was the first international tour to end without a result in any of the first-class matches.

Against Australia in 1990, Martin Snedden set a Test record by not scoring a run in 94 minutes.

Jeremy Coney's unbeaten 174 against England in 1984 was his first century in 131 first-class innings since 1976-77!

Against England in 1988, Richard Hadlee equalled Ian Botham's record of 373 Test wickets – then missed the rest of the series with a pulled muscle and had to wait nine months to break the record!

John Wright and Andrew Jones both averaged over 122.00 in the 1989-90 series against India. Ian Smith averaged 91.00.

John Bracewell achieved the Test double of 1,000 runs and 100 wickets – but only just. He scored 1,001 runs and took 102 wickets.

TEST • INDIA

In 1995 the Indian Communications Department refused to connect Sunil Gavaskar's phone unless he could provide a certificate proving he was a well-known sportsman!

Sunil Gavaskar's record run of 106 consecutive Tests ended when he refused to play in Calcutta in 1987 because of the crowd's reaction to him in previous matches.

Bhagwat Chandrasekhar took 242 Test wickets with a right arm withered by childhood polio.

Having taken a wicket with his first ball in Test cricket, against Sri Lanka in 1997, Nilesh Kulkarni bowled another 419 balls in the innings without taking a wicket!

In 1983, Kapil Dev became the first captain to take 9 wickets in a Test innings.

Against England in 1933, Ladha Amar Singh scored 0 and 1, took 0-134, and was later criticised for playing in tennis shoes.

Wally Hammond's view of Amar Singh: 'With the new ball he was perhaps better than anyone I have ever seen.' He died of pneumonia at 29.

Sunil Gavaskar's 236 not out against the West Indies in 1983 was his 30th Test century, a new world record and still the highest Test score by an Indian batsman.

Rather surprisingly, India's highest individual Test score, Sunil Gavaskar's 236 not out against the West Indies in 1983, is the lowest for any Test-playing country.

India's inaugural home Test, against England in 1933, was the first to include play on a Sunday.

In 1983, Gursharan Singh became the first substitute fielder to hold four catches in a Test match.

Sunil Gavaskar broke two of Geoff Boycott's world records in the same innings in 1983, scoring his 8,115th Test run and his 65th Test fifty.

TEST • INDIA

Sunil Gavaskar broke another of Geoff Boycott's world records with his 48th century partnership, shared with Ravi Shastri against the West Indies in 1984.

The 4th Test of the 1982-83 series against the West Indies was the first in which all 20 first-innings wickets fell to catches.

In his 50th Test (1983), Kapil Dev scored a hundred. took his 200th Test wicket, and became the youngest player to complete the double of 2,000 runs and 200 wickets: 24 years 68 days.

At Old Trafford in 1982, Sandeep Patil took a record six boundaries from an over by Bob Willis, including one off a no-ball.

In the Golden Jubilee match against England in 1980, the rest day was brought forward because of an eclipse of the sun.

At Lahore in 1978, Bishan Bedi played his 60th Test, a new Indian record, and took his 250th wicket.

In the 4th Test against New Zealand in 1964-65, Srinivas Venkataraghavan dismissed every batsman at least once.

Anil Kumble took his 10 wickets in an innings against Pakistan on the pitch that had been vandalised by opponents of the tour!

At Bombay in 1977, India used only one ball throughout the 154 overs of England's first innings.

Miniature fast bowler Ramakant 'Tiny' Desai scored 32 not out against New Zealand in 1968 despite having his jaw broken by a bouncer.

India lost the 1975-76 series in the Caribbean because Bishan Bedi declared at 97-5 in protest at intimidatory bowling. Viswanath broke a finger, Gaekwad was hit on the ear, Brijesh Patel had stitches in his mouth.

At the Oval in 1982, Ian Botham not only scored 208, his highest Test score, he also removed Sunil Gavaskar from the match by breaking his shin with a square drive!

TEST • INDIA

The Edgbaston pitch for the 1st Test of the 1996 series was so uneven that Nayan Mongia let through 24 byes and new cap Sunil Joshi broke a finger, as did Nick Knight.

Former Test opener Raman Lamba died after being hit by a ball in a club game in 1998.

A few minutes after Sourav Ganguly was out for 99 against Sri Lanka in 1997, Greg Blewett was out for 99 for Australia against New Zealand.

The only Indian bowler to be no-balled for throwing in a Test was Abid Ali in 1968. He threw the ball deliberately in protest against New Zealand batsman Gary Bartlett.

Rajindernath, who kept wicket against Pakistan in 1952, was one of the few Test players with only one name!

In his last Test, against the West Indies in 1959, Vinoo Mankad bowled 55 overs in an innings at the age of 41.

In 1947 an English cricket writer described Abdul Kardar's bowling as being that of an 'Indian mystic,' which appeared in print as an 'Indian mistake.'

Sachin Tendulkar scored a record 7 centuries before his 21st birthday.

At Edgbaston in 1996, Sachin Tendulkar reached a Test hundred with a six off Min Patel.

Sachin Tendulkar made his Test debut in 1989. More than six years later, at Edgbaston in 1996, he was still the youngest player in the team.

Sachin Tendulkar was the youngest player to score a Test fifty.

India's first win in the 1967-68 series against New Zealand ended a run of 7 consecutive defeats against England and Australia.

Three batsmen who were dismissed by the first ball they faced in Test cricket were victims of Kapil Dev: Chris Kuggeleijn (New Zealand), Ian Bishop (West Indies) and Jimmy Cook (South Africa).

TEST • INDIA

The first Indian Test team to play at home, against England in 1933-34, had two English selectors: AL Hosie and AE West. One of the umpires in the first Test was England Test cricketer Bill Hitch.

Rusi Modi scored only one Test century but it was enough to save a match against the West Indies in 1948 after India had followed on.

In his first Test as England coach David Lloyd saw India dismissed for 214, the same score that he made against the same opposition in 1974.

Gogumal Kishenchand made a duck in each of his five Tests (1947-52) and bowled the ball from which Don Bradman completed his hundredth first-class hundred.

The first bowler to run a non-striker out while backing up was Vinoo Mankad of India, who saw off Bill Brown at the SCG in 1947. This kind of dismissal is still known as a 'Mankad' in Australia.

India were the first country to play Test cricket against England after the last War, in 1946. They were the first side to travel to England by air.

1946 was such a cold summer that Vijay Merchant played in woollen underwear, a flannel shirt, three sweaters and a woollen muffler.

Kapil Dev took a world record 434 Test wickets, but none in the 1986-87 home series against Australia. Instead he headed the batting averages with 60.00.

India fielded all four of their world-class spinners in the 3rd Test against England in 1967 – Bedi, Chandrasekhar, Prasanna and Venkataraghavan – but lost by 132 runs.

TEST • INDIA

Bedi, Chandrasekhar, Prasanna and Venkataraghavan took a combined total of 853 Test wickets.

At Old Trafford in 1952, India were dismissed twice in a single day, for 58 and 82, losing by an innings and 207.

Motganhalli Jaisimha scored 74 and 101 against Australia in 1968 a few days after arriving to join the tour.

The highest fourth-innings total to win a Test match was India's 406-4 in Trinidad in 1976 – after Clive Lloyd had declared.

India's win at the Oval in 1971 was their first in England, at the 22nd attempt. It was enough to win a series in England for the first time and put an end to England's record run of 26 Tests without defeat.

Chetan Chauhan's 61 against Pakistan in December 1979 included the slowest first-class fifty made in India: more than five hours.

The first five Indian batsmen to score a century on their debut didn't score another. The jinx was eventually broken by Gundappa Viswanath in 1973.

On his Test debut, against Australia in 1969, Gundappa Viswanath scored a duck in his first innings and a hundred in the second.

The three Indian princes who played Test cricket for England all made centuries in their first Tests against Australia: Ranjitsinhji, Duleepsinhji and the Nawab of Pataudi senior.

When Sri Lanka scored their record 952-6 in 1997, it was almost the first time three bowlers conceded 200 runs each in a Test innings: Rajesh Chauhan 276, Anil Kumble 223, Nilesh Kulkarni 195. All three bowled more than 70 overs each.

There were six centuries in each of the two Tests of the 1997 series against Sri Lanka, three by each side.

TEST • INDIA

In 1993 Vinod Kambli became only the third batsman to score consecutive double centuries. Of the ten Indian players who bowled in an innings against Australia in 1969, none took a wicket.

Maninder Singh, a Bishan Bedi look-alike with his beard, patka and left-arm spin, twice took ten wickets in a Test, but not in his debut series, against Pakistan in 1982-83, when his 3 wickets cost 148.00 apiece.

Maninder Singh made a pair against the West Indies in 1987, each time caught by Richie Richardson off Courtney Walsh.

Surinder Amarnath, brother of Mohinder and son of Lala, scored a century in his debut Test innings, against New Zealand in 1976.

Although India were well beaten in the 1936 series in England, their opening bat Vijay Merchant was one of Wisden's Five Cricketers of the Year.

In the first Test of the 1992-93 series between India and England, Srinivas Venkataraghavan became the first former Indian Test player to umpire a Test.

India's total of 524-9 against New Zealand in 1976 was the highest without a century (they scored 6 fifties).

The one-off Test against Sri Lanka in 1990 was India's first at home for two years, during which they played 14 away from home without a win.

In the 1963-64 series against England, 'Bapu' Nadkarni conceded only 278 runs in 212 overs, including a record 21 consecutive maidens. He took only 9 wickets but finished top of the batting averages with 98.00. In one Test against Pakistan in 1961, he conceded only 67 runs in 86.4 overs, 62 of them maidens.

In the 3rd Test of the 1933-34 series against England, Naoomal Jeoomal retired hurt in the first innings and was absent hurt in the second.

TEST • INDIA

Kapil Dev missed only one match in his Test career, when he was dropped for playing a rash shot against England in 1984.

Kapil Dev's 400th Test wicket was an lbw decision given by umpire Tony Crafter, who was setting a new Australian record by standing in his 33rd Test.

CK Nayudu, India's first captain, played in seven Tests, all against England, the first when he was 36. He was also the only man to play first-class cricket in six decades, from 1916 to 1963, when he was 68.

Rustomji Jamshedji (1933) and Cota Ramaswami (1936) both played in their only Test after their 40th birthday.

Lala Amarnath's 118 on his debut in 1933 was India's first century in Test cricket – and his last, even though he played in 23 more matches.

The only time India won three Tests in a series away from home was in New Zealand in 1967-68.

In the 1st Test of the 1967-68 series against New Zealand, all eleven Indian batsmen reached double figures in the second innings.

In the 2nd Test of the 1976-77 series against New Zealand, all eleven Indian batsmen reached double figures in the second innings, six of them making fifties.

Bhagwat Chandrasekhar made 23 ducks in Test cricket but was not out in all three matches of the 1976-77 series against New Zealand.

Roger Binny's best Test figures, 6-56 in 1987, included a spell of 4-9 in five overs.

Sunil Gavaskar's 214th and last Test innings was one of his greatest: 96 out of 204 (the next highest score was 27 extras) which almost won a Test against Pakistan in 1987.

India's win over Sri Lanka in the 1st Test of the 1993-94 series was their 50th in the 286 Tests they'd played up to then.

TEST • INDIA

The win in Sri Lanka in 1993 ended India's run of 26 Tests away from home without a win since beating England in 1986.

The first time a batsman from each side scored a debut Test hundred was at Bombay in 1933 when Lala Amarnath hit 118 and England's Bryan Valentine 136.

In 1996 Sourav Ganguly became only the third batsman to make a century in each of his first two Test innings.

Mohammad Azharuddin has twice captained India in England. His average in 1990 (85.20) was ten times higher than in 1996 (8.40).

Navjot Singh Sidhu's maiden Test double century, against the West Indies in 1997, took more than 11 hours, the second-slowest in Test cricket.

Needing only 120 to beat the West Indies in 1997, India lost their last 8 wickets for 26 and were all out for 81. Only Venkat Laxman (19) and extras (15) reached double figures.

The match against Pakistan in Lucknow in 1952 was the only Test in India to be played on a matting wicket. India's Nyalchand Shah sent down 64 overs in his only bowl in Test cricket.

Kapil Dev took over half of his first-class wickets (835) in Test matches (434).

The captain of the first India team to tour England was the Maharaja of Porbandar, who stood down from the Test match, as did his vice-captain Prince Ghanshyam Sinhji of Limbdi.

It's said that the Maharaja of Porbandar collected more Rolls Royces than runs during the 1932 tour!

TEST • INDIA

The captain of the second India team to tour England was Sir Gajapatairaj Vijaya Ananda, the Maharajkumar of Vizianagram, who didn't stand down from the Tests, in which he averaged 8.25 with the bat.

Yadavendra Singh, the Yuvaraj of Patiala, later a Maharaja and Lieutenant Colonel, top-scored in his only Test, against England in 1934.

Hanumant Singh was the Maharajkumar of Banswana. He fielded for both sides as a substitute in the 2nd Test of the 1961-62 series against England.

The last time England won a Test series in India before 1976-77 was in 1933-34, when they were captained by Douglas Jardine, who was born in Bombay and averaged 96.25 in Tests against India.

England's Colin Cowdrey, who was born in India, averaged 103.00 in the 1963-64 series.

England's John Jameson, who was born in India, made his highest Test score (82) against India.

Part of India's great spinning tradition may have originated with England slow left-armer Hedley Verity who took 38 wickets at 16.45 in six Tests against India.

Although India lost at Lord's in 1952, Vinoo Mankad gave one of the great all-round Test performances, scoring 72 and 184 and taking 5 wickets in 97 overs, 36 of them maidens.

6'6 pace bowler Abey Kuruvilla, who made his debut in 1997, is thought to be India's tallest ever Test cricketer.

India's visit in 1996-97 attracted a total attendance of 191,256, a record for a three-Test series in South Africa.

Five current and future England captains played against India at Headingley in 1967: John Edrich, Geoff Boycott, Tom Graveney, Brian Close and Ray Illingworth.

Only four five-Test series have ended 0-0 with five draws. India were involved in three of them, including two in a row against Pakistan.

TEST • INDIA

India's win in 1999 was their first against Pakistan since 1980.

When India lost 5-0 in 1959, eight England batsmen averaged over 50.00 in the series.

Against England in 1961, Budhi Kunderan became the first Indian wicketkeeper to make 5 dismissals in a Test innings – and became Tony Lock's 2,000 first-class wicket.

Against England in 1963-64, Budhi Kunderan became the first wicketkeeper to score 500 runs in a Test series.

Amir Elahi was picked as a bowler in his only Test for India but didn't bowl. So he played five times for Pakistan instead.

Jahangir Khan and Dilawar Hussain played for India. Their sons Majid Khan and Waqar Ahmed played for Pakistan.

Test batsman Syed Wazir Ali had a brother (Syed Nazir Ali) who played for India and a son (Khalid Wazir) who played for Pakistan.

Anshuman Gaekwad, who scored two Test centuries, was the son of Datta Gaekwad, a former captain of India.

The Nawabs of Pataudi senior and junior, father and son, both captained India in England, in 1946 and 1967 respectively.

Test batsman Pankaj Roy had a son (Pranab) and a nephew (Ambar) who played for India.

Two brothers played in India's first home Test, in 1933: Ladha Amar Singh and Ladha Ranji.

Two brothers played against England in the 1961-62 series: Amritsar Milkha Singh and Amritsar Kripal Singh.

Kripal Singh's 100 not out on his debut in 1955 was his only century in 20 Test innings.

Bishan Bedi bowled some marathon spells in the 1972-73 series against England, conceding only 1.69 runs per over, averaging 41 overs per innings, and taking 25 wickets.

Dilawar Hussain top-scored in each innings of his Test debut in 1934, scoring 59 and 57 despite retiring hurt after being hit by a bouncer.

TEST • INDIA

Vijay Mehra played in his first two Tests at the age of 17 in 1955, then had to wait eight years for his third.

CK Nayudu was India's first Test captain (1932). His brother CS had an 18-year Test career (1934-52).

India's inaugural Test (1932) was Lall Singh's only cap. He was the first Test cricketer born in Malaysia.

India used three slow bowlers at Lord's in 1967 but the best figures (6-29) were those of England off-spinner Ray Illingworth.

When India were all out for 42 at Lord's in 1974, the innings lasted 77 minutes. The highest scores were Eknath Solkar's 18 and Gundappa Viswanath's 5!

In successive Tests against England in 1959, two Indian batsmen had bones broken, Chandu Borde by Fred Trueman, Nari Contractor by Brian Statham.

In 1986 Sunil Gavaskar celebrated his 115th Test (a world record at the time) by becoming the first Indian to hold 100 Test catches.

When Srinivas Venkataraghavan was left out of the Indian team in 1969, there was such an outcry that his replacement Subroto Guha agreed to stand down. He played in the next three Tests.

When India used ten bowlers in an innings against Australia in 1969, none of them took a wicket.

Wicketkeeper 'Nana' Joshi made a pair against the West Indies in 1953, each time caught by Frank Worrell off Alf Valentine.

Syed Abid Ali achieved his best Test bowling figures (6-55) in the first of his 29 Tests (1967).

Subash 'Fergie' Gupte and Jasu Patel took 9 wickets in a Test innings in Kanpur in consecutive years.

After taking 14 wickets in one Test against Australia in 1959, Jasu Patel played in only two more.

TEST • PAKISTAN

The first Hindu to play Test cricket for Pakistan was Anil Dalpat in 1984.

Soon after becoming a separate country, in 1948, Pakistan entertained a Commonwealth team, whose blazers were embossed with the word 'PARKISTAN.'

In 1983-84, at the 12th attempt, Pakistan won a series against England. It was also the first time they'd won a Test against England at home.

The 100th player to play Test cricket for Pakistan was Mohsin Kamal against England in 1984.

Pakistan's 624 in 1983 was the highest innings total made against Australia since England scored 903-7 in 1938.

Pakistan first played a Test series against India in 1952-53 – and first won one in 1978-79.

Pakistan first won a Test match in India in 1952. The second time they did it was in 1987.

In the West Indies v Pakistan series of 1957-58, Garry Sobers and Conrad Hunte scored a total of 1,446 runs at an average of 103.28.

When Hanif Mohammad scored his famous 337 against the West Indies in 1958, he batted through the third, fourth and fifth days and into the sixth and last.

Hanif Mohammad played in Pakistan's first 24 Tests before injuring his knee against the West Indies in 1959.

Against New Zealand in 1969, Hanif and Sadiq Mohammad became only the second pair of brothers to open a Test innings, the first since EM and WG Grace in 1880.

The four Mohammad brothers – Hanif, Mushtaq, Sadiq and Wazir – scored a total of 10,938 Test runs and 29 Test centuries.

Hanif Mohammad and his son Shoaib played in a total of exactly 100 Tests. Shoaib scored a century on debut in 1987.

TEST • PAKISTAN

Waqar Hassan scored 189 in a record partnership of 308 against New Zealand. His brother Pervez Saijad, who took 59 Test wickets, was a psychology graduate.

When Wes Hall took a hat-trick against Pakistan in 1959, his first victim (Mushtaq Mohammad) was only 15 and his third (Nasim-ul-Ghani) only 17.

In the 1982-83 series against India, Pakistani batsmen scored 12 centuries, equalling the record set by Australia in the West Indies in 1954-55.

Pakistan gave away a total of 221 extras against England in 1982, five runs more than their top scorer. They lost the series 2-1.

In 1980 Javed Miandad became Pakistan's youngest ever captain: 22 years 260 days.

All eleven players who beat Australia in December 1981 refused to play under Javed Miandad's captaincy in March 1982.

Wicketkeeper and opening batsman Taslim Arif was on the field throughout the 2nd Test against Australia in 1980, scoring 210 not out.

In Australia's first Test in Pakistan for 15 years (1980), two slow left-armers recorded the best innings and match analyses of their Test careers: Iqbal Qasim 7-49 and 11-118, Ray Bright 7-87 and 10-111.

The 1st Test of the 1979-80 series, Pakistan's first in India for 18 years, was interrupted by a swarm of bees.

Because of rain at Headingley in 1978, Sadiq Mohammad went to the wicket nine times during his innings of 97.

Pakistan's team for the 3rd match of the 1977-78 series against England didn't include any of the Mohammad brothers for the first time in 90 Tests.

TEST • PAKISTAN

Wasim Akram hit a record 12 sixes in a Test innings, against Zimbabwe in 1996.

Wasim Raja hit a record 14 sixes in a Test series, against the West Indies in 1976-77. He was top scorer in each innings of the first two Tests.

Replying to India's 509 in 1989, Pakistan declared at 699-5. Three batsmen made hundreds, two others made fifties, the sixth hit 39 not out!

In the 1st Test against England in 1987-88, Abdul Qadir dismissed every batsman at least once.

In the 3rd Test against England in 1954, Mohammad Ghazali was dismissed for a pair within two hours.

Majid Khan, Wasim Bari and Sikander Bakht all made a pair in the 2nd Test against Australia in 1978-79.

Sarfraz Nawasz had a spell of 7 wickets for one run to win the Melbourne Test of 1979, the 100th played by Pakistan.

Zaheer Abbas scored 583 runs at an average of 194.33 in the 1978-79 series against India.

Zaheer Abbas batted with a runner in both innings of the 3rd Test against England in 1984.

A record 32 catches were taken in the England v Pakistan Test at Headingley in 1971.

Pakistan scored a record 12 centuries in the 1982-83 series against India.

Pakistan scored the highest 4th-innings in any Test match when they declared at 657-8 against the West Indies in 1958. They drew the match after being made to follow on.

Nazar Mohammad faced Pakistan's first ball in Test cricket, against India in 1952.

Nazar Mohammad scored Pakistan's first Test century while carrying his bat against India in 1952.

TEST • PAKISTAN

Nazar Mohammad's son Mudassar Nazar played 76 Tests for Pakistan. They were the only Pakistani batsmen to carry their bats through a Test innings.

Abdul Kardar, who captained Pakistan in their first 23 Tests, had played for India in 1946 under the name Abdul Hafeez.

In the 5th Test of the 1952-53 series in India, Abdul Kardar's declaration asked India to score 97 runs in 15 minutes!

Pakistan didn't lose a Test, let alone a series, at home to Australia between 1959 and 1998.

Pakistan didn't win a series against the West Indies between 1959 and 1997.

When Shoaib Mohammad shared a record stand of 174 in 1990, he broke a record set by his father Hanif and his uncle Wazir.

Against South Africa in 1997, Azhar Mahmoud and Ali Naqvi became the first two debutants to score centuries in the same Test innings.

The only Pakistani bowler to be no-balled for throwing in a Test was Haseeb Ahsan against India in 1960.

When Ijaz Ahmed and Aamir Sohail put on a record opening stand of 298 against the West Indies in 1997, it was the first time both Pakistani openers had scored centuries in the same Test innings.

Pakistan's physio, who used to work with Sri Lanka, is Dan Kiesel, who was born in Tel Aviv.

In the two-match series against Zimbabwe in 1996-97, Wasim Akram averaged 292.00 with the bat and 16.36 with the ball.

Five Pakistani batsmen averaged over 60.00 in the 1996 series in England.

When Peter Petherick took his hat-trick for New Zealand in 1976, the third victim, Intikhab Alam, did the decent thing and walked.

Against Australia in 1994, Salim Malik made 237 before becoming the third victim in Damien Fleming's hat-trick.

TEST • PAKISTAN

Salim Malik's 237 in 1994 was achieved thanks to a dropped catch by Australia's captain Mark Taylor, who eventually took a record 157 in Tests.

In the 3rd Test in the Caribbean in 1957-58, Pakistan captain Abdul Kardar made 57 and bowled 37 overs despite a broken finger.

Basit Ali shares the trivial little record of playing the most Tests without facing England (19).

Playing in his first Test for two years, Ramiz Raja was made captain in 1995, lost the job after Sri Lanka had won the series, then got it back against the same opposition in 1997.

Of the 13 wickets Waqar Younis took in the 1st Test of the 1993-94 series against Zimbabwe, 12 were all his own work: 5 bowled, 7 lbw.

Against the West Indies in 1986, Salim Malik had his arm broken by a ball from Courtney Walsh. He made 3 not out in the second innings as Pakistan won by 186 runs.

Against England in 1996, Salim Malik put on 130 with his brother-in-law Ijaz Ahmed.

A spate of injuries during the 1997 series against Sri Lanka forced Pakistan to open the bowling with two specialist batsmen: Ijaz Ahmed and Salim Malik.

Pakistan's oldest Test debutant was 47-year-old Miran Bux in 1955. He bowled 48 overs in India's only innings. It was his first season in first-class cricket!

Against Sri Lanka in 1981-82, Ashraf Ali and Rashid Khan both averaged over 100 as a result of being out only once in the series.

In the 1982 series in England, Mudassar Nazar averaged only 17.00 with the bat but topped the bowling averages after taking 6-32 to win the 2nd Test.

TEST • PAKISTAN

Imtiaz Ahmed played in Pakistan's first 39 Tests (1952-62).

In the 2nd Test of the 1958-59 series, Fazal Mahmood took 6-34 and 6-66 to dismiss the West Indies for 76 and 172 and win the match.

On the 1962 tour of England, Peter Parfitt scored three consecutive hundreds in a week against Pakistan, including an unbeaten 101 in the 4th Test.

Majid Khan's maiden Test century, against Australia in 1972-73, was scored in his 20th innings, eight years after his debut.

The 2nd Test against England in 1968-69 was the only one of the three not interrupted by riots. It was controlled by student leaders, with no police or army present.

The Daily Telegraph 1978: 'Javed Miandad was the eighth to go. He was stretched well forward when a ball from Doshi raped him on the pads.'

The 5th match of the 1991-92 series in Australia was the only Test in which no batsman was bowled. The 33 catches set another record.

The first player to be stumped for 99 in a Test was Maqsood Ahmed against India in 1955.

Against India in 1999, Wasim Akram became Pakistan's leading Test wicket-taker – then became the last victim when Anil Kumble took all 10 wickets in an innings.

In the same Test against New Zealand in 1955, two batsmen set a new highest score for Pakistan, Waqar Hussain's 189 followed by Imtiaz Ahmed's 209.

The gap of 17 years in Younis Ahmed's Test career (1969-87) meant he missed a record 103 matches.

Against India in 1987, Ijaz Faqih reached both his fifty and his hundred with a six.

TEST • PAKISTAN

Wasim Akram took his 299th and 300th Test wickets in consecutive balls, at the Oval in 1996.

Aftab Baloch, who scored 428 in a first-class match, made his Test debut in 1969 aged only 16.

Mohammad Ghazali, who played in two Tests, both against England in 1954, was dropped after making a pair in the second.

Haroon Rashid reached a century with his 6th six of the innings against England in 1977-78 and hit another into the Lord's pavilion the following summer.

In the 1957-58 series in the Caribbean, Mahmood Hussain bowled 115.1 overs in the first three Test innings and broke down after five balls in the 4th.

At Headingley in 1962, Munir Malik bowled unchanged from 3.00 in the afternoon till 1.30 the following day, taking 5-128 in 49 overs.

Mohammad Ilyas reached his century against New Zealand in 1965 by hitting four consecutive fours with his score on 96.

After touring Australia in 1972-73, Mohammad Ilyas played grade cricket in Sydney and applied for Australian citizenship.

Pakistan settled for a draw in their first Test in England (1954) by scoring only 81 runs off the bat in 83.5 overs.

After spending 7 hours at the crease to score 79 against Zimbabwe in 1996, Saqlain Mushtaq bowled 40 overs in the second innings.

Shoaib Mohammad batted almost 8 hours in making 86 against the West Indies in 1990.

The 2nd Test against New Zealand in 1996 was held up because the officials at Rawalpindi couldn't find a match ball.

In the 2nd Test against the West Indies in 1959, Pakistan scored only 145 and 144 but won by 41 runs.

TEST • PAKISTAN

Mushtaq Mohammad's form had been so bad that he'd dropped himself during the 1976-77 West Indies tour – then made 121 and 56 and took 5-28 and 3-69 to win the 4th Test by 266 runs.

Kapil Dev and Javed Miandad both made their 100th Test appearances in the Pakistan-India series of 1989-90.

Inzamam-ul-Haq missed a Test against India in 1999 after a bang on the head in the team coach had given him stomach ache (!).

Pakistan's total of 708 against England in 1987 was their highest in Test cricket and the highest in England since 1938.

At Bradford Cathedral in 1992, the Rev. Geoffrey Peters, Britain's first Pakistani vicar, prayed for divine intervention in the ball-tampering dispute.

When the Lahore scoreboard wrongly credited Shoaib Mohammad with his maiden double century in 1989, the players had to be called back so he could reach the landmark.

Wasim Akram dominated the bowling averages in the 1989-90 series in Australia, taking 17 wickets at 18.70. The next best figures were 5 and 34.00

Wasim Akram gave a fine all-round performance at Adelaide in 1990, taking 5 wickets in an innings and scoring a fifty and his maiden Test hundred.

Before Dean Jones hit two centuries in the same Test in 1990, his previous highest score in eight Test innings against Pakistan had been 21 not out!

Waqar Younis took five wickets in an innings four times in a row in 1990, then took four, then another five.

Aamer Malik kept wicket against the West Indies in 1991 after Moin Khan was hit in the face by a bouncer from Ian Bishop, whom Moin had caught in the first innings.

Seventeen wickets fell on the last day of the Lord's Test in 1992 before Pakistan eked out a win by two wickets.

In 1992, Imran Khan's record of 21 wickets in a series in England was equalled by Wasim Akram and broken by Waqar Younis.

TEST • PAKISTAN

Pakistan have won their last five series against England.

When Pakistan made their lowest ever total, 62 against Australia in 1981, tail-ender Sarfraz Nawasz scored 26 but no-on else made more than 6.

The first series in which Pakistan won three Tests was the 1982-83 rubber against Australia, which was won 3-0.

Pakistan dismissed the West Indies for 53, their lowest ever score, in 1986. In the very next Test, they were bowled out themselves for 77, their lowest total at home.

Javed Miandad played in most consecutive Tests for Pakistan: 53 from 1977 to 1984.

The only partnership of over 300 in any Pakistan v England Test was the 322 shared by Javed Miandad and Salim Malik in 1992.

The only bowler to take 10 wickets in a Pakistan v England Test more than once was Abdul Qadir, who did it four times.

When the West Indies made 790-3 at Kingston in 1958, two of the Pakistani bowlers conceded over 200 runs each: Fazal Mahmood – and Khan Mohammad, whose 259 was the highest number of runs conceded in a Test innings without taking a wicket.

Against New Zealand in 1978-79, opening batsman Talat Ali was dismissed by Richard Hadlee in each of his five innings in the series, including once when he was bowled after mistaking Hadlee's grunt for the umpire's call of no-ball.

During Pakistan's tour of England in 1987, English commentator Henry Blofeld said 'Gosh, it's difficult to identify these chaps. Sometimes they turn out to be brothers and cousins, and sometimes not to be related at all.'

Waqar Younis, who has taken 277 Test wickets. is missing the little finger on his left hand.

TEST • SRI LANKA

Sri Lanka's 97 against New Zealand in 1984 was the lowest all-out Test total to contain a fifty.

Three Ranatunga brothers have played Test cricket for Sri Lanka: Arjuna, Dhammika – and Sanjeewa, who scored hundreds in successive Tests against Zimbabwe in 1994.

Greg Chappell's last Test as Australia's captain was in Sri Lanka in 1983.

In 1983 New Zealand batsman John Wright had his nose broken by a bouncer from Rumesh Ratnayeke, who fainted at the sight of blood and had to be revived with smelling salts!

Sri Lanka lost their inaugural Test, against England in 1982, when their last 7 wickets fell for 8 runs.

Sri Lanka's first ever Test was Derek Underwood's last. He took 5-28 and 3-67 to finish with 297 Test wickets.

Sri Lanka had to wait until 1995 to win a Test away from home, in New Zealand – and until 1996 to win a Test by an innings for the first time, against Zimbabwe.

Brendon Kuruppu's 201 not out against New Zealand in 1987 was the slowest Test double century and the only unbeaten double hundred on a Test debut.

Sri Lanka have had some very fast run-scorers, but not in their first Test against Zimbabwe, in 1994, when they managed only 157 runs in 90 overs on the first day.

Only 117 runs were scored from 81 overs in a Sri Lanka v New Zealand Test in 1984, a record low for the last day of a Test.

Sidath Wettimuny was the first Sri Lankan opener to carry his bat through a Test innings, against New Zealand in 1983.

TEST • SRI LANKA

Sidath Wettimuny's 157 against Pakistan in 1982 was his maiden first-class century and the first for Sri Lanka in a Test match.

Aravinda De Silva completed his first Test century (1985) with a six off Imran Khan, and has repeated the feat twice since.

When Sri Lanka lost by an innings to India in 1990, five batsmen failed to score in the first innings and five in the second. Three made a pair.

Two 19-year-old Test debutants opened the bowling against Pakistan in 1994: Chaminda Vaas and Ravindra Pushpakumara, who took 4-225 between them.

Apart from Muttiah Muralitharan, two other current off-spinners have been investigated on suspicion of throwing: Kumara Dharmasena and Sajeewa de Silva.

Sri Lanka's total of 952-6 against India in 1997, the highest in Test cricket, was the only innings to include a fifty, a century, a double century and a triple century.

The partnership of 576 between Sanath Jayasuriya and Roshan Mahanama in 1997 broke the previous Test record by over 100 and fell one run short of the highest in all first-class cricket.

When Sri Lanka restricted their hosts to 367 in 1989, it was the first time in ten Tests that Australia hadn't reached 400.

Sanath Jayasuriya (1,271) and Aravinda de Silva (1,220) were the world's leading run makers in Tests in 1997.

When Aravinda De Silva scored a hundred in each innings against India, it was the second time he'd achieved the feat in 1997. In his last six Test innings at home, he'd scored six centuries.

Against India in 1997, Sanath Jayasuriya scored 199 to add to the 340 he'd made in the previous Test. His aggregate of 571 broke the record for a two-Test series set by Wally Hammond (563) in 1933.

TEST • SRI LANKA

In the 1995-96 series in Australia, Muttiah Muralitharan was so disturbed by being no-balled for throwing that he finished bottom of the averages, scoring 7.00 with the bat and 116.00 with the ball.

In Arjuna Ranatunga's 50th Test, against Pakistan in 1994, Sri Lanka fielded three off-spinners – Dharmasena, Muralitharan, Warnaweera – and lost by 301 runs.

The only two Sri Lankan batsmen to bat throughout a full days's play in a Test match were Asanka Gurusinha and Arjuna Ranatunga in 1986.

Sri Lanka gifted Zimbabwe 65 extras in a single innings during the 1994-95 series.

Sri Lanka's appearance in 1989 attracted only 15,461, the smallest crowd for any Test in Brisbane.

Three batsmen made a pair in the 1989 Test in India: Marvan Atapattu, Rumesh Ratnayake and Graham Labrooy. Another, Jayananda Warnaweera, made 0 and 0 not out.

Roshan Gunaratne played in only one Test, against Australia in 1983, making 0 not out in each innings.

Ronald de Alwis made 4 consecutive Test ducks from 1986 to 1988.

In 1991 wicketkeeper Hashan Tillekeratne set a new Test record by not conceding any byes in a New Zealand of total of 671-4.

Asanka Gurusinha twice took over 8 hours to score a Test century, against Australia in 1992 and Zimbabwe in 1994. In the very next Test against Zimbabwe, he spent more than 5 hours in scoring 63!

In the 2nd Test against Zimbabwe in 1994, there were 7 left-handers in the Sri Lankan team.

Sri Lanka used four left-arm bowlers in the same Test against New Zealand in 1997.

Before scoring his first Test century in his 28th Test, Hashan Tillekeratne had reached 80 seven times.

TEST • SRI LANKA

Against Zimbabwe in 1996, Jayantha Silva conceded only 35 runs in 33 overs, including 21 maidens.

Sri Lanka took part in one of the shortest Tests ever, making 24-3 when only 50 minutes were possible against India in 1993.

In the two-Test series against Pakistan in 1997, Aravinda De Silva put a poor run behind him by averaging 216.00.

Against New Zealand in 1983, Yohan Goonasekera took four catches in an innings off the bowling of Vinothen John.

Australia lost only 4 wickets in their first ever Test against Sri Lanka (1983), scoring 514-4 and winning by an innings.

In Australia's first ever Test against Sri Lanka (1983), David Hookes scored his only Test century, in his 24th innings.

After Sri Lanka had lost their first ever home Test against New Zealand (1984), a crowd demonstration was put down by riot police.

Duleep Mendis' 190 in 1984 lasted more than 10 hours, the longest Test innings at Lord's.

The 1st Test against India in 1985 was the first in which Sri Lanka dismissed their opponents in each innings.

Pakistan were all out for 230 in 1986 – and still won by an innings, dismissing Sri Lanka for 109 and 101.

Against India in 1986, batsman Asanka Gurusinha bowled 11 balls which cost 25 runs, including two sixes, but took his first two Test wickets.

When Sri Lanka were all out for 82 against India in 1990, Asanka Gurusinha made 52 not out, 63.41% of the total.

Aravinda De Silva played in most consecutive Tests for Sri Lanka: 35 from 1988 to 1995.

TEST • SRI LANKA

In his first bowl at Test level, Ravindra Pushpakumara would have had a hat-trick against Zimbabwe if another new cap, Paul Strang, hadn't survived the third ball.

Amal Silva's 102 not out against England in 1984 was his maiden first-class century.

The record for most dismissals by a Sri Lankan wicketkeeper in a series is 22 by Amal Silva in only three Tests against India in 1985-86.

The first Sri Lankan to score a hundred in each innings of a Test was Duleep Mendis against India in 1982. He made 105 each time.

In the 1st Test against South Africa in 1998, Sri Lanka were dismissed for 306 in each innings.

The first Sri Lankan to take a wicket in his first over in Test cricket was Franklyn Ahangama against India in 1985. His victim was another Test debutant Lalchand Rajput.

Marvan Atapattu's first four Test scores in India were all ducks. His fifth, in 1997, was 108.

Marvan Atapattu improved his Test average by 2,182% (!) in half an hour against New Zealand in 1997, adding 25 runs to his previous 1 run in 6 innings.

Against India in 1997, Lanka De Silva lost three teeth when a ball from Javagal Srinath broke through the grille of his helmet.

Asanka Gurusinha and Andrew Jones both hit a hundred in each innings of the 2nd Test of the 1990-91 series in New Zealand.

Five Test wicketkeepers played in the England v Sri Lanka match at Lord's in 1991: Jack Russell, Alec Stewart, Brendon Kuruppu, Asanka Gurusinha and Hashan Tillekeratne.

TEST • ZIMBABWE

When Dave Houghton made his record 266 against Sri Lanka in 1994, the next highest score was Andy Flower's 50!

A few days later, Houghton made 142 against the same opposition, amassing 466 runs in his three innings of the series at an average of 155.33.

The only batsman to make a higher score for Zimbabwe than Dave Houghton's Test best 266 was Ray Gripper, who hit 279 not out against Orange Free State in 1967-68.

Henry Olonga, Zimbabwe's youngest Test player, was no-balled for throwing in his first Test.

Henry Olonga's debut for Zimbabwe had to be postponed when it was discovered that he held a Kenyan passport.

The first black player to play for Zimbabwe in a Test was Henry Olonga in 1995.

The second and third black players to play for Zimbabwe made their debuts in the same match in 1996: Everton Matambanadzo and Mpumelelo Mbangwa.

Zimbabwe's draw with India in 1992 made them the first country to avoid defeat on their Test debut since Australia won the very first Test in 1877.

Zimbabwe were the only country to remain unbeaten after their first two Test matches. They lost their third to New Zealand.

Zimbabwe's inaugural Test in 1992 was the first to feature three umpires, 'Dickie' Bird sharing the duties with two Zimbabweans.

Zimbabwe's 456 against India was the highest total by any country in its inaugural Test innings.

Zimbabwe are the only Test-playing country not to have scored 600 in a Test innings. Their best, an impressive 544-4, was made against Pakistan in 1995.

TEST • ZIMBABWE

Dave Houghton was the only captain to score a hundred in any country's inaugural Test.

Zimbabwe's first overseas Test, in Delhi in 1993, ended in defeat by an innings.

John Traicos was the last player to play Test cricket for two separate countries: South Africa in 1970, Zimbabwe in 1992-93.

The gap of 22 years 222 days between John Traicos' last Test for South Africa and his first for Zimbabwe was the longest in any player's Test career.

When he made his Test debut for Zimbabwe, John Traicos was 45, twice the age he had been when he made his debut for South Africa.

John Traicos was almost 26 years older than his first Test victim for Zimbabwe, 19-year-old Sachin Tendulkar, who was bowled for a duck.

The manager of the 1995-96 tour of New Zealand was Denis Streak, father of pace bowler Heath Streak.

In 1998 national coach Dave Houghton raised £25,000 towards a new cricket academy by walking the 250 miles from Bulawayo to Harare.

Andy and Grant Flower were the only brothers to each score a fifty in the first innings of their Test debuts.

Before the start of the 1996-97 series in Sri Lanka, Alistair Campbell and Henry Olonga had to be rescued by lifeguards when they were swept out to sea.

Andy Flower scored 18 in three hours to save the 1st Test of the 1996-97 series in Pakistan.

In a domestic match in 1996, Test wicketkeeper Wayne James broke world records by making 13 dismissals and scoring 99 in each innings.

TEST • ZIMBABWE

The first batsman to score a century in each innings of a Test for Zimbabwe was Grant Flower against New Zealand in 1997.

The Zimbabwe team against New Zealand in 1997 was the first to include three pairs of brothers: Andy and Grant Flower, Gavin and John Rennie, Bryan and Paul Strang. Guy Whittall was also in the team; his cousin Andy was 12th man!

The first match of the 1996-97 series against England was the only Test match to end in a draw (not a tie) with the scores level.

In the 1993-94 series in Pakistan, both Andy Flower and Waqar Younis captained their countries for the first time.

In the 1993-94 series in Pakistan, both captains were their country's youngest ever: Andy Flower 25 years 217 days, Waqar Younis 22 years 15 days.

Ujesh Ranchod played in only one Test (1993) and took only one wicket, but it was a good one: that of Sachin Tendulkar.

The first time two wicketkeeper-captains opposed each other in the same Test was during the 1995-96 series between New Zealand and Zimbabwe: Lee Germon and Andy Flower.

The first Zimbabwean to score 1,000 Test runs was Dave Houghton in 1996, a week before Andy Flower.

Dave Houghton retired hurt after scoring a century against New Zealand in 1996, having broken his foot before he'd scored 60.

The match against South Africa in 1995 was the first Test between two African countries.

In the first ever meeting of the Test 'minnows,' at Harare in 1994, Sri Lanka presented Zimbabwe with 65 extras in the second innings, including 36 no-balls.

The three Tests of their inaugural series against Sri Lanka, in 1994, were all drawn – but Zimbabwe could claim to have won on points: they batted only once in each match.

TEST • ZIMBABWE

When Zimbabwe won a Test for the first time, against Pakistan in 1995, they were helped by the coin having to be tossed twice. Pakistan won the first toss, Zimbabwe won the second, batted first, and won by an innings!

In the 2nd Test against Pakistan in 1995, Waqar Younis broke Dave Houghton's thumb and Aamir Nazir broke Mark Dekker's finger.

The first century for England against Zimbabwe was made by Nasser Hussain in 1996 after he'd been dropped by Stuart Carlisle off the first ball he faced.

England's second century against Zimbabwe, by John Crawley in the same innings, was reached with a six.

Andy Flower and England's John Crawley both scored 112 in the same Test of the 1996-97 series.

The lowest innings total made against Zimbabwe was Pakistan's 147 in 1993.

The partnership of 269 by Andy and Grant Flower against Pakistan in 1995 was the highest by a pair of brothers in Test cricket.

Ali Shah's 62, his maiden Test fifty at the age of 37, was Zimbabwe's highest score of the 1996-97 series against Sri Lanka.

Against Sri Lanka in 1996, Zimbabwe were dismissed for 145 and 127, a new record for their lowest score against any country.

Andy Whittall captained Cambridge University for two seasons. When he made his Test debut in 1996, he had never played first-class cricket in Zimbabwe.

TEST • ZIMBABWE

In 1995 Heath Streak took 52 Championship wickets for a county with the same name as his national coach: (John) Hampshire.

When Paul Strang scored his maiden Test century in 1996, he shared a partnership of 87 with his brother Bryan, who made 42.

Paul Strang is the only Zimbabwean to score 100 runs and take 5 wickets in an innings of the same Test.

The only Zimbabweans to share a century partnership against England were Grant Flower and Alistair Campbell in 1996.

The only Zimbabwean to score two centuries against Pakistan was Grant Flower in 1995 and 1996.

Grant Flower has shared in Zimbabwe's record partnerships for five different wickets against Pakistan.

Dave Houghton, the only Zimbabwean to score a century against Sri Lanka, did it twice in the same series.

Zimbabwe's second Test against New Zealand in 1992 was the first to have a one-day international staged in the middle of it.

COUNTY CRICKET

COUNTY • POT LUCK

1 Who was Man of the Match when Somerset won the 1983 NatWest Trophy final?

2 Who has taken the best innings analysis of 10-40 for Middlesex?

3 Who won the Gold Award when Somerset won the 1981 B and H Cup final?

4 How many matches did Sussex lose in the Sunday League in 1982: 1, 4, 12?

5 Who in 1997 shared the highest partnership for Worcestershire?

6 Who has taken most wickets in a first-class season for Worcestershire?

7 Whose career began at Surrey and after two more counties ended with Surrey?

8 Which Yorkshire player made his highest first-class score of 221 for England A?

9 Which Essex wicketkeeper had the nickname 'Tonker'?

10 For which county did Northamptonshire's current captain formerly play?

11 Which Gloucestershire player played in the 1981 Ashes series?

12 Who was first to score six centuries in consecutive first-class innings?

13 Who took 11 wickets for Gloucestershire against the 1995 West Indians: Kamran Sheeraz, Mike Smith, Courtney Walsh?

14 Which two Warwickshire players shared the record for the highest fourth wicket partnership in the championship?

15 Who was the first Hampshire player to captain England?

COUNTY • POT LUCK

1 Which wicketkeeper has made most dismissals in a first-class career for Middlesex?

2 Who has taken most wickets in a first-class season for Gloucestershire?

3 Who has taken most wickets in a first-class season for Somerset: Ian Botham, Arthur Wellard, Jack White?

4 Who was appointed captain of Lancashire in 1962 without having appeared in first-class cricket?

5 Which Middlesex and West Indies Test player was born in Trinidad?

6 Which Leicestershire batsman had the nickname 'Danny'?

7 Who has scored the most first-class runs and centuries for Derbyshire?

8 Which Gloucestershire bowler had the nickname 'Charlie'?

9 Who has scored the world record number of 20 sixes in a first-class match?

10 Which Middlesex and England Test player was born in Jamaica?

11 Which Worcestershire allrounder had the nickname 'Dippers'?

12 Which Hampshire batsman carried his bat through an innings four times in a season: Jimmy Gray, Roy Marshall, Neville Rogers?

13 Which New Zealand Test player was Nottinghamshire's overseas player in 1997?

14 Which South African Test allrounder played for Warwickshire in 1986?

15 Which two batsmen scored first-class double-centuries for Lancashire in 1998?

COUNTY • POT LUCK

1 Which Leicestershire bowler went on the 1982 unofficial tour of South Africa and was banned from Test cricket for three years?

2 Which Kent wicket keeper has played the second most Tests for England?

3 Who won the Gold Award when Somerset won the 1982 B and H Cup final?

4 Which wicketkeeper has made most dismissals in a first-class season for Hampshire?

5 Who was Northamptonshire's overseas player in 1997?

6 Which fielder has taken most first-class catches for Leicestershire: David Gower, Maurice Hallam, John Steele?

7 Which two overseas bowlers from the West Indies played for Kent but did not play a Test: Hartley Alleyne, Tony Merrick, John Shepherd?

8 Who shared a county record opening stand of 372 in 1998?

9 When did Essex first win the county championship: 1898, 1948, 1979?

10 Who was the last Lancashire players to score a 50 in the first innings of his Test debut for England?

11 Who carried his bat through a championship innings twice for Warwickshire in 1998?

12 Who was Middlesex's overseas player in 1996 who played only one first-class match because of a back injury?

13 Who has taken the most wickets in a season for Essex: John Lever, Maurice Nichols, Peter Smith?

14 When did Glamorgan win the Sunday League?

15 Which two legspinners were on Northamptonshire's staff in the late 1980s?

THE OBSERVER

JOB

---

15 Andy Roberts and Ian Salisbury.

6 Maurice Hallam, 427. **7** Hartley Alleyne and Tony Merrick. **8** Justin Langer and Mike Gatting. **9** 1979. **10** Paul Allott. **11** Nick Knight. **12** Dion Nash. **13** Peter Smith, 172. **14** 1993.

1 Les Taylor. **2** Godfrey Evans, 91. **3** Vic Marks. **4** Leo Harrison, 83. **5** Mohammad Akram.

COUNTY • POT LUCK

1   Which Somerset player became cricket correspondent of The Observer after World War II?

2   When Warwickshire won the Sunday League in 1980, which England fast bowler came out of retirement to help them?

3   Who has bowled most overs in a championship innings?

4   Which future Sussex captain made his first-class debut for them in 1970 aged 16?

5   Which Derbyshire player scored a maiden first-class century in his 744th innings?

6   Who was the overseas player when Glamorgan last won the championship?

7   Who was the last Northamptonshire player to go on a full England tour?

8   Who was the leading wicket-taker in the 1998 first-class season?

9   Who was the last Gloucestershire player to score a Test century for England: Bill Athey, Chris Broad, Jack Russell?

10 Which pair of brothers have scored the most first-class runs for Sussex?

11 Who was the first person to score 2000 runs in a first-class season: EM Grace, WG Grace, Gilbert Jessop?

12 Who is the only batsman to have scored centuries in the Varsity Match, for Gentlemen against Players and for England against Australia at Lord's?

13 Against which county did Hampshire field a side containing five former players of that county in 1994?

14 Who was the last Somerset batsman to score four centuries in four consecutive first-class innings?

15 Who has taken more than 60 catches in a first-class season four times: Brian Close, Phil Sharpe, John Tunnicliffe?

1 Vic Marks. 2 John Snow. 3 Peter Such, 86. 4 John Barclay. 5 Bob Taylor. 6 Waqar Younis. 7 Paul Taylor. 8 Courtney Walsh, 106. 9 Jack Russell. 10 James and John Langridge, 63036. 11 WG Grace. 12 Percy Chapman. 13 Middlesex. 14 Jimmy Cook. 15 John Tunnicliffe.

Quiz 5

COUNTY • POT LUCK

1 Who was the last Nottinghamshire batsman to score a double-century and a century in the same first-class match: George Gunn, Derek Randall, Reg Simpson?

2 Which Nottinghamshire bowler took 10-175 in an innings for an International XI against a West Indies XI at Kingston in 1982-3?

3 How many championships have Glamorgan won in all?

4 Who has taken most first-class wickets for Derbyshire?

5 Which pair of brothers are currently on the Northamptonshire staff?

6 Which New Zealand Test batman averaged 49 for Leicestershire before World War II?

7 Who has scored most runs in a first-class season for Worcestershire: Doc Gibbons, Graeme Hick, Don Kenyon?

8 Who scored a century for Kent on his first-class debut in 1979?

9 Which minor county beat Glamorgan in the 1974 Gillette Cup? Devon, Lincolnshire, Radnorshire?

10 Who was the Surrey player who died after a car accident in Australia in 1997?

11 Who was first to score 3000 runs in a first-class season?

12 Which Surrey and West Indian bowler had the nickname 'Silvers'?

13 Who was the leading first-class wicket-taker in 1993?

14 Which Surrey player was selected in an England party of 12 in 1983 but never played a Test?

15 Who was Leicestershire's youngest wicket keeper?

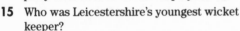

15 Ray Julian, 16.

11 KS Ranjitsinhji, 1899. 12 Sylvester Clarke. 13 Steve Watkin. 14 David Thomas.

6 Stuart Dempster. 7 Doc Gibbons, 2654. 8 Neil Taylor. 9 Lincolnshire. 10 Graham Kersey.

1 Derek Randall. 2 Eddie Hemmings. 3 8. 4 Les Jackson, 1670. 5 Alec and Graeme Swann.

Quiz 6
COUNTY • POT LUCK

1 Who scored 70* off 56 balls in a Sunday League match aged 16?

2 Which South African Test bowler has played for Warwickshire since 1987?

3 Which Leicestershire all-rounder had the nickname 'Luigi'?

4 Which two Middlesex and England Test players were born in St Vincent?

5 Which father and son have bowled leg-spin for Somerset?

6 Which Yorkshire player has represented England in ODIs but not in Tests?

7 Who has taken most wickets in a first-class career for Worcestershire?

8 Which Worcestershire wicketkeeper became a famous Test umpire and died during a first-class match?

9 Who was the second last Gloucestershire player to play a Test for England?

10 Who is the youngest Middlesex batsman to have scored 1000 runs in his first-class debut season: Denis Compton, Mike Gatting, Mark Ramprakash?

11 How many players did Glamorgan use when they won the championship in 1997?

12 Who has scored most centuries in a first-class career for Leicestershire: Les Berry, Brian Davison, Willie Watson?

13 Which Middlesex and England Test player was born in Barbados?

14 Which bowler who has played for Essex has taken the most Test wickets for England?

15 Who was Derbyshire's overseas player in 1998?

COUNTY • POT LUCK

1   Who was the joint leading run scorer in first-class cricket in England in 1992: Chris Adams, Kim Barnett, Peter Bowler?

2   Who was the leading run-scorer in first-class cricket in 1972: Alan Jones, Majid Khan, Tony Lewis?

3   Which Australian coached Leicestershire in the early 1990s?

4   Which two Nottinghamshire bowlers have taken 100 wickets in a first-class season most times?

5   Who scored 36049 first-class runs without being selected in a Test for England?

6   Who has scored most runs in a day for Middlesex: Denis Compton, Mike Gatting, Jack Robertson?

7   Who was Northamptonshire's overseas player in 1998?

8   Who was the last Warwickshire batsman to score a Test century against Australia?

9   Who has played the longest championship innings for Worcestershire?

10 Which bowler who has played for Hampshire has taken the most Test wickets?

11 Who has taken most wickets in a first-class season for Leicestershire: George Geary, Tony Lock, Jack Walsh?

12 Who was the last Somerset player to be selected for a full England tour?

13 Who scored a century for Kent on his first-class debut in 1981?

14 Which two fielders have taken most catches in a first-class season for Yorkshire?

15 Which West Indian Test batsman scored over 20000 first-class runs for Worcestershire?

COUNTY • POT LUCK

1 Who split Brian Lara's helmet during his record-breaking run in 1994?

2 Which Hampshire player is the only man to have kept wicket for England in a Test and kept goal for England in a full soccer international?

3 Who has scored the highest first-class innings of 318* for Gloucestershire: WG Grace, Tom Graveney, Wally Hammond?

4 Who was sacked as Northamptonshire's coach in 1998?

5 Which Essex batsman had the nickname 'Lager'?

6 Of which Essex player did Graham Gooch say: 'His epitaph will be the stories he created, stories which became bar-room legends around the county circuit'?

7 Which Middlesex batsman finished with 94 first-class centuries?

8 Who has taken the most first-class catches in a season since the reduction of the championship in 1969?

9 Which Gloucestershire player has the nickname 'Boo-Boo'?

10 Who was the last bowler to take 10 wickets in a first-class innings for Lancashire: Bob Berry, Brian Statham, Roy Tattersall?

11 Who was last to do the double of 2000 runs and 100 wickets in a first-class season?

12 Who was the leading run-scorer in first-class cricket in 1966: Alan Jones, Tony Lewis, Peter Walker?

13 Who was the last Lancashire bowler to take 100 wickets in a first-class season?

14 Who has scored a century as a nightwatchman for Worcestershire and England A?

15 Which Yorkshire wicket keeper made 412 championship appearances in succession?

Quiz 9

COUNTY • POT LUCK

1 Who poured salt over Jon Agnew's lunch in 1987 and had his kit thrown over the dressing-room balcony?

2 Which current Leicestershire batsman shared a stand of 283 for Oxford University against Hampshire?

3 Who has hit most sixes in a first-class innings for Warwickshire?

4 Which Essex and England allrounder had the nickname 'Suggsy'?

5 Who have shared the highest partnership for Middlesex?

6 Who has played the most championship matches in succession?

7 Who was the last Lancashire player to do the double of 1000 runs and 100 wickets in a first-class season: Wasim Akram, Len Hopwood, Jack Simmons?

8 Which Worcestershire player lost an arm during World War I and became a famous Test umpire?

9 Which Leicestershire player captained Ireland in the 1990s?

10 Which current Surrey player is the son of a former England wicketkeeper?

11 Who was the youngest Yorkshire player to be awarded a benefit?

12 Which West Indian wicketkeeper played for Nottinghamshire in the 1960s while studying at Nottingham University?

13 Which Yorkshire captain shares with WG Grace the record for captaining a county in the most seasons?

14 Who resigned as Nottinghamshire captain in the middle of the 1998 season?

15 Which Warwickshire bowler was the leading wicket taker in first-class cricket in 1971?

COUNTY • POT LUCK

1   Which Essex bowler has taken 100 wickets in a first-class season most times?

2   Who has taken most first-class wickets in a season for Lancashire?

3   Who was the Pakistan Test batsman sacked from Worcestershire for betting against his own county?

4   Who was the last batsman to score a double-century and a century in the same first-class match for Gloucestershire: Tim Hancock, Sadiq Mohammad, Zaheer Abbas?

5   Who scored 34 off an over from Alex Tudor?

6   Which wicket keeper has made most dismissals in a first-class career for Leicestershire: Paddy Corrall, Paul Nixon, Roger Tolchard?

7   Who retired as Middlesex's wicketkeeper after the 1998 season?

8   Who was first to score a century in the Gillette Cup final?

9   Which New Zealand Test player captained Surrey?

10 Who was the West Indian batsman who played for Sussex from 1968 to 1975: Roy Fredericks, Geoffrey Greenidge, Gordon Greenidge?

11 Who said: 'This is a Test match. It's not Old Reptonians versus Lymeswold, one off the mark and jolly good show'?

12 Which Somerset bowler has taken 100 wickets in a first-class season most times?

13 Which famous Test match radio commentator supported Hampshire?

14 Who said: 'I suppose I can gain some consolation from the fact that my name will be permanently in the record books?'

15 Who made a comeback for Gloucestershire after six years out of first-class cricket?

COUNTY • POT LUCK

1 Who was captain of Warwickshire when they first won the Sunday League?

2 Which Gloucestershire player has represented England in ODIs but not in Tests?

3 Who has taken the most catches in a first-class season for Glamorgan: Peter Walker, Allan Watkins, Wilf Wooller?

4 Who was the leading wicket-taker in the 1997 first-class season?

5 Who was the last Hampshire batsman to make a championship century outside mainland Britain?

6 Which Warwickshire player joined World Series Cricket and went on the 1982 unofficial tour of South Africa?

7 Which Worcestershire player was selected for England's A tour of Zimbabwe and South Africa in 1998-9?

8 Who were batting when Glamorgan won their final game in the Sunday League in 1993?

9 Who has taken the best bowling analysis in a first-class innings for Leicestershire?

10 Which current Nottinghamshire player was born in Pretoria?

11 Which Worcestershire fast bowler took over 100 Test wickets for West Indies?

12 Who scored 94 on his Lancashire debut and 106* on his England debut?

13 Who hold the record for the highest eighth wicket partnership in the championship?

14 Who was selected for England's ODI party in 1993 against Australia but did not play a game?

15 Who reached 1000 first-class runs in his first twelve innings for Warwickshire in 1990?

Quiz 12
COUNTY • POT LUCK

1 Which West Indian fast bowler played for Worcestershire from 1980 to 1982 but never played a Test?

2 Which Derbyshire bowler was known as 'Stan'?

3 What is Surrey's lowest total?

4 Who was the only player to represent England in both Centenary Tests, at Melbourne in 1976-7 and Lord's in 1980?

5 Which two Pakistani Test players played for Surrey between 1969 and 1978?

6 Who made a century for England against India at Kanpur in 1972-3?

7 Whose record for the highest innings for Warwickshire did Brian Lara beat in 1994?

8 Who is Northamptonshire's current batting coach?

9 Which allrounder from the West Indies scored 1000 runs in one season and took 100 wickets in another during the 1960s?

10 Whose partnership record did Percy Holmes and Herbert Sutcliffe beat when they scored 555 for Yorkshire against Essex at Leyton in 1932?

11 To which overseas player did Nottinghamshire prefer Jimmy Adams as a cheaper alternative in 1994?

12 Which wicket keeper has made the most dismissals in a first-class season for Warwickshire: Geoff Humpage, Keith Piper, Tiger Smith?

13 Which Essex and West Indian allrounder had the nickname 'Nobby'?

14 Who was appointed captain of Derbyshire for 1998?

15 Who took 8-21 against Sussex in the 1988 NatWest Trophy?

COUNTY • POT LUCK

1 Which South African Test batsman played for Sussex in the 1970s?

2 Who was the leading first-class wicket-taker in England in 1990, Neil Foster, John Lever, Derek Pringle?

3 Which Somerset allrounder helped Western Australia to win the Sheffield Shield in 1986-7?

4 Which wicket keeper has made the most dismissals in a first-class career for Warwickshire: Geoff Humpage, Keith Piper, Tiger Smith?

5 What is the highest position Hampshire have achieved in the championship under a right-handed captain?

6 Which pair of Sussex brothers have scored the most Test runs for England?

7 Which Essex and England batsman had the nickname 'Gnome'?

8 Who in 1920 set a record for the fastest first-class century in 35 minutes?

9 Which Nottinghamshire player was the youngest player to make a debut for Kenya, aged 15?

10 Who scored 79 off 91 balls on his first-class debut for Somerset in 1985 – and never bettered that score in the rest of his career?

11 Which two Australian bowlers from Queensland have been Surrey's overseas players?

12 Who has taken most first-class wickets in a career for Lancashire?

13 Which Gloucestershire allrounder had the nickname 'Jo'burg'?

14 Who won the Gold Award when Derbyshire won their B&H Cup final?

15 Which Yorkshire batsman had a son who captained Middlesex and England?

COUNTY • POT LUCK

1   Who won the Gold Award in the 1996 B and H Cup final?

2   Which two batsmen have scored most first-class centuries in a season for Worcestershire?

3   Which two Nottinghamshire players went on England's A tour of Zimbabwe and South Africa in 1998-9?

4   Who was originally signed as Northamptonshire's overseas player for 1998?

5   Which two Essex players have done the double of 1000 runs and 100 wickets in a season most times: Trevor Bailey, Maurice Nichols, Stuart Turner?

6   Who set a new record seventh wicket stand of 301 for Nottinghamshire against Durham in 1993?

7   Which Nottinghamshire and England bowler had the nickname 'Lol'?

8   Who was the last Yorkshire player to score 10,000 runs and take 100 wickets in first-class cricket?

9   Which Gloucestershire player is one of only two fielders to take seven catches in a first-class innings?

10 Who has scored the most centuries in a first-class season for Derbyshire?

11 Which Leicestershire bowler had the nickname 'Beast'?

12 Who has scored the fastest century in the NatWest Trophy?

13 Who are the only two Lancashire players who have made a Test century for England at Old Trafford?

14 Who was the last Worcestershire player to do the double of 1000 runs and 100 wickets in a first-class season?

15 Which Middlesex and England Test player was born in Trinidad?

1 Ian Austin. **2** Graeme Hick and Glenn Turner. **3** Chris Read and Paul Franks.
4 Paul Reiffel. **5** Maurice Nichols and Trevor Bailey. **6** Chris Lewis and Bruce French.
7 Harold Larwood. **8** Phil Carrick. **9** Tony Brown. **10** Peter Kirsten. **8**. **11** Nick Cook.
12 Graham Rose, off 36 balls v Devon. **13** Mike Atherton and Geoff Pullar.
14 Martin Horton, 1961. **15** Plum Warner.

COUNTY • DERBYSHIRE

1   Who is the only Derbyshire batsman to score a Test century for England: Kim Barnett, Donald Carr, Stan Worthington?

2   Which West Indian Test player was Derbyshire's overseas player in 1974: Rohan Kanhai, Viv Richards, Lawrence Rowe?

3   Which Derbyshire player has played the most Tests for England?

4   Which Indian Test player was Derbyshire's overseas player in 1973 and 1975: Bishen Bedi, Sunil Gavaskar, Srini Venkataraghavan?

5   Who has taken the most hat tricks for Derbyshire: Dominic Cork, Devon Malcolm, Dusty Rhodes?

6   Which two England batsmen joined Derbyshire from Yorkshire in the 1970s?

7   Which wicket keeper has made the most dismissals in a season for Derbyshire: George Dawkes, Harry Elliott , Bob Taylor?

8   When did Derbyshire last defeat the Australians?

9   What was the margin on the above occasion?

10 Who made the highest score of 185 for Derbyshire against the South Africans in 1998?

11 Who was the first Derbyshire player to be on the field throughout a completed championship match?

12 Who has scored most runs for Derbyshire in a one-day season?

13 Who has scored most centuries in a Sunday League season for Derbyshire?

14 Who took the best match analysis for Derbyshire in the championship in 1998?

15 Who shared a new eighth wicket record partnership for Derbyshire in 1996?

---

13 Dean Jones, 4. **14** Kevin Dean, 12-133. **15** Karl Krikken and Dominic Cork, 198.
8 1997. **9** One wicket. **10** Michael Slater. **11** Kim Barnett. **12** Dean Jones, 1151.
5 Dusty Rhodes. **6** John Hampshire and Phil Sharpe. **7** Harry Elliott, 90.
1 Stan Worthington. **2** Lawrence Rowe. **3** Bob Taylor. **4** Srini Venkataraghavan.

Quiz 2
COUNTY • DERBYSHIRE

1   Who has scored 1000 runs in a first-class season for Derbyshire most times?

2   Who has played the longest championship innings for Derbyshire?

3   Which South African Test player was Derbyshire's overseas player in 1995?

4   Which South African was one of Derbyshire's two overseas players in 1990?

5   Which four players kept wicket for Derbyshire in 1995?

6   Who was first to score a century for Derbyshire on his championship debut: Donald Carr, Daryll Cullinan, Chris Wilkins?

7   Who was the first Dane to play county cricket?

8   Who in 1992 scored Derbyshire's fastest championship century?

9   Which two Derbyshire pace bowlers were born in Dominica?

10 Which pair have made the most century opening partnerships for Derbyshire?

11 Which Derbyshire player has played the second most Tests for England: Dominic Cork, Devon Malcolm, Geoff Miller?

12 Who captained Derbyshire to victory in the 1981 NatWest Trophy final six weeks after being appointed?

13 Who was the highest scorer for Derbyshire on the above occasion: Peter Kirsten, Barry Wood, John Wright?

14 Who bowled the last over for Derbyshire in the 1993 B&H Cup final?

15 Which county did Derbyshire beat to take the Sunday League title, not having beaten them in any competition since 1982?

COUNTY • DERBYSHIRE

1   Who were the two leading wicket takers for Derbyshire when they won the Sunday League?

2   Who was Derbyshire's wicket keeper in the majority of their matches when they won the Sunday League: Peter Bowler, Karl Krikken, Bob Taylor?

3   Why was Derbyshire's game against Lancashire at Buxton halted on 2 June 1975?

4   Who is the only bowler to take four wickets in four balls for Derbyshire in first-class cricket?

5   Which Derbyshire batsman took his false teeth out and gave them to the umpire on a dodgy pitch?

6   Which Derbyshire fast bowler was told in his early days: 'you'll best get some ale down thee'? Bill Copson, Mike Hendrick, Alan Ward?

7   Who returned to Derbyshire in 1990 after three seasons with Essex?

8   Who was last to take ten wickets in a first-class innings for Derbyshire: Dominic Cork, Tommy Mitchell or Alan Ward?

9   Who was first to score 2000 runs in a first-class season for Derbyshire: Donald Carr, Denis Smith or John Wright?

10 Which two Derbyshire wicket keepers have scored 10,000 runs and made 1000 dismissals in their first-class careers: George Dawkes, Karl Krikken, Bob Taylor?

11 When did Derbyshire last come second in the championship?

12 Who was the coach – a former Somerset player – whom Dominic Cork said had too much influence at Derbyshire?

13 Which Derbyshire captain said: 'Derbyshire batsmen always labour under certain difficulties both psychological and technical. They have no tradition to inherit, no heroes to emulate': Kim Barnett, Brian Bolus, Guy Willatt?

14 Which South African player captained Derbyshire: Eddie Barlow, Peter Kirsten, Chris Wilkins?

15 What did Derbyshire do for the first time in their 2219th first-class match: a) bat consistently, b) tie the match, c) take all the opposition's wickets with spin?

14 Eddie Barlow. 15 Tie the match.

10 George Dawkes and Bob Taylor. 11 1996. 12 Andy Hayhurst. 13 Guy Willatt.

5 Ashley Harvey-Walker. 6 Mike Hendrick. 7 Geoff Miller. 8 Tommy Mitchell. 9 Donald Carr.

1 Simon Base and Adrian Kuiper, 19 each. 2 Peter Bowler. 3 Because of snow. 4 Bill Copson.

COUNTY • DURHAM

1 Who was Durham's first captain?

2 Which two former Gloucestershire players have captained Durham?

3 Who captained Durham to their highest championship position in 1998?

4 Who did Durham beat in their first competitive match?

5 Who scored the first century for Durham in the county championship?

6 Who bowled the first ball for Durham in the county championship?

7 In 1973, when Durham became the first minor county to beat a first-class county in the Gillette Cup, whom did they defeat?

8 In 1985, when Durham beat a first-class county for the second time in the Gillette/NatWest, whom did they defeat?

9 Who was the first Durham bowler to take 50 wickets in a championship season?

10 Who was Durham's first championship victory against?

11 Which Durham batsman has the nickname of 'Animal'?

1 David Graveney. 2 David Graveney and Phil Bainbridge. 3 David Boon.
4 Lancashire, in the Sunday League. 5 Ian Botham. 6 Ian Botham. 7 Yorkshire.
8 Derbyshire. 9 Simon Brown. 10 Glamorgan. 11 John Morris.

Quiz 2
COUNTY • DURHAM

1 Which Durham batsman had the nickname 'Ned'?

2 Who has scored most first-class runs for Durham?

3 Who has taken most first-class wickets for Durham?

4 What is Durham's highest position in the Sunday League?

5 Who has taken most wickets in a first-class innings for Durham?

6 Who has taken most wickets in a first-class match for Durham?

7 When Durham were trying to save their 1992 match against the Pakistanis, who left the ground early and was unavailable to bat?

8 Who was the first Durham batsman to carry his bat through a first-class innings (for 158*)?

9 Who was the second Durham batsman to carry his bat (for 158*)?

10 Who was signed from Middlesex to be county captain?

11 Which West Indian batsman has been Durham's overseas player?

12 Which Durham player is a painter and has an archaeology degree from Durham University?

1 Wayne Larkins. 2 John Morris. 3 Simon Brown. 4 Seventh in 1993. 5 Melvyn Betts, 9-64. 6 Alan Walker, 14-177. 7 Ian Botham. 8 Wayne Larkins. 9 Jon Lewis. 10 Mike Roseberry. 11 Sherwin Campbell. 12 Martin Speight.

COUNTY • ESSEX

1 Who has scored the fastest first-class century for Essex: Keith Boyce, Graham Gooch, Robin Hobbs?

2 Which Australian fast bowler spent a season on a scholarship with Essex: Dave Gilbert, Merv Hughes, Craig McDermott?

3 Who was Man of the Match when Essex won the 1985 NatWest Trophy final?

4 By what margin did Essex win that match?

5 How many did Nottinghamshire need to win off the last over in that match: 18, 12, 6?

6 Who bowled it?

7 Who was Man of the Match when Essex won the 1997 NatWest Trophy final?

8 Which Essex bowler took the most wickets in the Benson and Hedges Cup?

9 Who won the most Gold Awards in the Benson and Hedges Cup?

10 Who won the Gold Award in the 1979 Benson and Hedges Cup final?

11 Who won the Gold Award in the 1998 Benson and Hedges Cup final?

12 Which minor county beat Essex in the 1976 Gillette Cup: Devon, Hertfordshire, Rutland?

13 Who was the last batsman to score a double-century and a century in the same match for Essex?

14 Who was the last batsman to score four centuries in consecutive first-class innings: Allan Border, Keith Fletcher, Ken McEwan?

15 Who were dismissed for 14 by Essex in the championship at Chelmsford in 1983?

Quiz 2
COUNTY • ESSEX

1. Who was the last Essex player to do the double of 1000 runs and 100 wickets in a first-class season? Keith Boyce, Barry Knight, Stuart Turner?

2. Which former Kent captain played for Essex from 1977 to 1980?

3. Against whom did Essex make their lowest total of 30 in 1901: Glamorgan, the West Indians, Yorkshire?

4. Who was summoned from school to make his debut for Essex in 1980?

5. Which former Essex captain is a CBE: Allan Border, Doug Insole, Derek Pringle?

6. Which two former Essex captains are OBEs?

7. Which former Essex captain used to field a team at the Scarborough Festival: Doug Insole, Tom Pearce, Brian Taylor?

8. Which Essex player wrote 'Hit Hard And Enjoy It': Trevor Bailey, Dickie Dodds, Derek Pringle?

9. Which Essex player wrote 'Out Of The Wilderness': Allan Border, Graham Gooch, Derek Pringle?

10. Which Essex player became cricket correspondent of the 'Daily Herald'?

11. Which Essex player became cricket correspondent of 'The Independent'?

12. Which Essex captain was known as 'Johnny Won't Hit Today'?

13. Who played for Corinthian Casuals in the 1955-6 FA Amateur Cup final: Trevor Bailey, Keith Boyce, Doug Insole?

14. Which was Essex's first home?

15. Which two Essex players have been Test match radio commentators: Trevor Bailey, Ray East, Rev Frank Gillingham?

Quiz 3
COUNTY • ESSEX

1 Which Essex player has captained and coached England?

2 Which Essex player has captained and managed England?

3 Which Essex bowler also played for England at rugby as a full-back: Tony Jorden, Steve Malone, Derek Pringle?

4 Which Essex wicketkeeper had previously played for Yorkshire: Rodney Cass, Neil Smith, Mike Garnham?

5 Which Essex player made a pair against Australia on his Test debut in 1975?

6 Which Essex player made a pair against Australia in his last Test in 1958-9?

7 Who played only one more match for Essex after his last England Test in 1993?

8 Which Essex pace bowler was called up for England's 1994-5 tour of Australia but did not play a Test?

9 Which Essex pace bowler went on England's 1997-8 tour of the West Indies but did not play a Test?

10 Which Essex player tried to become a baseball pitcher in the United States?

11 Who cycled from third man at one end to third man at the other while fielding for Essex?

12 Who was renowned as the fastest bowler of his time: Charles Kortspright, Steve Malone, Derek Pringle?

13 Who played for Cambridge University, Yorkshire and England as an amateur before becoming an Essex professional, then an umpire and finally a bus driver?

14 Who was first to score 1000 runs and take 100 wickets in the Sunday League?

15 Which Essex fast bowler took 60 Test wickets before being killed on active service as a pilot in World War II?

COUNTY · GLAMORGAN

1 Which Glamorgan secretary offered to give spectators their money back when he thought Somerset had batted on too long?

2 Who said about Wes Hall, when Glamorgan played the West Indians in 1963: 'It was the first time two batsmen have crossed in the toilet'?

3 Who was the last batsman to have been dismissed 'handled the ball' in a championship match?

4 Who said about batting at Ebbw Vale: 'When I tap the pitch with my bat, someone else taps back'?

5 Who headed the Glamorgan bowling averages in 1976 but never played first-class cricket thereafter: Tony Allin, Gregory Armstrong, Jeff Jones?

6 Who has taken the best analysis in a first-class innings for Glamorgan: Jack Mercer, Don Shepherd, Waqar Younis?

7 Which two batsmen have scored the equal most first-class centuries for Glamorgan: Alan Jones, Matthew Maynard, Hugh Morris?

8 Who has taken most first-class wickets in a season for Glamorgan: John Clay, Don Shepherd, Waqar Younis?

9 Who have shared the highest partnership for Glamorgan?

10 Who have shared the highest opening partnership for Glamorgan?

11 Which wicketkeeper has made the most dismissals in a first-class season and career for Glamorgan: David Evans, Eifion Jones, Colin Metson?

12 What is the highest total by Glamorgan: 483, 582, 597-8?

13 What is the lowest total by Glamorgan: 17, 22, 29?

14 Which 37 year-old bowler did Glamorgan sign as captain in 1979?

15 Which 35 year-old bowler did Glamorgan sign as captain in 1983?

---

1 Wilf Wooller. 2 Tony Lewis. 3 Alun Rees, 1965, against Middlesex at Lord's. 4 Peter Walker.
5 Tony Allin. 6 Jack Mercer. 7 Alan Jones and Hugh Morris, 52. 8 John Clay, 176.
9 Adrian Dale and Viv Richards, 425*. 10 Alan Jones and Roy Fredericks, 330.
11 Eifion Jones, 933. 12 597-8 dec. 13 22. 14 Robin Hobbs. 15 Mike Selvey.

Quiz 2

COUNTY • GLAMORGAN

1. Which batsman who has played for Glamorgan has scored the most first-class centuries?

2. Who has taken most wickets in a first-class career for Glamorgan?

3. What is the highest first-class innings for Glamorgan: 243 by Alan Jones, 258 by Hugh Morris, 287* by Emrys Davies?

4. Who has scored most runs and centuries in a first-class season for Glamorgan: Majid Khan, Javed Miandad, Hugh Morris?

5. Which Glamorgan player has represented West Indies in ODIs but not in Tests?

6. Which Glamorgan player has toured with England A but not played a Test?

7. Who was Glamorgan's first team manager: Tom Cartwright, Duncan Fletcher, Barry John?

8. Who was the first Glamorgan player to captain England?

9. Which two Neath Grammar schoolboys have captained England?

10. Who led Glamorgan to their first championship?

11. Who was Glamorgan's youngest official captain at 22?

12. Which Glamorgan and England fast bowler took his career-best figures of 7-75 for Northamptonshire against Glamorgan?

13. Which Indian Test player has played for Glamorgan: Kapil Dev, Sunil Gavaskar, Ravi Shastri?

14. Which South African played for Glamorgan from 1975 to 1989: Rodney Ontong, Peter Swart, Corrie van Zyl?

15. Which two West Indian Test bowlers played for Glamorgan in the early 1980s?

EBBW VALE

1 Viv Richards, 114. 2 Don Shepherd, 2218. 3 Emrys Davies, 287*.
4 Hugh Morris, 10 and 2276. 5 Hamish Anthony. 6 Adrian Dale. 7 Tom Cartwright.
8 Tony Lewis. 9 Tony Lewis and Cyril Walters. 10 Wilf Wooller. 11 Hugh Morris.
12 Greg Thomas. 13 Ravi Shastri. 14 Rodney Ontong. 15 Winston Davis and Ezra Moseley.

COUNTY • GLAMORGAN

1   Who used to play football for Swansea and cricket for Glamorgan but has joined Sussex?

2   Which Glamorgan player, now the coach, had the nickname 'Bo'?

3   Which Glamorgan batsman had the nickname 'Ponty'?

4   Which Glamorgan captain had the nickname 'Walt'?

5   Which Glamorgan and England bowler had the nickname 'Boyo'?

6   Which former Middlesex and Glamorgan player had the nickname 'Smokey'?

7   Which former Somerset and Glamorgan player had the nickname 'Smokey'?

8   Which Glamorgan and England bowler has the nickname 'Watty'?

9   Who was the last Glamorgan player to do the double of 1000 runs and 100 wickets in a first-class season: Rodney Ontong, Jim Pressdee, Peter Walker?

10 Who was the first Pakistani to captain Glamorgan: Javed Miandad, Majid Khan, Younis Ahmed?

11 Who scored Glamorgan's first century in one-day cricket: Bernard Hedges, Alan Jones, Majid Khan?

12 Who scored Glamorgan's first century in the B and H Cup?

13 When Glamorgan won the Sunday League, who was their most economical bowler: Roland Lefebvre, Viv Richards, Steve Watkin?

14 Which fielder took the most catches in the Sunday League in that season: Tony Cottey, Roland Lefebvre, Matthew Maynard?

15 Which wicketkeeper made most dismissals in that season?

COUNTY • GLOUCESTERSHIRE

1   Which Gloucestershire player never played a Test but is now the chairman of England selectors?

2   Who has taken most hat-tricks for Gloucestershire: Charlie Parker, Mike Procter, Courtney Walsh?

3   Which two wicketkeepers have made the most dismissals in a first-class season for Gloucestershire: Jack Board, Barrie Meyer, Jack Russell?

4   Which fielder has taken the most first-class catches for Gloucestershire: WG Grace, Wally Hammond, Arthur Milton?

5   Who was first to score 1000 runs in an English first-class season before the end of May?

6   Who has carried his bat through a first-class innings most times for Gloucestershire: Alf Dipper, WG Grace, Arthur Milton?

7   Who has come closest to scoring a century before lunch on the first day of a Test for England?

8   Who has done the double of 100 runs and 10 wickets in a first-class match most times?

9   Who was first to score 100 first-class centuries entirely following World War II?

10 Who has scored 100 first-class centuries in the quickest time?

11 Who was first to score 10000 first-class runs for two counties?

12 What was Tom Graveney's highest score in the second innings of a Test: 54, 87, 151?

13 Which Gloucestershire player was a Wisden Cricketer of the Year in 1986 but never played a Test?

14 How many members of the Grace family played for Gloucestershire?

15 Who never played again for Gloucestershire shortly after being awarded his cap in 1979: Andy Brassington, Jim Foat, Brian Brain?

1 David Graveney. 2 Charlie Parker. 3 Jack Board and Barrie Meyer, 75.
4 Arthur Milton, 719. 5 WG Grace. 6 WG Grace, 17. 7 Charlie Barnett, 98*. 8 WG Grace.
9 Tom Graveney. 10 Wally Hammond, 12 years. 11 Tom Graveney. 12 54.
13 Phil Bainbridge. 14 Six. 15 Jim Foat.

COUNTY • GLOUCESTERSHIRE

1   Which Gloucestershire batsman was also an England rugby full-back?

2   In which season did Gloucestershire cap seven players: 1919, 1946, 1985?

3   Which famous Test umpire scored a century for Gloucestershire on his first-class debut in 1965?

4   Which Gloucestershire batsman was fired for batting too slowly in a limited-overs match: Phil Bainbridge, Chris Broad, Dean Hodgson?

5   Which wicketkeeper was capped by Gloucestershire and two other counties: Andy Brassington, Barrie Meyer, Roy Swetman?

6   Which two players born in Zimbabwe played for Gloucestershire in the 1980s?

7   Who was fired as captain in 1988 after seven years in charge?

8   Who succeeded him: Bill Athey, Courtney Walsh, Tony Wright?

9   Who was known as 'The Champion'?

10   Who was known as 'The Croucher'?

11   Who did Gloucestershire prefer Mike Procter to when it came to registering one of two South Africans who had played for their 2nd XI?

12   Who never played for England again after an incident in a lift with the chairman of England's selectors?

13   Who never played for England after fielding the ball with his boots in a Test at Lord's?

14   Which wicketkeeper has made the most first-class dismissals for Gloucestershire: Jack Board, Harry Smith, Jack Russell?

15   Which Gloucestershire captain suggested playing county cricket on Sundays and a knock-out competition half a century before either was introduced: WG Grace, Wally Hammond, Bev Lyon?

COUNTY · GLOUCESTERSHIRE

1 Who was the England A wicketkeeper who left Gloucestershire after one Sunday League match?

2 Which Australian Test bowler played for Gloucestershire in 1988: Terry Alderman, Dave Gilbert, Geoff Lawson?

3 Which Australian Test bowler played for Gloucestershire in 1991? Terry Alderman, Dave Gilbert, Paul Reiffel?

4 Who played for Gloucestershire at the beginning and the end of his career and for England in between?

5 Who took a career-best of 8-40 for the West Indians against Gloucestershire in 1969 and later joined the county?

6 Which two Pakistan Test batsmen played for Gloucestershire in the 1970s?

7 Which two Lancashire batsmen joined Gloucestershire in the 1960s?

8 Which current player was the public schools rackets and fives champion?

9 Which are the only two Gloucestershire wicketkeepers to have scored 10000 runs and made 1000 dismissals in their first-class careers?

10 Who played the most first-class innings without ever making a century?

11 Who never made a pair in 43 years of first-class cricket?

12 Who took 26 wickets in three consecutive innings in 1925, still a record for first-class cricket?

13 Why did Gloucestershire have only ten players when they played Surrey in 1914?

14 Who scored 161* for Gloucestershire on his championship debut in 1995?

15 Who captained Gloucestershire for 28 consecutive seasons, a record shared with Lord Hawke of Yorkshire?

1 Chris Read. 2 Terry Alderman. 3 Dave Gilbert. 4 Chris Broad. 5 John Shepherd.
6 Sadiq Mohammad and Zaheer Abbas. 7 David Green and Geoff Pullar. 8 Matt Windows.
9 Jack Board and Jack Russell. 10 Charlie Parker. 11 WG Grace. 12 Charlie Parker.
13 Because of World War I. 14 Andrew Symonds. 15 WG Grace.

Quiz 1
COUNTY · HAMPSHIRE

1 When did Hampshire first win the championship?

2 Who was captain on the above occasion?

3 When did Hampshire win their second championship?

4 Who was captain on the above occasion?

5 How many times have Hampshire won the Benson & Hedges Cup?

6 How many times have Hampshire won the Sunday League?

7 When did Hampshire win the Gillette/NatWest Trophy?

8 Who was captain on the above occasion?

9 Who would have been captain if Waqar Younis had not broken one of his fingers two days before the final?

10 Who was the Man of the Match when Hampshire won the NatWest Trophy?

11 Who is the only bowler to have taken 100 wickets in a first-class season for 20 consecutive years?

12 Who are the only two Hampshire batsmen to have scored a century for England against Australia?

13 Who scored 2395 first-class runs for Hampshire in his debut season: Matthew Hayden, Roy Marshall, Barry Richards?

14 Who batted with a broken arm for England against West Indies at Old Trafford in 1984?

15 Who is the only player to have scored a century and taken four wickets with four consecutive balls in the same first-class match: Kevan James, Malcolm Marshall, Peter Sainsbury?

1 1961. 2 Colin Ingleby-McKenzie. 3 1973. 4 Richard Gilliat. 5 Twice. 6 Three times. 7 1991.
8 David Gower. 9 Mark Nicholas. 10 Robin Smith. 11 Derek Shackleton.
12 Phil Mead and Robin Smith. 13 Barry Richards. 14 Paul Terry.
15 Kevan James v The Indians in 1996.

Quiz 2

COUNTY • HAMPSHIRE

1   Who was the leading wicket-taker in first-class cricket in 1974?

2   Who was the overseas bowler when Hampshire won the championship in 1973: Malcom Marshall, Andy Roberts, David O'Sullivan?

3   Who was the leading wicket taker in first-class cricket in every season from 1962 to 1965 inclusive?

4   Who took 5-13 against Derbyshire in the 1988 B&H Cup final?

5   Who won the Gold Award when Hampshire won the 1992 B&H Cup final?

6   Who was the last Hampshire to head the national batting averages?

7   Who was the last Hampshire player to score four centuries in consecutive first-class innings: Gordon Greenidge, Mark Nicholas, Barry Richards?

8   Which Hampshire player represented Holland in the 1996 World Cup?

9   Who was the first Anguillan to play county cricket?

10 Who was the first Antiguan to play for Hampshire?

11 Who was the second Antiguan to play for Hampshire?

12 Which two Hampshire players have represented England in ODIs but not in Tests?

13 Who shared the record for the highest sixth wicket partnership in the championship?

14 Who has scored most first class runs in a day for Hampshire: Gordon Greenidge, Richard Moore, Robin Smith?

15 Who was the last Hampshire player to score a double-century and a century in the same first-class match?

---

1 Andy Roberts. 2 David O'Sullivan. 3 Derek Shackleton. 4 Steve Jefferies. 5 Robin Smith.
6 Gordon Greenidge, 1986. 7 Gordon Greenidge. 8 Paul-Jan Bakker. 9 Cardigan Connor.
10 Danny Livingstone. 11 Andy Roberts. 12 Trevor Jesty and Shaun Udal.
13 Robert Poore and Edward Wynyard, 411. 14 Richard Moore. 15 Matthew Hayden.

Quiz 3
COUNTY • HAMPSHIRE

1   Which Hampshire bowler had the nickname 'Dougal'?

2   Which Hampshire batsman had the nickname 'Jets'?

3   Which Hampshire batsman had the nickname 'Pokers'?

4   Which Hampshire batsman had the nickname 'Kippy'?

5   Which Hampshire bowler had the nickname 'Trooper'?

6   Which Hampshire bowler had the nickname 'Butch'?

7   Which Hampshire batsman has the nickname 'Judge'?

8   Which Hampshire allrounder has the nickname 'Stan'?

9   Which Hampshire bowler has the nickname 'The Rat'?

10 Which current Hampshire player was born in Denmark?

11 Which current Hampshire player was born in the Channel Islands?

12 Which player born in Ireland played for Hampshire from 1973-1977?

13 Which Hampshire batsman was selected for an England A tour but never played a Test?

14 Who was Hampshire's overseas bowler from the West Indies in 1984?

15 Which Hampshire bowler took 1000 first-class wickets and his son 500, both with pace bowling?

COUNTY • KENT

1   How many times have Kent won the championship?

2   How many times have Kent won the Gillette/NatWest competition?

3   How many times have Kent won the Benson & Hedges Cup?

4   How many times have Kent won the Sunday League?

5   When did Kent last win a major competition?

6   When did Kent first win the championship: 1898, 1906, 1958?

7   When did Kent last win the championship?

8   Who won the Gold Award when Kent won the 1973 B & H Cup final?

9   Who won the Gold Award when Kent won the 1976 B & H Cup final?

10   Who won the Gold Award when Kent won the 1978 B & H Cup final?

11   Which Kent captain has won the most trophies?

12   Who is the only player to have won the Gold Award in a B & H Cup final after finishing on the losing side?

13   Who was Man of the Match when Kent won the 1967 Gillette Cup final?

14   Who was Man of the Match when Kent won the 1974 Gillette Cup final?

15   Who took 7-15 against Surrey in the 1967 Gillette Cup?

1 Six and one shared. 2 Two. 3 Three. 4 Four. 5 1995. 6 1906. 7 1978. 8 Asif Iqbal.
9 Graham Johnson. 10 Bob Woolmer. 11 Mike Denness. 12 Aravinda de Silva.
13 Mike Denness. 14 Alan Knott. 15 Alan Dixon.

Quiz 2
COUNTY • KENT

1 Who was the last Kent player to captain England in Tests?

2 Who has scored most first-class runs: Chris, Colin or Graham Cowdrey?

3 Who has scored fewest first-class runs:Chris, Colin or Graham Cowdrey?

4 Who has taken most first-class wickets:Chris, Colin or Graham Cowdrey?

5 Who said, after being appointed captain of England: 'I felt as if I had come third in an egg and spoon race at school and been awarded the prize because the first two had been disqualified'?

6 Who is the only bowler to have taken 10 wickets in a first-class innings on three occasions?

7 Who has taken the most first-class hat-tricks?

8 Who was last to take 150 wickets in a first-class season?

9 Who was the last batsman to score a double-century and a century in the same first-class match for Kent?

10 Who was the last Kent batsman to score four centuries in consecutive first-class innings: Mark Benson, Colin Cowdrey, Frank Woolley?

11 Who has scored most first-class runs in a day for Kent: Bill Ashdown, Aravinda de Silva, Frank Woolley?

12 Who was the last bowler to take four wicket in four balls for Kent: Tich Freeman, Fred Ridgway, Derek Underwood?

13 Who has played the longest championship innings for Kent?

14 Who was the last Kent player to head the national batting averages?

15 Who is the only fielder to have taken 1000 first-class catches?

COUNTY • KENT

1   Which two batsmen scored double-centuries for Kent in 1998?

2   Who was the last player to do the double of 1000 runs and 100 wickets in a first-class season for Kent?

3   Which three Kent wicket keepers have scored 10,000 runs and made 1000 dismissals in first-class cricket?

4   What is Kent's highest first-class total: 694, 760, 803-4 dec?

5   Who has scored the highest innings for Kent?

6   Who have shared the highest partnership of 366 for Kent?

7   Who has scored most runs in a first-class season and career for Kent?

8   Who has scored most first-class centuries for Kent?

9   Who has scored most first-class double-centuries for Kent?

10 Who was the 'Lion of Kent'?

11 Which Kent and England captain said: 'cricket is not only a game but a school of the greatest social importance'?

12 Which Kent batsman and Test umpire said: 'if they won't accept decisions, there is no point carrying on. Why should I?'

13 Which overseas player shared in Kent's record ninth wicket stand of 171 in 1997?

14 How many of Graham Dilley's 41 Tests did England win?

15 Which Kent player has represented England in ODIs but not in Tests?

11 Lord Harris. 12 Arthur Fagg, 1973. 13 Paul Strang. 14 Two. 15 Matthew Fleming.
7 Frank Woolley, 2894 and 47868. 8 Frank Woolley, 122. 9 Les Ames, 8. 10 Alfred Mynn.
Alan Knott. 4 803-4 dec. 5 Bill Ashdown, 332. 6 Simon Hinks and Neil Taylor.
1 David Fulton and Carl Hooper. 2 Leslie Todd, 1936. 3 Les Ames, Godfrey Evans and

Quiz 1

COUNTY • LANCASHIRE

1 How many championships have Lancashire won?

2 When did Lancashire last win a championship outright?

3 When did Lancashire last share the championship title?

4 When did Lancashire last finish as runners-up?

5 When did Lancashire first win a one-day trophy?

6 When did Lancashire win the Gillette/NatWest competition three years in a row?

7 Who captained Lancashire in these three years?

8 When did Lancashire first win two major competitions in one season: 1930, 1970, 1990?

9 Who was Lancashire's first manager?

10 Who scored 1000 runs in his first-class debut season in 1987?

11 Which Lancashire batsman was the first to score 1000 runs in under-19 Tests?

12 Which Lancashire wicket keeper shares the world record of 11 catches in a first-class match?

13 Which Lancashire batsman scored a century in his first first-class match and in his last 33 years later?

14 Which Lancashire bowler has taken 100 wickets in a first-class season most times?

15 Who scored the slowest ever championship century?

Quiz 2

COUNTY • LANCASHIRE

1 Which Lancastrian captained Tasmania in their first Sheffield Shield match?

2 Which Lancastrian has captained England in most Tests against Australia?

3 Who beat Len Hutton's 364 as the highest first-class innings played at The Oval?

4 Who was the 19 year old spinner who dismissed Don Bradman twice in the same match in 1948?

5 Which Lancastrian scored 1000 first-class runs before the end of May?

6 Which Lancastrian scored 2000 runs in a first-class season without a century?

7 Who is the only Lancashire wicket keeper to have made 100 dismissals in a first-class season?

8 Who has taken more first-class wickets than any other overseas bowler?

9 Who made his England debut in the last Test before World War II, scored 99 runs and never represented England again: Norman Oldfield, Eddie Paynter, Cyril Washbrook?

10 Who was the leading run scorer in first-class cricket in 1998?

11 Who was the leading wicket taker in first-class cricket in 1975: Peter Lee, Peter Lever, Jack Simmons?

12 Who was the leading wicket taker in first-class cricket in 1950: Bob Berry, Brian Statham, Roy Tattersall?

13 Who took four wickets in an over for England against South Africa at Headingley in 1947?

14 Which fielder has taken most catches in a first-class season for Lancashire: Mike Atherton, Ken Grieves, Ernest Tyldesley

15 Which three left-handed batsmen from Accrington have scored Test double-centuries for England?

Quiz 3

COUNTY • LANCASHIRE

1 Which Lancashire and England bowler had the nickname 'Plank'?

2 Which Lancashire and England batsman had the nickname 'Bumble'?

3 Which Lancashire and England batsman had the nickname 'Foxy'?

4 Which Lancashire and England bowler had the nickname 'Walt'?

5 Which Lancashire batsman had the nickname 'Filth'?

6 Which Lancashire and West Indies batman had the nickname 'Hubert'?

7 Which Lancashire and England wicket keeper has the nickname 'Chuck'?

8 Which two Lancashire players have played for England in ODIs but not in Tests?

9 Who has made the highest first-class score for Lancashire?

10 Who has scored most first-class centuries in a season for Lancashire: John Crawley, Charlie Hallows, Johnny Tyldesley?

11 Who has scored most first-class centuries and runs in a career for Lancashire?

12 Who has scored most first-class runs in a season for Lancashire?

13 What is Lancashire's highest first-class total – 663, 763, 863?

14 Who have shared the highest partnership for Lancashire?

15 Who has made the highest first-class score at Old Trafford: Mike Atherton, Jason Gallian, Archie MacLaren?

15 Jason Gallian, 312.

13 863 against Surrey, 1990. **14** Frank Watson and Ernest Tyldesley, 371.

10 Charlie Hallows, 11. **11** Ernest Tyldesley, 90 and 34222. **12** Johnny Tyldesley, 2633.

7 Warren Hegg. **8** Ian Austin and Graham Lloyd. **9** Archie MacLaren, 424.

1 Peter Lever. **2** David Lloyd. **3** Graeme Fowler. **4** Paul Allott. **5** Harry Pilling. **6** Clive Lloyd.

Quiz 1

COUNTY • LEICESTERSHIRE

1 How many times have Leicestershire won the county championship?

2 When did Leicestershire last win the championship?

3 Which county did Leicestershire beat to clinch the title on the above occasion?

4 Which two 26 year old batsmen scored centuries in the above match?

5 By what margin did Leicestershire win the above match: 211 runs, an innings and 211 runs, eight wickets?

6 Which four players captained Leicestershire in 1998?

7 Who scored most championship runs in 1998?

8 Who was the leading wicket taker in 1998?

9 When did Leicestershire win their previous county championship?

10 Who was their captain in that season?

11 Who was their overseas player in that season?

12 Who did they beat in the final match by an innings to clinch the title?

13 Who was the number 11 who hit 72 on the above occasion?

14 How many championship games did Leicestershire lose from 1996 to 1998?

15 What is Leicestershire's emblem?

Quiz 2

COUNTY • LEICESTERSHIRE

1 What is the name of Leicestershire's county ground?

2 What is the name of the previous county ground in Leicester?

3 Who was Leicestershire's overseas player in 1997: Hansie Cronje, Neil Johnson, Phil Simmons?

4 Who was Leicestershire's overseas player in 1995: Hansie Cronje, Neil Johnson, Phil Simmons?

5 When did Leicestershire win their first championship?

6 Who was their captain on the above occasion?

7 Who was their overseas bowler on the above occasion?

8 Which two Leicestershire players played their only Test match against Australia?

9 Who reappeared for Leicestershire in a single one-day knock-out match in 1992?

10 Who broke the record for the highest innings for Leicestershire on his championship debut for the county?

11 In 1955 who brought himself on against Surrey and took eight wickets without conceding a run?

12 In how many Tests did Roger Tolchard keep wicket for England?

13 Who played for Leicestershire and Doncaster Rovers on the same day in 1975?

14 Which Leicestershire batsman missed the whole of the 1985 season owing to a car accident?

15 Who took 8-17 on his first-class debut for Leicestershire in 1976?

COUNTY • LEICESTERSHIRE

1   What is the highest score in Tests by a Leicestershire batsman?

2   Who was first to take a hat-trick in a B&H Cup final?

3   Who won the Gold Award in the 1972 B&H Cup final?

4   Who won the Gold Award in the 1975 B&H Cup final?

5   Who won the Gold Award in the 1985 B&H Cup final?

6   Which non-championship side has twice beaten Leicestershire in the B&H Cup?

7   Which Leicestershire player has done the double of 1000 runs and 100 wickets in a first-class season the most times: Eric Astill, George Geary, Ray Illingworth?

8   Who was the last Leicestershire bowler to be the leading wicket taker in an English first-class season?

9   Which Leicestershire bowler has taken 100 wickets in a first-class season the most times?

10 Which two Leicestershire players have represented England in ODIs but not in Tests?

11 Who was the last Leicestershire player to score a double-century and century in the same first-class match: Brian Davison, Maurice Hallam, Clive Inman?

12 Who set a county record of 322 for the fifth wicket in 1998?

13 Who was the last Leicestershire bowler to take 100 wickets in a first-class season?

14 Who was the last Leicestershire player to do the double of 1000 runs and 100 wickets in a first-class season?

15 Who was the leading run scorer for England against Rest of the World in 1970?

and Phil Simmons. **13** Jon Agnew, 1987. **14** Jack van Geloven, 1962. **15** Ray Illingworth.
9 George Geary, 11. **10** Darren Maddy and Vince Wells. **11** Maurice Hallam. **12** Ben Smith
5 Peter Willey. **6** Minor Counties. **7** Eric Astill, 9. **8** Jack Walsh, 174 in 1948.
1 David Gower, 215. **2** Ken Higgs, 1974. **3** Chris Balderstone. **4** Norman McVicker.

COUNTY • MIDDLESEX

1 How many championships have Middlesex won?

2 When did Middlesex first win the championship: 1898, 1903, 1947?

3 When did Middlesex last win the championship?

4 Who was the captain on the above occasion?

5 Who has captained Middlesex to the most championships?

6 What was the official reason for Mike Gatting being deposed as England captain: a) a chambermaid b) excess weight c) Shakoor Rana

7 When did Middlesex win the Sunday League?

8 By what margin did Middlesex win the 1983 Benson and Hedges Cup final?

9 Who won the Gold Award on the above occasion?

10 By what margin did Middlesex win the 1986 Benson and Hedges Cup final?

11 Who won the Gold Award on the above occasion?

12 Who was the last bowler to taken ten wickets in an innings in the championship?

13 Who was the last Middlesex player to captain England in a Test?

14 Who has made the highest first-class score for Middlesex: Denis Compton, Mike Gatting, Jack Robertson?

15 Which Middlesex bowler has taken the most Test wickets for England?

1 Ten and two shared. 2 1903. 3 1993. 4 Mike Gatting. 5 Mike Brearley and Mike Gatting, 3 each. 6 A chambermaid. 7 1992. 8 Four runs. 9 Clive Radley. 10 Two runs. 11 John Emburey. 12 Richard Johnson. 13 John Emburey. 14 Jack Robertson, 331. 15 Angus Fraser, 177.

COUNTY • MIDDLESEX

1 Who has scored the most first-class runs in any calendar year and when?

2 Who has scored most centuries in a first-class season for Middlesex?

3 Who has scored most runs in a first-class season for Middlesex?

4 Which Middlesex player has represented England in ODIs but not in Tests?

5 Which Middlesex batsman has played the longest innings for England outside Ashes Tests: Bill Edrich, Mike Gatting, Clive Radley?

6 Who was the leading run-scorer in first-class cricket in 1995?

7 Who was the joint leading run-scorer in first-class cricket in 1992?

8 Who was the last Middlesex batsman to head the national first-class batting averages: John Carr, Desmond Haynes, Mark Ramprakash?

9 Which Middlesex player's wife wrote 'Cricket XXXX Cricket' about England's 1986-7 tour of Australia: Phil Edmonds's, John Emburey's, Mike Gatting's?

10 Which Middlesex batsman has made the highest score in Tests: Denis Compton, Mike Gatting, Patsy Hendren?

11 Who took 85 first-class wickets in his only season for Middlesex in 1980?

12 Who was Man of the Match when Middlesex won the 1977 Gillette Cup final?

13 Who was Man of the Match when Middlesex won the 1980 Gillette Cup final?

14 Who was Man of the Match when Middlesex won the 1984 NatWest Trophy final?

15 Who was Man of the Match when Middlesex won the 1988 NatWest Trophy final?

COUNTY • MIDDLESEX

1   In the middle of which season did Mike Gatting resign as captain?

2   Who was Mike Gatting's successor as Middlesex captain?

3   Who was Middlesex captain before Mike Gatting?

4   Who was Middlesex's coach in 1998?

5   Which amateur spin bowler captained Middlesex from 1961 to 1962: Ian Bedford, Colin Drybrough, Walter Robins?

6   Who was Middlesex's overseas player in 1997?

7   Who took 7-12 against Minor Counties East in the B and H Cup?

8   Who took 7-22 against Hampshire in the B and H Cup?

9   Which Middlesex and England bowler had the nickname 'Ernie'?

10   Which Middlesex and England bowler had the nickname 'Goat'?

11   Which Middlesex and England bowler had the nickname 'Flash'?

12   Which Middlesex and West Indies bowler had the nickname 'Diamond'?

13   Which Middlesex and England wicketkeeper had the nickname 'Nobby'?

14   Which Middlesex and England batsman had the nickname 'Gladys'?

15   Who scored three Test centuries for England in the 1962 season?

1 1997. 2 Mark Ramprakash. 3 Mike Brearley. 4 John Buchanan. 5 Ian Bedford.
6 Jacques Kallis. 7 Wayne Daniel. 8 Jeff Thomson. 9 John Emburey. 10 Phil Edmonds.
11 Norman Cowans. 12 Wayne Daniel. 13 Paul Downton. 14 Graham Barlow.
15 Peter Parfitt.

COUNTY • NORTHAMPTONSHIRE

1 What is Northamptonshire's highest position in the championship?

2 When did Northamptonshire win their first major competition?

3 Who captained Northamptonshire on the above occasion?

4 Who was Man of the Match on the above occasion?

5 When did Northamptonshire win the B&H Cup?

6 Who was captain on the above occasion?

7 Who won the Gold Award on the above occasion?

8 What was Northamptonshire's highest position in the Sunday League?

9 Who defeated Northamptonshire in 1973 when a non-championship side beat a first-class county in the B&H Cup for the first time?

10 Which non-championship side beat Northamptonshire in the 1990 B&H Cup?

11 Who was Man of the Match when Northamptonshire won the 1992 NatWest Trophy final?

12 How many times have Northamptonshire lost the Gillette/NatWest final?

13 Which minor county beat Northamptonshire in the 1988 NatWest Trophy: Cheshire, Devon, Huntingdonshire?

14 Who are the only two Northamptonshire batsmen to have scored a Test century for England against Australia?

15 In addition to the 11 Sri Lankans, who else made his Test debut in the inaugural Test between Sri Lanka and England at Colombo in 1981-2: Geoff Cook, Allan Lamb, Wayne Larkins?

1 Second on four occasions . 2 1976, Gillette Cup. 3 Jim Watts. 4 Peter Willey.
5 1980. 6 Jim Watts. 7 Allan Lamb. 8 Third in 1991. 9 Oxford University. 10 Scotland .
11 Alan Fordham. 12 Five. 13 Cheshire. 14 Allan Lamb and Raman Subba Row.
15 Geoff Cook.

QUiz 2

COUNTY • NORTHAMPTONSHIRE

1　Of bowlers who have played for Northamptonshire, who has taken the most Test wickets?

2　Who has taken most wickets in a first-class season for Northamptonshire: Bishen Bedi, George Tribe, Frank Tyson?

3　Who was first to take a hat-trick in the Gillette Cup?

4　Who took two hat-tricks in the space of six weeks in 1961?

5　Who has done the double of 1000 runs and 100 wickets in a first-class season the most times after Wilfred Rhodes and George Hirst?

6　Which Northamptonshire allrounder did the double of 1000 runs and 100 wickets in a first-class season seven times?

7　Who has played the longest championship innings for Northamptonshire?

8　Which Northamptonshire player has gone the most first-class innings without scoring a run?

9　Who was the first bowler to take 100 wickets in a championship consisting of four-day matches only?

10　Who was the leading wicket taker in first-class cricket in 1995?

11　Who was the leading wicket taker in 1973?

12　Which two Northamptonshire allrounders have done the double of 1000 runs and 100 wickets in a first-class season for another county?

13　Who scored a double-century on his first-class debut in 1996?

14　Who scored a century on his first-class debut in 1985: Nigel Felton, Alan Fordham, Alistair Storie?

15　Who was the last Northamptonshire batsman to score a double-century and a century in the same first-class match?

---

1 Kapil Dev, 434. 2 George Tribe, 175. 3 David Larter. 4 Mike Dilley. 5 Vallance Jupp, 10.
6 George Tribe. 7 Richard Montgomerie, 582 minutes. 8 Mark Robinson, 12. 9 Anil Kumble.
10 Anil Kumble, 105. 11 Bishen Bedi, 105. 12 Freddie Brown (Surrey) and Vallance Jupp
(Sussex). 13 David Sales. 14 Alistair Storie. 15 Allan Lamb.

COUNTY • NORTHAMPTONSHIRE

1   Who has made the highest first-class score for Northamptonshire?

2   Whose record did he beat?

3   Who has made the most first-class centuries in a career for Northamptonshire?

4   Of batsmen who have played for Northamptonshire, who has made the most first-class centuries?

5   Who has made the most first-class centuries in a season for Northamptonshire: Dennis Brookes, Robert Haywood, Allan Lamb?

6   Who has made the most first-class runs in a career for Northamptonshire: Dennis Brookes, Allan Lamb, David Steele?

7   Who has the best analysis in a first-class innings for Northamptonshire: Bishen Bedi, Vallance Jupp, Frank Tyson?

8   Who has taken the best analysis in a first-class match for Northamptonshire?

9   Who have shared the highest first-class partnership for Northamptonshire?

10 Whose record did they beat?

11 Which batsman and captain had the nickname 'Legger'?

12 Which batsman had the nickname 'Ned'?

13 Which batsman had the nickname 'Stainless'?

14 Which allrounder had the nickname 'Chippie'?

15 Which bowler had the nickname 'Typhoon'?

---

1 Mal Love, 322*. 2 Raman Subba Row, 300. 3 Dennis Brookes, 67. 4 Allan Lamb, 89.
5 Robert Haywood, 8. 6 Dennis Brookes, 28980. 7 Vallance Jupp, 10-127.
8 George Tribe, 15-31. 9 Mal Love and David Ripley, 401.
10 Alan Fordham and Allan Lamb, 393. 11 Allan Lamb. 12 Wayne Larkins. 13 David Steele.
14 Richard Williams. 15 Frank Tyson.

COUNTY • NOTTINGHAMSHIRE

1 How many championships have Nottinghamshire won?

2 When did Nottinghamshire last win the championship?

3 Who captained them on the above occasion?

4 When did Nottinghamshire win the Sunday League?

5 Who captained them on the above occasion?

6 When did Nottinghamshire win the Benson and Hedges Cup?

7 Who won the Gold Award on the above occasion?

8 Who hit the last ball from John Lever for four to win the match?

9 When did Nottinghamshire win the Gillette/NatWest competition?

10 Who was Man of the Match in the final of the above competition?

11 Which county beat Nottinghamshire by one run in the 1985 NatWest Trophy final?

12 Who scored 16 of the 18 runs needed off the final over on the above occasion?

13 Which two Nottinghamshire fast bowlers bowled 'Bodyline'?

14 On which England tour of Australia did they do so?

15 Which of them was never selected for England again?

COUNTY • NOTTINGHAMSHIRE

1   Who hit six sixes in an over for Nottinghamshire?

2   Who was the bowler on the above occasion?

3   Who committed suicide in 1903 after heading the national first-class batting averages in the previous season?

4   Who scored 156* against Australia in 1950-1?

5   Who scored 162* against Australia in 1986-7?

6   Who scored 164 against Australia in 1886?

7   Who scored 169* against Australia in 1938?

8   Who scored 174 against Australia in 1976-7?

9   Who scored 175 against Australia in 1985?

10 Which Nottinghamshire allrounder has done the double of 1000 runs and 100 wickets in a first-class season most times: John Gunn, Richard Hadlee, Garfield Sobers?

11 Who was last to do the double of 1000 runs and 100 wickets in a first-class season?

12 Who is the only other player to have done the double since 1967?

13 Who was the last Nottinghamshire player to head the national first-class batting averages?

14 Who was the last Nottinghamshire batsman to be the leading run-scorer in a first-class season in this country?

15 Which Nottinghamshire player took the record of 208 wickets in a first-class career for Cambridge University?

COUNTY • NOTTINGHAMSHIRE

1 Which Nottinghamshire bowler took 100 first-class wickets in 1988 in addition to Franklyn Stephenson?

2 Who was the leading wicket-taker in first-class cricket in this country in 1953 and 1954: Harold Butler, Bruce Dooland, Arthur Jepson?

3 Who was captain and manager of Nottinghamshire in 1974: Jack Bond, Mike Smedley, Clive Rice?

4 Which Nottinghamshire bowler was the joint leading wicket-taker with 98 wickets in 1972, and died in 1980?

5 Which Nottinghamshire bowler has taken over 100 Test wickets for India?

6 Which Australian allrounder has the highest batting average for Nottinghamshire of 164: Bruce Dooland, Keith Miller, Steve Waugh?

7 Which Nottinghamshire wicketkeeper made his first-class debut at 16?

8 Which Nottinghamshire wicketkeeper made his first-class debut at 17?

9 Who scored three centuries in the 1986-7 Ashes series in Australia?

10 Who went on the England A tour of the West Indies in 1991-2 but was never selected for a Test?

11 Which town in Nottinghamshire has produced many Test and first-class cricketers, the latest of them Tim Robinson and Paul Franks?

12 Who scored 98 as a nightwatchman for England against Australia?

13 Who scored 95 as a nightwatchman for England against Australia?

14 Who has taken most wickets in a first-class season for Nottinghamshire: Bruce Dooland, Richard Hadlee, Tom Wass?

15 Who has taken most wickets in a first-class career for Nottinghamshire: Bruce Dooland, Sam Staples, Tom Wass?

COUNTY • SOMERSET

1   What is Somerset's highest championship position?

2   When did Somerset first win a major competition?

3   When did Somerset first win two competitions in one season?

4   When did Somerset win the same competition in successive seasons?

5   When did Somerset last win a competition?

6   Who captained Somerset to all the above trophies?

7   What is the highest first-class innings for Somerset?

8   Who was the last batsman to score 3000 runs in a first-class season?

9   Who did not make his debut in county cricket until the age of 35 and then scored 7604 runs at 72 in his next three seasons?

10 In which year did Somerset have three official captains?

11 Who has scored most runs in a first-class season for Somerset?

12 Who has scored most runs and centuries in a first-class career for Somerset?

13 Who has scored most centuries in a first-class season for Somerset?

14 Which three Test players abruptly left Somerset at the end of the 1986 season?

15 Who was the captain of Somerset in 1986?

COUNTY • SOMERSET

1   Which Somerset bowler had the nickname 'Crusoe'?

2   Which Somerset batsman had the nickname 'Dasher'?

3   Which Somerset batman had the nickname 'Sir Len'?

4   Which Somerset allrounder had the nickname 'Budgie'?

5   Which Somerset and England bowler had the nickname 'Farmer'?

6   Which Somerset bowler had the nickname 'Ghost'?

7   Which Somerset bowler had the nickname 'The Demon of Frome'?

8   Who has made the highest score for Somerset in the Sunday League?

9   Which wicket keeper made eight dismissals in the B&H Cup against Combined Universities in 1980?

10 Who is the only Somerset wicket keeper to have scored 10,000 runs and made 1000 dismissals in a first-class career?

11 Who has scored the fastest first-class century for Somerset?

12 Who has scored the fastest double-century for Somerset?

13 Who scored 45* aged 17 in a one-day game in 1974 after being hit in the mouth by Andy Roberts?

14 Who has made the most first-class appearances for Somerset?

15 Who scored a maiden first-class century for Somerset, his third county, in 1998?

QUIZ 3
COUNTY • SOMERSET

1 From which competition were Somerset disqualified in 1979?

2 At what score did they declare on the above occasion?

3 Who made a century on his first-class debut for Somerset against the 1953 Australians: Bill Alley, Colin McCool, Peter Wight?

4 Who is the oldest to have scored a first-class century for Somerset?

5 Which Somerset captain was born on a Red Indian reservation?

6 Who scored the fastest century of the 1935 season on his first-class debut against Essex at Frome?

7 Who have shared Somerset's highest partnership in first-class cricket?

8 Who was the first Somerset player to captain England?

9 Which two New Zealand Test players have represented Somerset?

10 Which two Indian Test players have represented Somerset?

11 Which two Pakistani Test players have represented Somerset?

12 Which two South African Test players have represented Somerset?

13 Which batsman who has played for Somerset has scored most Test runs?

14 Which batsman who has played for Somerset has scored most first-class runs?

15 Who scored 322 for Somerset II in 1997?

1 B&H Cup. 2 1–0. 3 Peter Wight. 4 Ernest Robson, 51. 5 Dennis Silk. 6 Harold Gimblett.
7 Herbert Hewett and Lionel Palairet, 346. 8 Jack White. 9 Martin Crowe and Tom Lowry.
10 Abbas Ali Baig and Sunil Gavaskar. 11 Mushtaq Ahmed and Khan Mohammad.
12 Jimmy Cook and Richard Snell. 13 Sunil Gavaskar, 10122. 14 Jim Parks, 36673.
15 Marcus Trescothick.

COUNTY • SURREY

1   When did Surrey win seven championships in a row?

2   How many times have Surrey won the championship outright: 9, 15, 21?

3   When did Surrey last win the championship?

4   Who are the only county to have won more champioships than Surrey?

5   When did Surrey first win the B&H Cup?

6   Who won the Gold Award on the above occasion?

7   When did Surrey last win the B&H Cup?

8   Who won the Gold Award on the above occasion?

9   When did Surrey win the Gillette/NatWest competition?

10   Who was Man of the Match on the above occasion?

11   When did Surrey win the Sunday League?

12   Which two Surrey players have played for England in ODIs but not in Tests?

13   Who was the last bowler to take 200 wickets in a first-class season?

14   Which Surrey fielder is one of only two players to have taken seven catches in a first-class innings?

15   Which four Surrey batsmen have scored 100 first-class centuries?

COUNTY • SURREY

1 Which Surrey bowler was the leading wicket taker in first-class cricket in 1991?

2 Which Surrey bowler was the leading wicket taker in first-class cricket in 1980?

3 Which Surrey bowler was the leading wicket taker in first-class cricket in 1958?

4 Who was the last Surrey batsman to head the national first-class batting averages?

5 Who scored the fastest first-class century in 1981 in 62 minutes?

6 Who scored a duck and a century on his Test debut against Australia in 1993?

7 Which 33 year old bowler made his Test debut for England in 1994?

8 Who took seven wickets in 11 balls against Sussex in 1972?

9 Who took four wickets in five balls for Surrey in 1985: Sylvester Clarke, Tony Gray, Pat Pocock?

10 Who carried his bat through a Surrey innings for 357*?

11 Which Surrey player has done the double of 1000 runs and 100 wickets in a first-class season most times?

12 Which pair put on 63 century opening stands in first-class cricket?

13 Who held the record for the most first-class dismissals by a wicket keeper until John Murray broke it?

14 What is Surrey's highest total: 770, 811, 903-7?

15 Which Surrey batsman has scored the most first-class centuries?

COUNTY • SURREY

1   What is the highest score in Tests by a Surrey player?

2   Who set a record of 3309 first-class runs in 1901?

3   Which two Surrey pace bowlers toured Australia with England in the 1990s without playing a Test?

4   Which Surrey allrounder toured Australia in 1998-9 without playing a Test?

5   Who has played the longest championship innings for Surrey?

6   Which two brothers played a Test for England in 1997?

7   Who has scored 2000 runs in a first-class season most times?

8   Who was the second batsman after WG Grace to score 1000 first-class runs by the end of May?

9   Who is the only Surrey batsman to have a first-class career average over 50?

10   Who scored a century for Surrey on his first-class debut in 1993?

11   Who was the first allrounder to do the treble of 1000 runs, 100 wickets and 50 catches in a first-class season?

12   Who has scored most first-class runs in a day for Surrey: Ali Brown, Andy Ducat, Jack Hobbs?

13   Who has hit most sixes in a first-class season for Surrey?

14   Who was the last bowler to take ten wickets in a first-class innings for Surrey?

15   Who took ten wickets or more in a championship match three times for Surrey in 1998?

COUNTY • SUSSEX

1   What is Sussex's highest position in the county championship?
2   When did Sussex win their first Gillette Cup?
3   When did Sussex win their second Gillette Cup?
4   Who was captain on the above occasions?
5   How many times have Sussex won the Gillette/NatWest competition in all ?
6   When did Sussex win the Sunday League?
7   Who was captain on the above occasion?
8   When did Sussex last win a major competition?
9   Which Sussex captain became Bishop of Liverpool?
10 Which Sussex captain became Lord Ted?
11 Which Sussex captain became Jam Sahib of Nawanagar?
12 Which Sussex captain became Indian High Commissioner in Australia?
13 Who has scored most first-class runs and centuries in a career for Sussex?
14 Who has scored most first-class runs and centuries in a season for Sussex?
15 Which Test player moved from Worcestershire to Sussex because of the livelier night life?

COUNTY • SUSSEX

1 Who was the wicketkeeper who moved from Surrey and captained Sussex from 1978 to 1980?

2 Which Sussex batsman scored 173 for England against Australia?

3 Which Sussex batsman scored 174 for England against Australia?

4 Which Sussex batsman scored 175 for England against Australia?

5 Which two Sussex players have represented England in ODIs but not in Tests?

6 Which Sussex batsman turned down an invitation to play Test cricket for Sri Lanka so he could be selected for England but never was?

7 Which Sussex batsman was dismissed by his first ball in Test cricket in 1995?

8 Which fielder has taken most catches in a first-class career and season for Sussex?

9 Apart from the above, who is the only other fielder to take 50 first-class catches in a season for Sussex?

10 Who is the only Sussex wicketkeeper to have scored 10000 runs and made 1000 dismissals in his first-class career?

11 Which Sussex captain was followed by his men 'out of curiosity', according to George Cox junior: Ted Dexter, Robin Marlar, David Sheppard?

12 Which Sussex player scored his maiden first-class century in a Test for England?

13 Who was the last Sussex batsman to score four centuries in consecutive first-class innings: John Langridge, Alan Wells, Colin Wells?

14 Which Sussex batsman was the grandson of a British Prime Minister?

16 Which Sussex allrounder has done the double of 1000 runs and 100 wickets in a first-class season most times?

1 Arnold Long. 2 KS Duleepsinhji. 3 Ted Dexter. 4 KS Ranjitsinhji.
5 Ian Gould and Colin Wells. 6 Gehan Mendis. 7 Alan Wells. 8 John Langridge, 76 and 779.
9 Alan Oakman. 10 Jim Parks. 11 Robin Marlar. 12 Billy Griffith. 13 John Langridge.
14 Mark Faber (grandson of Harold Macmillan). 15 Maurice Tate, 8.

COUNTY • SUSSEX

1 Who did the double of 1000 runs and 200 wickets in a first-class season most times?

2 Which Sussex player was England's last man out to lose a Test against Australia by three runs?

3 Who scored 158 against Derbyshire in the 1997 NatWest Trophy?

4 Which two non-championship teams defeated Sussex in the B and H Cup?

5 Who was Man of the Match when Sussex won the 1964 Gillette Cup final?

6 Who was Man of the Match when Sussex won the 1978 Gillette Cup final?

7 Who was Man of the Match when Sussex won the 1986 NatWest Trophy final?

8 Which Sussex allrounder toured Pakistan with MCC Under-25s but never played a Test?

9 Which Sussex bowler has taken 100 wickets in a first-class season most times?

10 Which Sussex bowler took 14-57 on his first-class debut and captained and managed England in their first ever Test match?

11 Which Sussex bowler captained England before becoming a Hollywood film star?

12 Which two England captains were brothers who played for Sussex?

13 Which Sussex player captained England in 1954: Ted Dexter, Hubert Doggart, David Sheppard?

14 Who was the last Sussex player to captain England?

15 Which Sussex player is the only allrounder to have done the double of 3000 runs and 100 wickets in a first-class season?

Quiz 1

COUNTY • WARWICKSHIRE

1   How many times have Warwickshire won the championship?

2   When did Warwickshire win their second championship?

3   Who captained Warwickshire on the above occasion?

4   When did Warwickshire win their third championship?

5   Who captained Warwickshire on the above occasion?

6   When did Warwickshire last win the championship?

7   How many times have Warwickshire won the Gillette/NatWest competition?

8   When did Warwickshire win the Benson & Hedges Cup?

9   In what year did Warwickshire become the first county to win three competitions?

10 Which trophy did they not win on the above occasion?

11 Who was the captain in the above season?

12 Who were the four West Indies Test players in Warwickshire's championship-winning side of 1972?

13 Who bowled an 18-ball over for Warwickshire against Middlesex at Coventry in 1982?

14 Whose Test career lasted half-an-hour in 1984?

15 Who was the bowler who terminated the above's Test career?

QUIZ 2

COUNTY • WARWICKSHIRE

1 What is the highest score in Tests for England by a Warwickshire batsman?

2 What is the highest score in Tests by a batsman who has played for Warwickshire?

3 Who are the only father and son to have captained Warwickshire?

4 Which Warwickshire player captained Oxford University in 1997?

5 Which Warwickshire player captained Cambridge University in 1997?

6 Who was the last Warwickshire player to captain England?

7 Which Warwickshire player had the nickname 'Yogi'?

8 Which Warwickshire player had the nickname 'Gunga'?

9 Which Warwickshire player had the nickname 'Molar'?

10 Which Warwickshire and England bowler had the nickname 'Gladys'?

11 Which Warwickshire and England bowler had the nickname 'Goose'?

12 Which Warwickshire and England bowler had the nickname 'Harry'?

13 Which Warwickshire batsman was chosen for England in 1966 before he had made a first-class century?

14 Who is the only Warwickshire batsman to have scored a double-century in a limited overs match?

15 Which fielder has taken most catches in a first-class season and career for Warwickshire?

1 262* by Dennis Amiss. 2 375 by Brian Lara. 3 Mike and Neil Smith. 4 Mark Wagh. 5 Anurag Singh. 6 Norman Gifford, ODI 1985. 7 Anton Ferreira. 8 Asif Din. 9 Andy Moles. 10 Gladstone Small. 11 Bob Willis. 12 Tim Munton. 13 Dennis Amiss. 14 Alvin Kallicharran, 206 v Oxfordshire. 15 Mike Smith, 52 and 422.

COUNTY • WARWICKSHIRE

1   Of which Warwickshire captain was it written by Colin Cowdrey: 'His approach to a problem was to sit in a chair with the Daily Telegraph crossword, dose off, wake up, finish the crossword and then fire some broadsides': Brian Lara, Dermot Reeve, Mike Smith?

2   Which Warwickshire batsman has scored most Test runs for West Indies?

3   Who toured Pakistan with MCC under-25 in 1966-7 but never played a Test?

4   Who is the last Warwickshire batsman to score a double century and a century in the same first-class match?

5   Who has scored the most runs in a first-class season for Warwickshire?

6   Who has scored the most runs and centuries in a first-class career for Warwickshire?

7   Which Indian Test spinner took 100 wickets in a first-class season for Warwickshire?

8   Which West Indian Test spinner took 100 wickets in a first-class season for Warwickshire?

9   Who was the last Warwickshire batsman to score a Test century for England?

10 Who was Warwickshire's first choice as overseas player for 1994?

11 Which Warwickshire pace bowler has taken 79 Test wickets for England since World War II?

12 Which Warwickshire pace bowler has taken 55 Test wickets for England since World War II?

13 Who has taken the most wickets in a first-class season for Warwickshire?

14 Who has take the most wickets in a first-class career for Warwickshire?

15 Which Warwickshire player made his England Test debut in 1998?

Quiz 1

COUNTY • WORCESTERSHIRE

1 When did Worcestershire win their first trophy?

2 Who was captain on the above occasion?

3 How many championships have Worcestershire won?

4 When have Worcestershire won the championship twice in successive seasons?

5 When did Worcestershire last win the championship?

6 Who was captain on the above occasion?

7 In what year did Worcestershire win two competitions?

8 When did Worcestershire win the B&H Cup?

9 Who won the Gold Award on the above occasion?

10 How many times have Worcestershire won the Sunday League?

11 When did Worcestershire win the Gillette/NatWest competition?

12 Who was Man of the Match on the above occasion?

13 Which non-championship side beat Worcestershire in the NatWest Trophy in 1998?

14 Which two non-championship sides have beaten Worcestershire in the B&H Cup?

15 Who was the last Worcestershire player to captain England in a Test?

14 Oxford and Cambridge Universities, and Combined Universities. 15 Tom Graveney.
8 1991. 9 Graeme Hick. 10 Three. 11 1994. 12 Tom Moody. 13 Scotland.
1 1964. 2 Don Kenyon. 3 Five. 4 1964 and 1965, 1988 and 1989. 5 1989. 6 Phil Neale. 7 1988.

QUIZ 2

COUNTY • WORCESTERSHIRE

1 By what other name were Worcestershire known in their early years?

2 How many cup finals at Lord's did Worcestershire lose before they won for the first time?

3 Which Worcestershire batsman scored 287 against Australia on his Test debut?

4 Which other Worcestershire batsman scored a century against Australia on his Test debut: Graeme Hick, Basil d'Oliveira, Nawab of Pataudi senior?

5 Which Worcestershire bowler took a wicket with his first ball in Test cricket in 1991?

6 Which Worcestershire bowler took a wicket with his first ball in Test cricket in 1947?

7 Which Worcestershire bowler has taken 100 wickets in a first-class season the most times?

8 Which Worcestershire player was Man of the Match in the first Gillette Cup final?

9 Which batsman brought up his 100th first-class century when playing for Worcestershire in 1964?

10 Why did the above batsman have to miss the 1961 first-class season?

11 Which batsman brought up his 100th first-class century when playing for Worcestershire in 1982?

12 Which batsman brought up his 100th first-class century when playing for Worcestershire in 1998?

13 Who is the youngest batsman to have scored 2000 runs in a first-class season?

14 Which two Worcestershire players have captained Indi·

15 Why was play delayed during the championship matc·
Somerset at Worcester in 1979: a) the Severn Bore ꜰ
the ground b) a streaker chained herself to the stumpꜱ
groundsman rolled the starting handle of his roller into the ᵪ

---

1 Fostershire. 2 Five. 3 Reggie Foster. 4 Nawab of Pataudi senior. 5 Richard Illingworth.
6 Ray Howorth. 7 Reg Perks, 16. 8 Norman Gifford. 9 Tom Graveney. 10 Because he was
qualifying by residence after leaving Gloucestershire. 11 Glenn Turner. 12 Graeme Hick.
13 Graeme Hick. 14 Nawab of Pataudi senior and Kapil Dev.
15 The groundsman rolled the starting handle of his roller into the pitch.

QUIZ 3

COUNTY • WORCESTERSHIRE

1   Which Nottinghamshire batsman joined Worcestershire in 1999?

2   Who was the last batsman to score four centuries in consecutive first-class innings for Worcestershire?

3   Who was the last batsman to score a double-century and a century in the same first-class match for Worcestershire?

4   Who hold the record for the highest fifth wicket partnership in the championship?

5   Who was last to take ten wickets in a first-class innings for Worcestershire?

6   Who has taken the best analysis in a first-class innings for Worcestershire?

7   Who is the youngest batsman to have scored 50 first-class centuries?

8   Why was Tom Graveney banned from playing Test cricket in 1969: a) for abusing an umpire b) for playing in a Benefit match on the Sunday rest day of a Test c) for failing to turn up to net-practice?

9   Which Worcestershire allrounder was run out going for his 100th run in a Test?

10   Who was the last fulltime county cricketer and league footballer?

11   Who in 1983 became the first Worcestershire batsman for 55 years to score a century on his first-class debut?

12   Who joined the England party on a tour of Australia in the 1990s and scored 40* in the Perth Test?

13   Who joined the England party on a tour of Australia in the 1990s and scored 67 in the Perth Test?

14   Which two batsmen with the same surname but unrelated have opened the batting for Worcestershire since 1990?

15   Which two Pakistan Test players have scored 1000 runs in a first-class season for Worcestershire?

Quiz 1

COUNTY • YORKSHIRE

1 How many times have Yorkshire won the championship outright: 6, 17, 29?

2 When did Yorkshire last win the county championship?

3 Who was the captain on the above occasion?

4 Which England bowler retired at the end of the above season?

5 Which England allrounder left Yorkshire after a contractual dispute at the end of the above season?

6 Who captained Yorkshire from 1971-1978 without winning a trophy?

7 When did Yorkshire first win the Gillette/NatWest competition?

8 Who was Man of the Match on the above occasion?

9 In what other year did Yorkshire win the Gillette/NatWest competition?

10 Who was Man of the Match on the above occasion?

11 When did Yorkshire win the Sunday League?

12 Who was the captain on the above occasion?

13 How old was he?

14 When did Yorkshire win the Benson & Hedges Cup?

15 Who won the Gold Award on the above occasion?

COUNTY • YORKSHIRE

1   Who was the first Yorkshire bowler to take a wicket with his first ball in Test cricket?

2   Who was the first Yorkshire batsman to score a Test century?

3   Which Yorkshire batsman scored 315* at Lord's in 1925, a record for the ground which lasted only one year?

4   Which Yorkshire wicket keeper made his Test debut for England at 39?

5   What record did Richard Stemp set when he joined Yorkshire?

6   Which Yorkshire and England bowler had the nickname 'Rocket'?

7   Which Yorkshire and England bowler had the nickname 'Chilly'?

8   Which Yorkshire and England batsman had the nickname 'Moggy'?

9   Which Yorkshire and England batsman had the nickname 'Fiery'?

10   Which Yorkshire allrounder had the nickname 'Fergy'?

11   Which Yorkshire batsman has the nickname 'Bingo'?

12   Who captained the England A tour of Zimbabwe and South Africa in 1998-9?

13   Which Yorkshire allrounder used to play for Manchester United?

14   Which non-championship side beat Yorkshire in the 1976 B&H Cup?

15   Which minor county beat Yorkshire in the 1984 NatWest Trophy?

1 George Macaulay. 2 George Ulyett. 3 Percy Holmes. 4 Arthur Wood. 5 He was the first modern player born outside the county. 6 Graham Stevenson. 7 Chris Old. 8 Martyn Moxon. 9 Geoff Boycott. 10 Phil Carrick. 11 David Byas. 12 Michael Vaughan. 13 Arnie Sidebottom. 14 Oxford and Cambridge Universities. 15 Shropshire.

COUNTY • YORKSHIRE

1 Who made the most dismissals by any wicket keeper in a career in the B&H Cup?

2 Who was the last to take ten wickets in a first-class innings for Yorkshire: Chris Old, Tommy Smailes, Fred Trueman?

3 Which two Yorkshire bowlers have taken the most first-class hat-tricks for Yorkshire: Schofield Haigh, George Macaulay, Fred Trueman?

4 Which West Indian batsman was Yorkshire's overseas player in 1993?

5 Why did the above leave mid-way through 1994: a) too much committee in-fighting b) mental and physical exhaustion c) a volcanic eruption back home?

6 Who has scored most runs in a first-class season and career for Yorkshire?

7 Who has scored most centuries in a first-class season and career for Yorkshire?

8 Who said: 'I am only setting records for Hutton to break'?

9 Who took 10-10 against Nottinghamshire in 1932: George Macaulay, Wilfred Rhodes, Hedley Verity?

10 Which Yorkshire wicketkeeper has made the most first-class dismissals: David Bairstow, Richard Blakey, David Hunter?

11 Who was the leading wicket-taker for Yorkshire in the championship in 1998?

12 Who called himself 't'Finest Bloody Fast Bowler that ever drew breath'?

13 Who was the first Yorkshire player to score 2000 runs in a first-class season?

14 Who said: 'When you're a batter and a bowler you enjoy yourself twice as much'?

15 Who has taken the most wickets for Yorkshire in a first-class season and career?

COUNTY • DERBYSHIRE

Derbyshire were founded in 1870 and played their first season in the championship in 1895.

By some reckonings Derbyshire were unofficial county champions in 1874 as they won three and drew one of their four matches.

In 1997 Kim Barnett shared a third wicket record partnership of 316* with Adrian Rollins against Leicestershire.

Adrian Rollins and his brother Robert of Essex are one of ten pairs of brothers who were contracted to play first-class cricket in the 1998 season.

Matthew Cassar is the husband of the England wicketkeeper Jane Cassar.

Kim Barnett was selected for England's 1988-9 tour of India which was cancelled for political reasons.

Henry Bagshaw, who played for Derbyshire from 1887 to 1902 and stood as a first-class umpire from 1907 to 1923, was buried in his umpire's coat and with a cricket ball in his hand.

The first to score a first-class century for Derbyshire against the Australians was Laurie Johnson, from Barbados, in 1964.

Frederick Spofforth, Australia's 'Demon' bowler, played for Derbyshire from 1889-91 when the county did not have first-class status and captained them in 1890.

Harry Elliott did not concede a bye in 25 completed innings in 1936.

The ninth wicket partnership of 283 between John Chapman and Arnold Warren against Warwickshire at Blackwell in 1910 remains the world record for the ninth wicket.

In 1897-8 William Storer became the first Derbyshire player to represent England against Australia. In addition to being a batsman, he kept wicket and bowled leg breaks.

COUNTY • DERBYSHIRE

Both William Storer and his son Harry took 232 first-class wickets and played soccer for Derby County.

Les Jackson took 143 first-class wickets at 10.99 in 1958, the lowest bowling average since World War II for any bowler taking 100 wickets in a season.

Harold Rhodes took 119 first-class wickets at 11.04 in 1965.

After leaving Yorkshire in 1968 Fred Trueman represented Derbyshire in the Sunday League in 1972.

The first bowler to take a hat-trick for Derbyshire was John Platts in 1881. On his first-class debut for MCC in 1870 Platts bowled fast and hit George Summers of Nottinghamshire on the head, an injury from which he died a few days later. Platts subsequently slow.

Derbyshire have never played more than 28 championship matches in a season.

Bob Berry became the first player to be capped by three counties: Lancashire, Worcestershire and Derbyshire.

Peter Gibbs, an Oxford blue and opening batsman for Derbyshire, scored 11 first-class centuries before becoming a playwright.

Ashley Harvey-Walker, who scored a century on his first-class debut against Oxford University, became assistant groundsman at the Wanderers in Johannesburg before being shot dead in a bar aged 52.

Jim Hutchinson, who played for Derbyshire from 1920 to 1931 and was a famous cover-fielder, celebrated his 100th birthday in 1996.

Denis Hill-Wood, an Oxford blue who played five matches for Derbyshire in 1928 and 1929, was chairman of Arsenal from 1959 until his death in 1982.

WELL DONE JIM... 1996

COUNTY • DERBYSHIRE

Guy Jackson was invited to captain England's 1927-8 tour to South Africa but declined owing to illness.

Karl Krikken made the most dismissals in 1996, 67, along with Rob Turner.

Karl Krikken is the son of Brian Krikken, who kept wicket in two matches for Lancashire and one for Worcestershire.

In 1996 Colin Wells, batting with a foot injury against Surrey at The Oval, took tea in the middle so as not to climb the pavilion steps.

In the same game Paul Aldred batted 87 minutes with a broken wrist to help achieve a draw. Derbyshire finished second in the championship.

Les Jackson took 1670 wickets for Derbyshire at 17.11 yet played only two Tests for England, in 1949 and 1961.

Mike Hendrick took 87 Test wickets for England without ever taking five in one innings.

Derbyshire have gone through four first-class seasons without a championship win, in 1897, 1901, 1920 and 1924.

In 1920 Derbsyhire lost 17 of their 18 championship matches. The other one was abandoned.

In the match between Derbyshire and Warwickshire at Derby in 1922 father and son Bill and Bob Bestwick bowled to another father and son, William and Bernard Quaife.

George Dawkes caught three catches off consecutive balls by Les Jackson against Worcestershire in 1958.

England won the 1948-9 Test against South Africa in Durban with a leg bye off Cliff Gladwin from the last possible ball.

COUNTY • DERBYSHIRE

The second to score a double-century for Derbyshire was Charles Ollivierre, who scored 229 against Essex at Chesterfield in 1904. Born in the West Indies, Ollivierre qualified by residence and was paid by the Hill-Wood family to play as an amateur from 1901 to 1907.

Derbyshire are the only county to have conceded an individual innings of 300 and yet won the match, and they have done so twice: when Percy Perrin made 343* for Essex in 1904, and when Jason Gallian made 312 for Lancashire in 1996.

Derbyshire's biggest victory was by an innings and 379 runs against Sussex in 1995.

When Dominic Cork took 9-43 against Northamptonshire in 1995 he would have become the first Derbyshire bowler to take ten wickets in an innings since 1935 if Colin Wells had taken a slip catch off him.

In 1994 no Derbyshire batsman reached 1000 first-class runs for the first time since 1927, apart from war years.

Twice in the space of a fortnight in 1994 Derbyshire conceded 81 extras in a championship innings, a world record at the time.

Three generations of the Richardson family have played for Derbyshire: Arthur, who led them to the championship in 1936, his son William and grandson Alastair.

Dominic Cork made a century as nightwatchman for England's Young Cricketers in 1990 against Pakistan's.

Derbyshire County Council withdrew a grant of £14,000 when Kim Barnett went on the the 1989-90 unofficial tour of South Africa.

Derbyshire won their semi-final in the NatWest Trophy in 1981, as well as the final, by virtue of losing fewer wickets with the scores level.

COUNTY • DERBYSHIRE

The most runs off a single hit in a first-class match is 10 by Samuel Hill-Wood for Derbyshire against MCC at Lord's in 1900.

Peter Kirsten was the leading run-scorer in first-class cricket in England in 1980 with 1895 runs. In his career he scored 7722 first-class runs at 49.50 for Derbyshire.

Bill Copson is one of only two bowlers to have taken five wickets in six balls in first-class cricket, against Warwickshire at Derby in 1937.

Karl Krikken was given out 'handled the ball' in the match against the Indians at Derby in 1996.

Alan Ward was sent off by his captain Brian Bolus for refusing to bowl against Yorkshire at Chesterfield in 1973.

Alan Ward played 115 first-class matches for Derbyshire from 1966 to 1976, and played five Tests for England, before joining Leicestershire. In his first-class career he took 460 wickets at 22.

In 1895 George Davidson became the first Derbyshire player to do the double of 1000 runs and 100 wickets in a first-class season.

Michael Frederick of Barbados played a Test for West Indies in 1953-4 yet played only six first-class matches in his whole career, including two for Derbyshire in 1949.

In 1985 Derbyshire's batsmen hit 18 sixes in their Sunday League match against Worcestershire at Knypersley.

In 1992 Chris Adams made Derbyshire's highest Sunday League score of 141*.

Dominic Cork recorded the most expensive analysis in the Sunday League: 8-0-96-1 against Nottinghamshire in 1993.

COUNTY • DERBYSHIRE

Alan Ward is the only player to have taken four wickets in four balls in the Sunday League.

Bob Taylor was selected for England's 1972-3 tour of India and Pakistan but could not go owing to an ear infection.

Mike Hendrick took 6-7 in a Sunday League match against Nottinghamshire in 1972.

Fred Swarbrook, who made his first-class debut for Derbyshire aged 16, suffered the yips as a left-arm spinner and retired from county cricket aged 28.

Brian Bolus was the first man to captain two different counties – Nottinghamshire the other – in two consecutive seasons.

The only two spinners to take 1000 first-class wickets for Derbyshire are Tommy Mitchell and Edwin Smith.

Mike Page has taken most catches in a first-class season for Derbyshire, 49.

The last Oxbridge blue to represent Derbyshire was Gul Khan.

Derbyshire finished third in 1934 and second in 1935 before winning the championship the following year.

Tommy Mitchell took most wickets in a first-class season for Derbyshire, 168.

The first time three Derbyshire players played together for the same England Test side was when Mike Hendrick, Geoff Miller and Bob Taylor did so in 1978.

COUNTY • DURHAM

Durham were founded in 1882 and were admitted to the championship in 1992.

Durham finished bottom of the championship in their first two seasons, 1993 and 1993.

All Durham players are awarded their county caps.

Durham were the only county to make the 1993 Australians follow-on.

At the end of the above game Ian Botham retired from first-class cricket.

Durham went through the 1995 season without drawing a championship match, the first time a county had done so since 1955.

Durham moved into their purpose-built ground at Riverside in 1995.

Durham went through the 1996 season without a championship win, one of only four counties to do so since World War II.

In 1996 Durham's only win against a first-class county was against Essex in the Sunday League. Their total of six points was the lowest in the League's history.

Simon Brown took over the captaincy when Mike Roseberry resigned in August 1996.

David Cox began batting at number 11 in 1996 and finished top of Durham's first-class batting averages.

Paul Collingwood took a wicket with his first ball in first-class cricket against Norhamptonshire and scored 91.

COUNTY • DURHAM

The only batsmen to have scored 1000 runs in a championship season for Durham so far have been Wayne Larkins, Paul Parker, Phil Bainbridge, John Morris, Mark Saxelby, Sherwin Campbell and Jon Lewis.

Lance Cairns, who took 130 Test wickets for New Zealand, played for Durham between 1979 and 1988.

Wasim Raja of Pakistan and Mohinder Amarnath of India have also played as professionals for Durham.

Simon Davis took 7-32 for Durham against Lancashire in the NatWest Trophy in 1983.

In 1998 Paul Collingwood set a sixth wicket record of 193 with David Boon against Warwickshire, and a seventh wicket record of 110 with Mike Foster against Nottinghamshire.

Dean Jones hit a century in each innings for Durham against the Pakistanis in 1992, having done so for Australia against Pakistan at Adelaide in 1989-90.

Durham's 305-9 against Glamorgan in 1991 is the highest total by a minor county in the Gillette/NatWest competition.

When David Graveney represented Durham in 1992, he was playing for his third county in three consecutive seasons (Gloucestershire and Somerset the previous ones).

Durham shared the Minor Counties championship with Norfolk and Worcestershire in its inaugural season of 1895.

From 1976 Durham set a record of 65 matches without defeat in the Minor Counties championship.

COUNTY • ESSEX

Essex were founded in 1876 and played their first season in the championship in 1895.

The most runs in a day in a first-class match in England is 721 by the Australians against Essex in Southend in 1948.

Essex had to launch an appeal for £1000 in 1924 in order to survive.

Essex never had a county ground or home of their own between selling Leyton and buying Chelmsford.

In 1928 Essex used 38 different players, including one Reverend and three Captains.

In 1972 and 1976 Essex used 14 different players.

In 1991 Essex were 51 points behind the leaders Warwickshire in the championship but won six of their last seven matches to take the title by 13 points.

Essex went through the 1995 season without drawing a championship match, the first time a county had done so since 1955.

Mark Ilott was fined £1000 after a pushing incident with Robert Croft during the NatWest Trophy semi-final against Glamorgan in 1997.

Play was suspended in Essex's match against Cambridge University in April 1981 because it was too cold.

When Essex finished bottom of the county championship in 1998, it was only the second time in their history.

Nobody has taken 100 wickets in a first-class season at greater cost than Ray Smith who took 125 at 37.26 in 1947.

COUNTY • ESSEX

Essex are the only county with a partnership of 200 or more for every wicket in first-class cricket.

The best innings analysis for Essex is 10-32 by Henry Pickett, a pace bowler, against Leicestershire at Leyton in 1895.

Henry Pickett disappeared from his home aged 45. His body was found on the beach at Aberavon but not identified until three months after his death.

In 1991 Nasser Hussain shared a new county record partnership of 314 for the fourth wicket with Salim Malik against Surrey, and another of 316 for the fifth wicket with Mike Garnham against Leicestershire.

In 1992 Nasser Hussain shared a new county record partnership of 347* for the third wicket with Mark Waugh against Lancashire at Ilford.

Mark Ilott took a hat-trick of lbws against Northamptonshire at Luton in 1995.

Essex and Durham are the only first class counties never to have been dismissed for a total below 30.

David East equalled Wally Grout's world record of eight dismissals in an innings when he took eight catches out of the nine Somerset wickets to fall at Taunton in 1985.

Graham Gooch had match figures of 9-68 against Lancashire at Ilford in 1985.

Graham Gooch was no-balled for throwing when impersonating John Emburey during the match between England and East Zone at Jamshedpur in 1981-2.

Doug Insole became chairman of the Test and County Cricket Board.

Geoff Hurst played one match for Essex as a wicket keeper in 1962 before scoring a hat-trick for England in the 1966 World Cup final.

COUNTY • ESSEX

Keith Fletcher was the first captain of a county side to win all four domestic competitions.

In 1989 Essex were docked 25 points for an unsatisfactory pitch at Southend. Worcestershire won the championship that year by six points ahead of Essex.

Graham Gooch's 120 in 1979 was the first century in a B and H Cup final.

In 1977 Ken McEwan scored 28 off one over from Kerry O'Keefe of the Australians and 27 off one over from Mark Allbrook of Cambridge University.

Brian Hardie took 142 minutes to score four runs against Hampshire in 1974.

David Acfield won a gold medal for fencing at the 1970 Commonwealth Games.

'Hopper' Read took six wickets in his only Test for England against South Africa in 1935.

Trevor Bailey took 7-34 and opened the batting for England on the first day of the fifth Test against West Indies at Kingston in 1953-4.

Percy Perrin's 343* against Derbyshire at Chesterfield in 1904 is the highest score for Essex.

Percy Perrin hit 68 fours, the most in any first-class innings, on the above occasion.

In 1985 Graham Gooch and Brian Hardie put on two double-century opening stands on successive days against Nottinghamshire, firstly in the NatWest Trophy final and secondly in the Sunday League.

COUNTY • ESSEX

The opening stand of 202 by Graham Gooch and Brian Hardie on the above occasion set a new record for the highest partnership in any Lord's final.

The highest total in a B&H Cup final was 290-6 by Essex against Surrey in 1979.

Three times Essex finished with equal most points at the head of the Sunday League before they won their first trophy in 1979.

Graham Gooch and Ken McEwan shared a record second wicket partnership in the Sunday League of 273 against Nottinghamshire in 1983.

When Essex won the Sunday League in 1985 they won only one of their first seven games.

Two of the first three bowlers to take 300 wickets in the Sunday League played for Essex: John Lever and Stuart Turner.

Claude Ashton, a triple Cambridge blue, represented England at soccer before being killed in 1942 when his plane collided with that of RWK Winlaw (Surrey).

Sir Hubert Ashton, a triple Cambridge blue, MP and Essex batsman, scored 4025 first-class runs at an average of 38.

Jack Bailey took 7-32 on his first-class debut for Essex against Nottinghamshire in 1953.

The slowest century in a first-class match in Britain was made by Keith Fletcher for England against Pakistan at The Oval in 1974 in 7 hours 38 minutes.

John Childs made his Test debut for England against West Indies at Old Trafford in 1988 aged 37.

COUNTY • ESSEX

Johnny Douglas was the Olympic middleweight boxing champion in 1908.

Johnny Douglas – one of two Essex and England all-rounders to go to Felsted, along with Derek Pringle – was drowned when the SS Oberon collided with another ship in dense fog in 1930.

The highest score by any number 11 in first-class cricket is 163 by Peter Smith against Derbyshire at Chesterfield in 1947.

Essex won two major competitions in 1979,1984 and 1985.

Maurice Nichols has taken 100 wickets in a first-class season most times for Essex, 11.

In 1979 John Lever was the joint highest wicket taker in first-class cricket with 106 wickets.

In 1983 John Lever was the joint highest wicket taker in first-class cricket with 106 wickets.

In 1989 Derek Pringle was the joint leading wicket taker in first-class cricket with 94 wickets.

Essex dismissed Middlesex for 41 in the 1972 Gillette Cup.

Gordon Barker hit a century on his first-class debut for Essex against the Canadians in 1954, and later coached Derek Pringle, John Stephenson and Nick Knight at Felsted.

Stephen Peters scored a century on his first-class debut against Cambridge University in 1996 aged 19.

COUNTY • ESSEX

Jack O'Connor and Doug Insole have scored the most first-class centuries in a season for Essex, nine.

The best analysis in a first-class match for Essex is 17-119 by Walter Mead, a slow-medium off-break bowler, against Hampshire in 1900.

In 1998 only two Essex batsmen scored more than 550 runs in the championship, Stuart Law and Ronnie Irani.

Ray East set a Sunday League record, since broken, for the most expensive spell: 8-0-79-1 against Glamorgan in 1979.

Ray East took five wickets in a Sunday League innings four times, a record (since broken) he shared with David Hughes and Denis Marriott.

Ray East wrote the book 'A Funny Turn'.

Roy Sheffield kept wicket for Essex in the 1930s, worked as a cowboy in South America, was arrested as a Bolivian spy and wrote a novel based on the incident 'Bolivian Spy?'

Mike Garnham and Derek Pringle drove through Africa from North to South.

Frederick Nicholas, who scored 2255 first-class runs for Essex at an average of 22, was the grandfather of Mark Nicholas (Hampshire).

Bill Reeves, who became an umpire after taking 581 first-class wickets for Essex, told the Yorkshire bowler George Macaulay: 'There's only one man made more more appeals than you, George, and that was Dr Barnardo.'

COUNTY • GLAMORGAN

Glamorgan were founded in 1888 and were admitted to the championship in 1921.

Glamorgan defeated Sussex in their inaugural championship match at Cardiff Arms Park in 1921.

The highest aggregate in a three day championship match was 1641 runs by Glamorgan and Worcestershire at Abergavenny in 1990.

The fewest runs in a full day's play in the county championship was when Glamorgan scored 134-3 off 95 overs against Hampshire at Portsmouth in 1964 to draw the match.

Glamorgan went through the 1979 season without a championship win, one of only four counties to do so since World War II.

The equal highest number of defeats in a championship season is 20 by Glamorgan in 1925.

Glamorgan went through the 1969 season without a championship defeat, only the fourth county to do so.

Alan Butcher played against his son Mark in a Sunday League match between Glamorgan and Surrey in 1991.

Emrys Davies scored a century and took a hat-trick for Glamorgan against Leicestershire in 1937.

In 1951 Peter Walker completed the treble of 1000 runs, 100 wickets and 50 catches in a first-class season.

Matthew Maynard hit 34 off an over from Kent's wicket keeper Steve Marsh at Swansea in 1992.

Cyril Smart hit 32 off an over from Hampshire's Gerald Hill at Cardiff in 1935.

Steve James was the first batsman in the country to reach 1000 first-class runs in 1997.

COUNTY • GLAMORGAN

Glamorgan dismissed the Sri Lankans for 54 at Cardiff in 1998.

Glamorgan used 18 different pairs of opening batsmen in 1998.

In 1997 Glamorgan were dismissed for 31 by Middlesex at Cardiff.

Waqar Younis took 7-25 against Leicestershire and 8-17 against Sussex in consecutive innings in 1997: 15 wickets for 42 runs off only 18.5 overs.

Steve James's 162 against Nottinghamshire in 1997 at Colwyn Bay was the highest first-class innings on that ground.

For the last day of the above game Robert Croft was flown to the ground by helicopter after his induction into the Bardic Circle at the National Eisteddfod.

Philip North would have played in the same game – his first match for Glamorgan for eight years – if he had not overslept.

Glamorgan's first victory over a first-class touring team was against the West Indians at Cardiff in 1923.

George Geary took 10-18 for Leicestershire against Glamorgan at Pontypridd in 1929, the best innings analysis against Glamorgan.

Jimmy Cook scored 313* for Somerset against Glamorgan at Cardiff in 1990, the highest innings against Glamorgan.

Maurice Turnbull became Glamorgan's first Test player when he represented England against New Zealand in 1929-30.

Maurice Turnbull was killed on active service in Normandy in 1944 by a sniper's bullet.

Emrys Davies was selected for England's 1939-40 tour of India which had to be abandoned.

COUNTY • GLAMORGAN

When Glamorgan clinched their first championship title against Hampshire at Bournemouth, the umpire who upheld the lbw appeal against Hampshire's number 11 was the former Glamorgan batsman Dai Davies, who said to the bowler John Clay: 'that's out and we've won the championship!'

John Clay, who played his last game for Glamorgan aged 51, took 1317 first-class wickets at 19 runs each.

The first Glamorgan player to take a hat-trick was Trevor Arnott, who played cricket and rugby for Cardiff, in 1926.

Glamorgan's first regular professional in pre-championship years was Billy Bancroft, who won 33 caps for Wales as a rugby full-back.

Viv Richards was unfit to play for Glamorgan in the 1989 season.

William Bates, an opening batsman for Glamorgan nicknamed 'The Marquis', was the father of Eddie Bates who played soccer for and managed Southampton.

Ossie Wheatley took most wickets in a first-class season for Cambridge University, 80.

Robert Croft was fined £1000 after a pushing incident with Mark Ilott in the NatWest Trophy semi-final against Essex in 1997.

Glamorgan's run of 12 consecutive wins in the Sunday League in 1993 equalled the previous record held by Middlesex.

In 1993 Sunday League matches saw the introduction of coloured clothes and white balls, and the matches consisted of 50 overs a side.

In the four seasons before 1993 Glamorgan had finished in the bottom three in the Sunday League.

COUNTY • GLAMORGAN

In 1961 Don Shepherd hit a 50 against the Australians in 15 minutes and another against Derbyshire in 16 minutes.

Lord Justice Griffiths scored 137 runs and took 102 wickets in his first-class career as William Hugh Griffiths.

In 1927 Glamorgan pulled off a great shock when they beat the championship leaders Nottinghamshire by an innings in the last game so that the title went to Lancashire.

Glamorgan have finished bottom of the championship nine times.

Gilbert Parkhouse scored a century against every contemporary first-class county.

Alan Jones scored a century against every contemporary first-class county except Middlesex.

Percy Bush, the leading Welsh fly-half at the turn of the century, played four matches for Glamorgan before first-class status.

Tony Cordle, who emigrated from Barbados, took 701 first-class wickets for Glamorgan at 27 and is the uncle of Gerald Cordle the former Cardiff winger.

Glamorgan wicket keeper David Evans was awarded a Churchill scholarship in 1967-8 to study coaching around the world and deliver lectures on umpiring.

The left-arm fast bowler Jeff Jones won his first England cap in 1963-4 at Bombay before winning his Glamorgan cap.

Jeff Jones was the leading first-class wicket taker on England's 1965-6 tour of Australia and New Zealand with 48 wickets.

Keith Jarrett, who won 10 rugby caps for Wales, played two first-class matches for Glamorgan in 1967.

Ezra Moseley joined Glamorgan in 1980 before representing his native Barbados.

Rodney Ontong and Steve Barwick were badly injured in a car accident in 1988 after Glamorgan's match against Essex.

COUNTY • GLAMORGAN

Frank Ryan, who took over 1000 first-class wickets as a left-arm spinner, was born in America and served in the Royal Flying Corps in World War I.

Frank Ryan was once found fast asleep under the covers one morning, after forgetting where Glamorgan were staying. He was released in 1931.

Lord Silkin played one match for Glamorgan in 1938 as Sam Silkin.

Batting at number 11 for Glamorgan against the Indians at Cardiff in 1946, Peter Judge was bowled first ball by Chandra Sarwate. Glamorgan followed on, and with little time left, Judge opened Glamorgan's second innings and was dismissed first ball again by Sarwate.

The first time Glamorgan beat the Australians was at Swansea in 1964, by 36 runs. On the second day the crowd was 20,000.

In the above game Don Shepherd was the sole survivor of the Glamorgan team which had last defeated a touring side, the 1951 South Africans. He took 9-93 off 69 overs.

In 1968 Glamorgan made history by defeating the Australians for the second time in consecutive tours, by 79 runs.

Glamorgan have not won the Benson & Hedges Cup or the Gillette/NatWest competition.

In the match against Yorkshire at Swansea in 1965 Jim Pressdee took 9-43 in the first innings and Don Shepherd 9-48 in the second.

Norman Riches was considered Glamorgan's finest batsman before WWI but could only play during his holidays from Guy's Hospital where he was a dentist.

Robert Croft batted 190 minutes to make 37* and save the third Test against South Africa at Old Trafford in 1998.

COUNTY • GLOUCESTERSHIRE

Gloucestershire were founded in 1871, and were one of the original members of the championship in 1890.

They were unofficial county champions in 1873 (shared), 1874, 1876 and 1877.

Wally Hammond holds the records for the most runs in a first-class season and career for Gloucestershire (2860 and 33664), and the most centuries in a first-class season and career (13 and 113).

Gilbert Jessop scored the fastest first-class 150 in 63 minutes for Gentlemen of the South against Players of the South at Hastings in 1907.

Gilbert Jessop scored the fastest first-class double-century in 120 minutes for Gloucestershire against Sussex at Hove in 1903, a record since equalled by Clive Lloyd.

Gilbert Jessop is the only batman to have hit two centuries before lunch in a first-class match, for Gloucestershire against Yorkshire at Bradford in 1900.

Fourteen of Jessop's centuries were scored in an hour or less. Before 1907 only hits out of the ground were worth six runs, so many of Jessop's strokes were worth only four.

WG Grace was first to score 10 first-class centuries in a season, in 1871.

WG Grace was the only first-class victim of Sir Arthur Conan Doyle, who played 10 first-class matches for MCC from 1900 to 1907.

WG Grace captained England in the first international bowls match in 1903.

Charlie Parker took two hat-tricks in the match against Middlesex at Bristol in 1924.

Charlie Parker conceded the most runs in a championship innings when he took 6-231 against Somerset at Bristol in 1923.

COUNTY • GLOUCESTERSHIRE

Charlie Barnett hit 11 sixes in one innings against Somerset at Bath in 1934, a county record until Andrew Symonds broke it.

Gloucestershire tied their match with the 1930 Australians at Bristol. The tourists had not lost to a first-class county since 1912.

Allan Border played one first-class match for Gloucestershire in 1977.

Jack Russell became Gloucestershire's youngest wicket keeper when he made his first-class debut aged 17 against the Sri Lankans in 1981 while still at school. He made eight dismissals.

The highest partnership for Gloucestership is 395 for the first wicket by Martin Young and Ron Nicholls against Oxford University in 1962.

In 1995 Gloucestershire lost to Surrey after making them follow on 175 runs behind on first innings.

The Australian Arthur Mailey called his autobiography 'Ten For 66 And All That' after taking 10-66 against Gloucestershire at Cheltenham in 1921.

The Nottinghamshire bowler Ken Smales took 10-66 against Gloucestershire at Stroud in 1956.

The lowest total to include a double-century is 298 by Gloucestershire against Glamorgan at Newport in 1956 when Tom Graveney scored 200.

Gloucestershire were not defeated at home by any county until Nottinghamshire did so in 1879.

Gloucestershire's match against Lancashire at Old Trafford in 1884 was abandoned when Mrs HM Grace, mother of WG Grace, died.

COUNTY • GLOUCESTERSHIRE

WG Grace was paid £3000 to tour Australia in 1891-2. His testimonial in 1895 raised £9073.

WG Grace declared Gloucestershire's innings closed against Sussex at Bristol in 1898 when his own score was 93*. He had made every score between 0 and 100 except 93.

'It's Grace before meat, Grace after dinner and Grace all the time': Tom Emmett, Yorkshire's pace bowler.

'What, are you going, Doctor? There's still one stump standing': Charles Kortright of Essex after bowling WG Grace.

With EM and GF Grace, WG provided the first instance of three brothers playing in the same Test when they did so against Australia in 1880.

The first triple century in first-class cricket was WG Grace's 344 for MCC against Kent in 1876.

WG Grace left Gloucestershire in 1899 to set up London County. In all cricket he is estimated to have scored 80,000 runs and taken 7000 wickets.

'I have the greatest affection for the county of my birth, but for the committee as a body the greatest contempt': WG Grace on his resignation from the Gloucestershire captaincy, 1899.

Dallas Page, Gloucestershire's captain at the time, was killed in a car accident in 1936 when returning home from the last game of the season.

Gloucestershire's match against Sussex at Bristol on 3 June 1909 was suspended because of snow.

COUNTY • GLOUCESTERSHIRE

Jack Russell was the fourth England player to make his maiden first-class century in a Test.

Jack Russell made his first-class and Test debut against Sri Lanka.

Jack Russell took three catches off three consecutive balls from Courtney Walsh and David Lawrence against Surrey at The Oval in 1986.

WG Grace made only one first-class century outside England, against Victoria at Melbourne in 1891-2.

Walter Gilbert, a cousin of the Graces, ceased to play for Gloucestershire and emigrated to Canada in 1886 after a scandal involving money stolen from a dressing-room.

Percy Mills took five wickets for no runs against Somerset at Bristol in 1928.

Tom Goddard took 17 wickets in a day against Kent at Bristol in 1939.

Only three bowlers have taken more wickets on first-class debut than Fred Roberts, who took 14-171 against Yorkshire in 1887.

John Mortimore bowled 14 maiden overs in succession against Glamorgan at Margam in 1962.

Tom Goddard had figures of 8.2-0-98-0 against Kent at Dover in 1937.

Sam Cook took a wicket with his first ball on his debut against Oxford University in 1946.

In his last match before leaving to join Worcestershire, Tom Graveney shared in the county record second wicket stand of 256 with Tom Pugh against Derbyshire in 1960.

COUNTY • GLOUCESTERSHIRE

In 1931 Bev Lyon made the revolutionary move of declaring Gloucestershire's first innings at 4-0 against Yorkshire at Sheffield. He persuaded Yorkshire to do the same so the rain-affected match became a third-day contest for full points.

In his only season for Gloucestershire, 1997, Shaun Young made the highest Sunday League score for Gloucestershire, 146* against Yorkshire.

Gloucestershire have finished bottom of the championship six times.

Wally Hammond turned amateur in 1938 and was appointed captain of England.

Lord Harris succeeded in having Wally Hammond banned from county cricket in 1922 because he did not have a birth qualification to play for Gloucestershire. On meeting Lord Harris at Lord's the president of Worcestershire, Lord Deerhurst said: 'may I congratulate you on having buggered the career of another young cricketer.'

Wally Hammond holds the record for the most runs in May, 1042 in 1927, and for the most runs in August, 1281 in 1936.

Wally Hammond scored 31165 first-class runs in the 1930s, the record for one decade.

Wally Hammond scored 36 double-centuries in first-class cricket, second only to Don Bradman's 37.

On the 1928-9 tour of Australia, Wally Hammond scored 1553 first-class runs, still the record for any visiting batsman in Australia.

During the Cheltenham Week of 1928 Wally Hammond took 15-128 against Worcestershire, then scored 139 and 143, and took 10 catches, in the match against Surrey. His 10 catches in the match and 78 catches in the 1928 season remain records.

COUNTY • GLOUCESTERSHIRE

The lowest total by Gloucestershire is 17 against the Australians at Cheltenham in 1896.

The highest total against Gloucestershire is 774-7 declared by the Australians at Bristol in 1948.

Jack Crapp became Gloucestershire's first professional captain in 1953.

Mike Procter is the only player to have scored a century and taken a hat-trick in the same first-class match twice.

Mike Procter is the only bowler to have taken two first-class hat-trick of lbws.

The only hat-trick of stumpings in a first-class match occured when Charles Townsend had three batsmen stumped off three consecutive balls by William Brain in the match between Gloucestershire and Somerset at Cheltenham in 1893.

The first three players to do the double of 2000 runs and 100 wickets in a first-class season were all Gloucestershire players: WG Grace, Charles Townsend and Gilbert Jessop.

Bill Athey was the last Gloucestershire batsman to score four centuries in four consecutive first-class innings.

WG Grace was first to score 1000 first-class runs in a calendar month, in August 1871.

In 1873 WG Grace became the first person ever to do the double of 1000 runs and 100 wickets.

In 1977 Gloucestershire were leading the championship at the start of the last round of matches, only to lose against Hampshire.

COUNTY • HAMPSHIRE

Hampshire were founded in 1863 and were admitted to the county championship in 1895.

James Aylward's 167 for Hampshire against England in 1777 was the highest individual innings recorded to that time.

When Hampshire cricket was born on Broad Halfpenny Down, the players drank punch – 'not your modern cat-lap milk punch, but good unsophisticated John Bull stuff that would make a cat speak', according to John Nyren.

Charles Fry moved from Sussex to Hampshire in 1909 to direct the Hamble-based training ship 'Mercury'.

Phil Mead scored 280* against Nottinghamshire in 1921 yet still finished on the losing side.

George Brown hit the first ball of the match against the 1930 Australians from Alan Fairfax out of the ground.

Malcolm Marshall's aggregate of 134 first-class wickets in 1982 remains the most in a season since 1966.

In 1963 Hampshire played a first-class match against MCC All England XI to celebrate the county's centenary.

Hesketh Vernon Hesketh-Pritchard, who took 106 wickets in the 1904 season, was a noted traveller and writer.

Hampshire's record fourth wicket stand of 263 against Middlesex in 1970 was shared by two batsmen born in the West Indies, Roy Marshall and Danny Livingstone.

Six Hampshire players have been born in Barbados: Roy Marshall, John Holder, Larry Worrell, Gordon Greenidge, Malcolm Marshall and Elvis Reifer.

COUNTY • HAMPSHIRE

Major Robert Poore averaged 91.23, the highest in a first-class season to that time, in 1899.

Robert Poore, who became a Brigadier-General, was a fine swordsman, tennis and polo player who also played three Tests for South Africa against England in 1895-6.

Hampshire went through the 1973 season without a championship defeat, only the sixth county to do so.

Derek Shackleton took 8-4 against Somerset at Weston-super-Mare in 1955.

Hampshire have had only nine official captains since World War II.

Johnny Arnold played cricket for England against New Zealand in 1931 and soccer for England against Scotland in 1932-3.

Trevor Jesty took 10 years to make his maiden first-class century.

Robin Smith was the South African under-19 shotput champion.

The former captain of Hampshire Desmond Eagar was the father of cricket photographer Patrick Eagar.

David White was no-balled by Syd Buller when playing against Lancashire in 1965. He stumbled in delivery and flung the ball in apparent fun at the batsman.

David White was no-balled three times by Paul Gibb when playing against Sussex in 1960.

Phil Mead holds the record for the most runs in a first-class season and career for Hampshire (2854 and 48892).

Phil Mead holds the record for the most centuries in a first-class season and career for Hampshire (12 and 138).

COUNTY • HAMPSHIRE

Charles Llewellyn, who played for Hampshire and South Africa, made his highest first-class score of 216 for Hampshire against the South Africans at Southampton in 1901.

Charles Llewellyn, who took 1013 first-class wickets at 23, is regarded as the first bowler of the left-arm chinaman.

Alec Kennedy was lbw in six consecutive innings in 1924.

When Hampshire were dismissed for 258 by Derbyshire in 1991, with Chris Smith scoring 114 and Kevan James 101, it was the lowest total in English first-class cricket to contain two individual hundreds.

When Robin Smith scored a century on his first-class debut for Hampshire against Lancashire at Bournemouth in 1983, his brother Chris also made a century.

Hon. Lionel Tennyson, who averaged 23 with the bat in first-class cricket and 31 in Tests for England, scored 63 and 36 with his right hand against Australia in 1921 after injuring his left.

Hon. Lionel Tennyson, grandson of the poet Alfred, entitled his autobiography 'From Verse to Worse'.

When Gordon Greenidge scored 259 against Sussex in 1975, he reached 50, 100, 150 and 200 with sixes. His innings contained 13 sixes in all, a record in the championship at the time.

Tom Jameson, who played 53 matches for Hampshire between 1919 and 1932, was the Amateur Squash champion twice.

Phil Mead scored the most championship centuries, 132.

Hampshire have finished bottom of the championship five times, and equal last once.

COUNTY • HAMPSHIRE

'I wonder if there has been another player who understood the science of batsmanship as much as Mead': Herbert Sutcliffe of Yorkshire and England.

'He took guard with the air of a guest who, having been offered a weekend by his host, obstinately decides to reside for six months': Raymond Robertson-Glasgow on Phil Mead.

When Hampshire made their lowest championship total of 15 against Warwickshire at Edgbaston in 1922, they scored 521 in the follow-on and won by 155 runs.

Arthur Ridley made 104 for Hampshire against Kent at Faversham in 1876 without a boundary.

Edward Sprot reached his century in 45 minutes against Gloucestershire at Bristol in 1911.

When Hampshire and Kent tied at Southampton in 1950, the two sides bowled the same number of balls.

Jack Newman was sent off by his captain Lionel Tennyson after kicking down the stumps in the match against Nottinghamshire at Trent Bridge in 1922.

Two Catholic priests have played for Hampshire: Canon John Greig, who scored 249* against Lancashire at Liverpool in 1901, and Father Peter Utley who took 90 first-class wickets with his pace bowling in 1927 and 1928.

Robert Fowler, the star of Fowler's Match between Eton and Harrow in 1910, played three matches for Hampshire in 1924, was appointed captain of England's tour of the West Indies in 1924-5 which was postponed, and died in 1925.

COUNTY • HAMPSHIRE

Phil Mead has made the most first-class catches for Hampshire, 629, other than wicket keepers.

Peter Sainsbury has made the most first-class catches in a season for Hampshire, 56.

Arthur Jacques was 27 and had taken 175 first-class wickets at 21, when he was killed in action in Loos, France, in World War I.

Arthur Hill took 4-8 in his only spell of Test bowling for England against South Africa in 1895-6.

Arthur Hill averaged 62.75 with the bat in his four Test innings, all against South Africa. He captained Hampshire at rugby and hockey.

George Brown scored over 25,000 runs, took over 600 wickets, and made 78 stumpings in first-class cricket.

Cecil Abercrombie represented Scotland at rugby, averaged 40 in16 first-class matches, and was killed in the naval battle off Jutland in 1916, aged 30.

Harry Altham, who played for Hampshire from 1919 to 1923 and was a famous historian of the game, is buried in Winchester Abbey.

Ronnie Aird, who scored 4482 first-class runs and played for Hampshire from 1920-1938, became Secretary and President of MCC.

Groucho Marx visited Lord's when Ronnie Aird was MCC Secretary. When Aird asked him if he was enjoying the cricket, Marx replied: 'great. What time does it start?'

Lord Strathavon played as an amateur for Hampshire in 1819 but appeared for the Players against the Gentlemen in that year as he was their financial backer.

COUNTY • KENT

Kent were founded in 1842 and merged with another club in 1870. They were one of the original 'Big Six', the only non-Test county.

If a ball hits the lime tree inside the boundary on the St Lawrence ground at Canterbury it is worth four runs.

The only two batsman thought to have hit a ball over the lime tree are the West Indians Learie Constantine and Carl Hooper.

The last first-class match to end on the first day was between Kent and Worcestershire at Tunbridge Wells in 1960, when Kent won by an innings and 101 runs.

Chris Tavare scored the slowest 50 in a first-class match in England when he took 350 minutes to do so for England against Pakistan at Lord's in 1982.

Dean Headley took three hat-tricks in the championship in 1996.

The first bowler to take four wickets in four balls was Joseph Wells, the father of HG Wells, for Kent against Sussex in 1862.

Dr Julian Thompson dismissed Brian Lara for a pair, his first, in the match between Kent and the West Indians in 1995.

Doug Wright became Kent's first professional captain in 1954.

Arthur Fielder scored 112* at number 11 in 1909 against Worcestershire, one of only three instances of a number 11 making a first-class century in the championship.

Arthur Fielder and Frank Woolley added 235 for the tenth wicket on the above occasion, still a record in the championship.

Tich Freeman took 51 wickets in seven consecutive first-class innings in 1932, a world record.

Tony Catt scored 162 as a nightwatchman against Leicestershire at Maidstone in 1962.

COUNTY • KENT

Ian Akers-Douglas was the British Rackets champion in 1933, and played 48 first-class matches for Kent.

David Halfyard retired from Kent in 1964 after a car accident, became a first-class umpire, then played for Nottinghamshire from 1968 to 1970.

Graham Dilley was capped by England before he was capped by Kent.

George Downton, father of the England wicket keeper Paul, played eight matches for Kent as an amateur wicket keeper.

In the same year that he made his first-class debut for Kent, 1909, Doug Carr played for England against Australia. A wrist spinner, he took 7-282 in his only Test.

Colin Blythe has the best analysis for a first-class innings and match for Kent: 10-30 and 17-48 against Northamptonshire at Northampton in 1907.

Colin Blythe was the first bowler to take 17 first-class wicket in a day when he did so on the above occasion.

Colin Blythe, who took 100 Test wickets at 18, was killed in action near Passchendaele in 1917 aged 38.

James Seymour's Benefit match, against Hampshire in 1920 was used as a legal Test case which went to the House of Lords. The final ruling was that cricketers' benefits should not be subject to income tax.

James Seymour took 40 catches or more in a first-class season six times.

Aravinda de Silva shared in two record partnerships during his season with Kent in 1995: 368 for the fourth wicket with Graham Cowdrey and 315 for the sixth wicket with Mark Ealham. The former partnership is the all time record for any wicket for Kent.

COUNTY • KENT

Kevin Jarvis took 674 first-class wickets and scored 403 first-class runs.

Stuart Waterton made his NatWest Trophy debut in the 1984 final.

Charles Thornton, one of the first great hitters, twice struck a ball over 160 yards in practice.

Under Lord Harris Kent beat the Australians five times up to and including 1899.

Kent finished in the first five places in the championship 16 times between the World Wars without winning the title.

Wally Hardinge scored 75 first-class centuries and was capped for England at cricket in 1921 and for England at soccer in 1910.

In his only Test 'Father' Marriott took 11 wickets for England against West Indies in 1933. As a master at Dulwich College, he could only play in the holidays.

Tich Freeman took 2058 first-class wickets in the 1920s, the most in any decade.

Tich Freeman is the only bowler to have conceded more than 5000 runs in a first-class season, 1928, but he took the record of 304 wickets in return for 5489 runs.

Tich Freeman is the only bowler to have bowled more than 12,000 balls in a first-class season, 12234 in 1933.

Tich Freeman conceded the most runs in a first-class match in Britain when he took 8-331 for Kent against Middlesex at Folkestone in 1934.

COUNTY • KENT

Frank Woolley made every first-class score from 0 to 111.

Derek Underwood scored his maiden first-class century in his 618th innings against Sussex at Hastings in 1984.

Derek Underwood's best innings analysis was 9-28 against Sussex at Hastings in 1964.

Steve Marsh equalled the world record of eight dismissals in a first-class innings against Middlesex at Lord's in 1991.

The record number of stumpings in a first-class match is nine by Fred Huish against Surrey at The Oval in 1911.

Godfrey Evans took 97 minutes to get off the mark in the 1946-7 Ashes Test at Adelaide.

Les Ames scored 123 before lunch on the third day of the England v South Africa Test at The Oval in 1935.

In 1950 Les Ames became the first professional to be appointed an official Test selector.

Dean Headley took a wicket with his first ball on his first-class debut for Kent, although having previously played for Middlesex.

Tony Pawson played football for Great Britain at the 1952 Olympics and later became world fly-fishing champion.

Kent won the championship in four seasons out of eight shortly before World War I.

Bob Woolmer bowled 8.1 overs in the Sunday League match against Hampshire in 1972, one ball more than the legal maximum, off which three runs were scored. John Graham completed the over.

Bob Woolmer was the first bowler to reach 50 wickets in the Sunday League.

Bob Woolmer was banned by England for playing for World Series Cricket and for going on the 1982 unofficial tour of South Africa.

COUNTY • KENT

Kent have finished bottom of the championship only twice in their history.

Neil Taylor won four Gold Awards in his first five B and H Cup matches.

Frank Woolley scored 1000 runs in a first-class season 28 times, equalling the record set by WG Grace.

In 1928 Frank Woolley was not selected for the winter tour of Australia after scoring 3352 runs in the season.

Frank Woolley's highest first-class innings was 305* for MCC against Tasmania at Hobart in 1911-12.

Frank Woolley is the only player to have scored 2000 runs and taken 100 wickets in a first-class season on four occasions.

Chris Tavare scored 82* to win the Man of the Match on his ODI debut for England against West Indies in 1980.

Charles Absolom, who scored a 50 in his only Test for England in 1878-9 and was a noted all-round athlete, was killed in Trinidad when a crane collapsed on him.

Hon. Ivo Bligh, whose England side recaptured the Ashes in 1882-3, averaged 18 as a batsman for Kent.

James Allan, when making his first-class debut for Oxford University in 1953 before joining Kent, took three wickets before conceding a run.

Carl Hooper scored the equal fastest championship century in 1998 off 72 balls, against Worcestershire.

Kent won two major competitions in 1973, 1976 and 1978.

COUNTY • LANCASHIRE

Lancashire were founded in 1864 and were one of the original 'Big Six'.

Lancashire's total of 589 against Derbyshire at Blackpool in 1994 is the largest by a county following on.

Lancashire have beaten Somerset four times in a single day in the county championship.

Seven Lancashire batsmen have scored Test centuries for England against South Africa.

Lancashire scored 166-0 declared and 66-0 to defeat Leicestershire by ten wickets at Old Trafford in 1956. It was the first instance in first-class cricket of a side winning without losing a wicket.

Starting with his Test debut against South Africa at Trent Bridge in 1998, Andy Flintoff scored 89 runs in his last twelve first-class innings of the season and took one wicket.

Cyril Washbrook became Lancashire's first professional captain in 1954.

Dick Tyldesley took five wickets for no runs against Leicestershire at Old Trafford in 1924.

It was Lancashire who proposed a two-day county championship on economic grounds in 1919. The experiment was abandoned after one season.

Lancashire have never finished bottom of the championship.

Cecil Parkin never played for England again after criticising in print his captain Arthur Gilligan for failing to bowl him in a Test against South Africa in 1924.

Cecil Parkin told an earlier England captain, the allrounder Johnny Douglas, when an Australian batsman came in: 'you go on for an hour and bowl him in, then I'll come on and bowl him out.'

COUNTY • LANCASHIRE

John Crawley's seven championship centuries in 1998 were the most by a Lancashire batman since Winston Place in 1947.

The Australian Ted McDonald was the first famous overseas player, signed in 1924 for £500 a year. His fast bowling helped Lancashire to four of their championships.

Apart from scoring over 20,000 first-class runs and captaining Lancashire in 1963 and 1964, the Australian Ken Grieves was a goal keeper for Bury, Stockport County and Bolton Wanderers.

Of the current staff, Mike Atherton, Mark Chilton, John Crawley and Gary Yates went to Manchester Grammar School.

David Hughes hit 24 off the penultimate over from John Mortimore to win the 1971 Gillette Cup semi-final against Gloucestershire.

When turning down an appeal for bad light by Jack Bond in the above match, Arthur Jepson the umpire said: 'You can see the moon. How far do you want to see?'

Archie MacLaren came out of retirement in 1921 and at the age of 49 led his own side to the only first-class victory over the Australian tourists of that year.

Arthur Mold was the most famous fast bowler of his day with a suspect action. After taking 1673 wickets at 15, his first-class career was ended when he was no-balled for throwing in 1901.

Albert Hornby, of 'O my Hornby and my Barlow long ago', averaged 23 with the bat in 286 matches for Lancashire whom he captained.

COUNTY • LANCASHIRE

Albert Hornby, son of the above, averaged 24 with the bat in 283 matches for Lancashire, whom he captained.

Eddie Paynter scored 591 runs in Ashes Tests at an average of 84.42.

Allan Steel took 164 first-class wickets at nine runs each in 1878 and captained England to three wins in their three Tests against Australia in 1886.

Farokh Engineer scored 1000 runs in a first-class season in India in 1964-5, but never in England.

Peter Martin was the leading wicket taker in the 1997 Sunday League.

George Duckworth became baggage-manager and scorer for England after he retired.

Lancashire scored 352-6 in the B&H Cup against Hampshire in 1990, only to have the match annulled because of rain and another game played instead.

Harry Makepeace is the oldest batsman to make a maiden Test century. He was 40 when he did so in the Ashes Test at Melbourne in 1920-1.

In 1927 Ernest Tyldesley became the first to score ten consecutive first-class scores of 50 or more.

Walter Brearley, the amateur fast bowler, had so many disputes with the Lancashire committee that he left the county in 1911 and was selected for England in 1912 while representing Cheshire.

Lancashire's match against Oxford University in 1925 was the last 12-a-side match in England to have been ranked as first-class.

Ken MacLeod scored a century in 63 minutes for Lancashire against Somerset at Bath, represented Cambridge University as a 100 yards sprinter and long jumper, and played for Scotland as a rugby wing before World War I.

COUNTY • LANCASHIRE

Ken MacLeod, a Jamaican pace bowler, was signed by Lancashire in 1987 and played six first-class matches.

Lancashire's captain in 1934, Peter Eckersley, won the toss 27 times in 30 county matches.

It was calculated by the cricket historian GB Buckley that in the period from 1873 to 1936 Lancashire were the luckiest county at winning the toss, winning 703 and losing 590.

Cyril Washbrook enjoyed what was a record benefit of £14,000 in 1948.

Jack Simmons enjoyed what was a record benefit of £128,000 in 1980.

In five of the seven seasons between 1981 and 1987 Lancashire lost more time to rain and bad light away in the championship than at home.

Graeme Fowler scored 100 runs or more in each innings of the match against Warwickshire at Southport in 1982 with a runner.

Graeme Fowler remained on 39 for 90 minutes when he was batting against Warwickshire at Edgbaston in 1989. It remains the longest period without adding to an individual innings in a first-class match in Britain.

Les Poidevin, who topped Lancashire's batting averages in 1905, represented Australia in the Davis Cup.

Albert Hornby was the first person to captain England at cricket and rugby.

Peter Marner was the first to score a century in the Gillette Cup, 121 against Leicestershire in 1963.

Brian Statham was the first bowler to take five wickets in the Gillette Cup in the above match.

COUNTY • LANCASHIRE

John Crawley's 286 for England A against Eastern Province in Port Elizabeth in 1993-4 was the highest score by an England player on tour since 1965-6.

Jason Gallian took a wicket with his first ball on his first-class debut for Lancashire against Oxford University in 1990.

When Warren Hegg scored 130 in his fourth first-class match aged 18, he was the youngest century-maker for Lancashire for 30 years.

Dick Barlow – of 'O my Hornby and my Barlow' – carried his bat for 5* in Lancashire's total of 69 against Nottinghamshire in 1882. He was also a sprinter.

Johnny Briggs took 100 wickets in a season most times for Lancashire, 11.

Johnny Briggs made six Test tours of Australia and took 118 wickets for England before dying in Cheadle Asylum aged 39.

Syd Barnes, who took 189 wickets in 27 Tests, took 225 wickets at 19 in his 46 matches for Lancashire.

Sir John Brocklebank played four matches for Lancashire in 1939 before becoming chairman of Cunard.

Six batsmen in one innings were dismissed 'c. Farrimond b. McDonald' in the match between Lancashire and Kent in 1930.

Six batsmen in one innings were dismissed 'c. Maynard b. Watkinson' in the match between Lancashire and Glamorgan in 1983.

Glen Chapple scored 34 and 32 off two consecutive overs from Tony Cottey and a century in 21 minutes against Glamorgan at Old Trafford in 1993. The runs were offered to expedite a declaration.

Steve O'Shaughnessy scored a century in 35 minutes against Leicestershire in 1983. The runs were offered to expedite a declaration.

COUNTY • LEICESTERSHIRE

Leicestershire were founded in 1879 and were admitted to the county championship in 1895.

Leicestershire organized the first domestic limited overs competition. In 1963 they competed against Derbyshire, Nottinghamshire and Northamptonshire for the Midlands Knock-Out Cup.

The first major cricket ground in Leicester was at Wharf Street, where some of the biggest matches in the Midlands were staged between 1825 and its closure in 1860.

The only instance of ten different fielders taking a catch during a first-class innings was when Leicestershire did so against Northamptonshire at Leicester in 1967.

Charles de Trafford, Leicestershire's captain from 1890 to 1906, seldom batted with gloves.

Albert Knight was one of the first professional cricketers to write a book, 'The Complete Cricketer', published in 1906.

The fastest first-class 50 was made in eight minutes off 13 balls by Clive Inman against Nottinghamshire at Trent Bridge in 1965. He was offered the runs to expedite a declaration.

When Ben Smith score his first double-century, against Surrey at The Oval in 1998, he went from 88 to his century in two shots: a seven (three and four overthrows) and a six.

Eric Astill became Leicestershire's first professional captain in 1935 and led them to sixth, their highest position to that point.

Leicestershire's captain in 1936 was the New Zealand amateur Stuart Dempster.

COUNTY • LEICESTERSHIRE

Cecil Wood carried his bat through an innings 17 times, the most instances along with WG Grace.

The first batsman to carry his bat and make a century in each innings of a first-class match was Cecil Wood, who scored 107* and 117* against Yorkshire in 1911.

Leicestershire beat Cambridge University by 522 runs at Cambridge in 1984, the largest first-class victory by a runs margin by any county.

In 1971 John Steele scored a century for Leicestershire and his brother David a century for Northamptonshire. It was the first time two brothers had scored a century for opposing sides in the same match in England, and they did it again in 1973.

When Leicestershire played Somerset at Ashby-de-la-Zouch in 1963, the pitch was found to be 23 yards long and a new one had to be measured out.

Charles Palmer, captain of Leicestershire in the 1950s, occasionally bowled high full-tosses designed to land on the stumps.

Leicestershire's first two championship winning sides both lost only one match, to Surrey at The Oval.

Jack Birkenshaw played in the first championship-winning side, and coached and managed the other two.

Leicestershire used only 13 players in the championship in 1996.

Leicestershire finished in the top half of the championship only four times before World War II.

Dickie Bird scored 2701 first-class runs at 19.72 for Leicestershire.

David Constant scored 1385 first-class runs at 20.67 for Leicestershire.

Jon Dakin took a hat-trick as Middlesex were dismissed for 62 in the Sunday League in 1998.

COUNTY • LEICESTERSHIRE

John King scored 205 against Hampshire at Leicester in 1923 at the age of 52.

In 1994 Paul Nixon became the first Leicestershire wicket keeper to score 1000 runs in a first-class season since Tommy Sidwell in 1928.

Eric Astill shared a stand of 327 for the fifth wicket with Percy Holmes for MCC against Jamaica at Kingston in 1925-6, which remains a record for the fifth wicket in the West Indies.

Eric Astill served as an officer in both World Wars, was a champion billiards player and a noted musician, especially on the ukelele.

Paddy Clift took a hat-trick with his first three balls after lunch against Derbyshire in 1985.

David Gower set a world record of 119 consecutive Test innings without making a duck.

Charles Palmer played one Test for England on the 1953-4 tour of the West Indies when he went as manager.

Terry Spencer, who took 1320 first-class wickets for Leicestershire, was the nephew of Haydon Smith, who took 1076 first-class wickets for Leicestershire.

Leicestershire have finished bottom of the championship seven times, and equal bottom twice.

In 1935 George Geary and Haydon Smith bowled unchanged through four consecutive championship innings.

Leicestershire's highest total is 701-4 declared against Worcestershire at Worcester in 1906.

The partnership of 228 between Ray Illingworth and Ken Higgs against Northamptonshire at Leicester in 1977 is the third highest tenth wicket stand for any county in the championship.

COUNTY • LEICESTERSHIRE

Every record partnership for Leicestershire has been set since World War II, except 160 for the ninth wicket in 1902.

The first six Yorkshire batsmen were caught by Roger Tolchard at Headingley in 1973.

Roger Tolchard had to return home early from England's 1978-9 tour of Australia after being hit on the head while batting at Newcastle, NSW.

Horace Snary was not out in 41% of his first-class innings: 114 out of 249.

Sir Arthur Hazlerigg captained Leicestershire from 1907-1910. His son Sir Arthur Hazlerigg captained Leicestershire in 1934.

Maurice Tompkin, who scored almost 20,000 first-class runs, died of cancer shortly after going on MCC's 1955-6 tour of Pakistan aged 37.

Mike Turner, secretary of Leicestershire for over 30 years, played ten matches for the county as a leg break bowler.

Leicestershire were dismissed for 36 by Sussex in the Sunday League in 1973, their lowest total in the competition.

Laurie Potter captained Young Australia and Young England.

Tony Lock captained Leicestershire to second position in 1967, their highest championship position to that date.

Alex Skelding, who took 593 first-class wickets for Leicestershire, became famous as one of the most humorous umpires.

The England bowler Syd Barnes, having had an appeal for LBW turned down by Alex Skelding, caught a stray dog and presented it to the umpire saying: 'Now all you want is a white stick.'

COUNTY • LEICESTERSHIRE

Alex Skelding did not retire as an umpire until he was 72.

In one of his two Tests, against West Indies at The Oval in 1976, Chris Balderstone made a pair.

Norman Armstrong was first to score 2000 runs in a season for Leicestershire, 1933.

Dick Pougher took five wickets for no runs when playing for MCC against the Australians at Lord's in 1896.

Nigel Briers carried his bat for 60* out of 108 against Northamptonshire in 1991.

The record for the most centuries in a first-class season for Leicestershire is held by three batsmen: Les Berry, Brian Davison and Willie Watson, seven each.

The record for the most hat-tricks for Leicestershire is shared by five bowlers, with two each.

The lowest total against Leicestershire is 24, recorded on two occasions, by Glamorgan in 1971 and by Oxford University in 1985.

The highest score against Leicestershire is 341 by George Hirst in 1906.

Leicestershire beat the Australians in 1975.

When still a second-class county, Leicestershire beat the Australians in 1888.

Phil Whitticase lost seven teeth after being struck in the mouth by Neil Williams of Essex in 1995.

Set a target of 204 off 20 overs to beat Northamptonshire in their championship match in 1998, Leicestershire won by four wickets with five balls to spare. At 179 runs per 100 balls it was the fastest successful run-chase ever recorded in the championship.

COUNTY • MIDDLESEX

Middlesex were founded in 1864 and were one of the original 'Big Six'.

When nine Middlesex players were late to arrive for the second day of their match against Kent at Tunbridge Wells in 1963 owing to traffic, they had to declare their innings then borrow eight substitute fielders from Kent.

Middlesex did not play Derbyshire in the championship until 1929, Northamptonshire until 1930 and Glamorgan until 1931.

When Middlesex dismissed Glamorgan at Cardiff in 1997 for 31, it equalled the lowest total by any county against Middlesex.

John Carr had a sequence of 854 first-class runs for once out in 1994.

The fastest 50 off genuine bowling was made by Jim Smith in 11 minutes against Gloucestershire at Bristol in 1938.

Gubby Allen was born in Australia and captained England in an Ashes series in Australia.

Ahsan-ul-Haq, who played for Middlesex at the turn of the century, scored a first-class century in 40 minutes for Muslims when batting at number 11 in 1924-5. He had arrived late.

Patsy Hendren has taken the most first-class catches for Middlesex, apart from wicket keepers, 561.

Andy Miller was first to score a century for Combined Universities in the B and H Cup.

Three of the first four batsmen in Middlesex's first innings against Kent in 1921 were dismissed 'hit wicket bowled Freeman.'

COUNTY • MIDDLESEX

Denis Compton became Middlesex's first professional captain when he shared the captaincy with Bill Edrich in 1951.

In 1947 Leslie Compton opened the bowling against Somerset at Taunton, and put his pads on to keep wicket at the end of each over.

Nigel Haig was accused of lifting the seam in the match between Middlesex and Worcestershire at Lord's in 1925.

Shortly after he had been left out of England's 1997-8 tour of Australia, Phil Tufnell was stung by a wasp which had flown up his trouser leg.

John Warr had a Test bowling average for England of 281.00.

Middlesex's home match against Nottinghamshire in 1939 was played at The Oval because Lord's was required for the Eton v Harrow match.

In 1977 Middlesex played a 'home' championship match against Somerset at Chelmsford owing to a clash with the Gillette Cup.

Fred Titmus represented Middlesex in five consecutive decades, starting in 1949 aged 16.

Charles Studd was the first Middlesex player to do the double of 1000 runs and 100 wickets in a first-class season, before becoming a missionary in China and The Congo.

Andrew Stoddart captained Middlesex and England, scoring 996 Test runs, and played for England at rugby, before shooting himself aged 52.

After rising to speak at a cricket dinner and knocking over his chair, Patsy Hendren declared: 'That's by no means the first time I've heard the sound of falling timber behind me.'

Middlesex have never finished bottom of the county championship.

COUNTY • MIDDLESEX

Middlesex were runners-up from 1936 to 1939, and again in 1946.

Mike Gatting was the second captain of a county, after Keith Fletcher, to win all four domestic competitions.

Five Middlesex players were chosen for England's 1964-5 tour of South Africa.

Jim Swanton played three first-class matches for Middlesex before becoming the cricket correspondent of the Daily Telegraph.

John Warr once described EW Swanton's prose style as 'Somewhere between Enid Blyton and the Ten Commandments'.

Ian Peebles took 610 first-class wickets for Middlesex, and 45 Test wickets for England, before becoming cricket correspondent of the Sunday Times.

Three Middlesex and England players have been born in Scotland: Gregor McGregor, Ian Peebles and Eric Russell.

Albert Trott remains the only batsman to have hit a six over the Lord's pavilion, off Monty Noble in the match between MCC and the Australians in 1899.

Middlesex were the only county to defeat the 1976 West Indians.

The first four Middlesex batsmen scored centuries when Middlesex made 642-3 dec against Hampshire at Southampton in 1923.

Leslie Compton became the oldest player to make his debut for England at soccer in 1950-1 at the age of 38.

Joe Hulme, who scored 12 first-class centuries for Middlesex, played for Blackburn Rovers, Arsenal, Huddersfield Town and England before World War I.

COUNTY • MIDDLESEX

'A Lot of Hard Yakka' – Triumph and torment: a county cricketer's life – by Simon Hughes was voted 1997 Sportsbook of the Year.

Both Frank Mann and his son George Mann captained Middlesex and England, led successful England tours to South Africa, averaged 24.6 with the bat for Middlesex and took two first-class wickets for them.

Norman Cowans received his first England cap in 1982-3 and his Middlesex cap in 1984.

Middlesex's team for their match against Essex at Lord's in 1981 consisted entirely of Test players. This was the first instance in English first-class cricket.

Peter Parfitt holds the record for most catches in a first-class season for Middlesex, 46.

Patsy Hendren holds the record for most catches in a first-class career for Middlesex, 561.

Although they were dismissed by Somerset for only 86 at Lord's in 1899 Middlesex still won by an innings and seven runs. The game was completed in 185 minutes, the shortest on record in first-class cricket.

Bernard Bosanquet, 'father' of the googly and grandfather of the television newsreader Reggie, was the first man to score a century in each innings and take 10 wickets in a championship match, for Middlesex against Sussex at Lord's in 1905.

John Emburey's 46 for England against Tasmania at Hobart in 1986-7 contained 10 fours and a six.

In the fourth innings of their match against Nottinghamshire at Trent Bridge in 1925 Middlesex scored 502-6 to win.

When batting for Middlesex against Somerset at Lord's in 1933 Harry Lee was caught by his brother Frank off the bowling of his brother Jack for 82.

COUNTY • MIDDLESEX

Sir Timothy O'Brien, who played for Middlesex from 1881 to 1898, and captained England in one Test, once threatened to fight WG Grace on the pitch.

Plum, later Sir Pelham, Warner was the second person to carry his bat through a Test innings when he scored 132* against South Africa at Johannesburg in 1898-9.

Sir Pelham Warner was chairman of the England selectors and cricket correspondent of the Morning Post simultaneously.

The best bowling analysis in the B&H Cup was 7-12 by Wayne Daniel against Minor Counties East in 1978.

Harry Enthoven scored 102* out of 107 added for the tenth wicket with Fred Price against Somerset at Lord's in 1930.

Albert Trott took four wickets in four balls and a hat-trick against Somerset at Lord's in 1907 to hasten the end of his own Benefit match.

Viscount Chelmsford played six first-class matches for Middlesex before becoming Viceroy of India from 1916-1921. He was the uncle of the explorer Wilfred Thessiger.

Mike Brearley scored the most runs in a first-class career for Cambridge University, 4310 at 38.48.

Ian Peebles took most wickets in a first-class season for Oxford University, 70.

When batting for MCC against Yorkshire in 1946 Jack Young shard a tenth wicket stand of 75 with Walter Robins without making a run himself.

Rev. Edgar Killick scored 206 against Warwickshire in his only first-class innings in 1931.

George Beldam who represented Middlesex as an amateur from 1900-1907, scoring 6575 runs at 30, was the first cricket photographer of note.

COUNTY • NORTHAMPTONSHIRE

Northamptonshire were founded in 1878. They joined the championship in 1905 after winning the Minor Counties championship in the two previous years.

Northamptonshire are the only county which has produced partnerships of 300 or more for the first six wickets.

Northamptonshire had the smallest county membership in 1984, of 1976 members.

The lowest innings in the county championship is 12 by Northamptonshire against Gloucestershire at Gloucester in 1907.

The lowest match aggregate in the championship is 42 by Northamptonshire (27 and 15) against Yorkshire at Northampton in 1908.

Six Northamptonshire batsmen have scored Test centuries for England against West Indies.

Northamptonshire came second in 1912, using only 12 players in their 18 championship matches, winning 10 and losing one.

Northamptonshire were penalized 25 points for an unfit pitch at Northampton in their match against Sussex in 1998.

In 1996 Allan Lamb and Ian Botham lost the libel case which they had brought against Imran Khan.

Keith Andrew did not concede a bye while 2132 runs were scored against Northamptonshire in 1965.

When Northamptonshire advertised the county captaincy in 'The Cricketer' in 1953, they received two replies.

Dennis Brookes became Northamptonshire's first professional captain in 1954.

COUNTY • NORTHAMPTONSHIRE

Northamptonshire's highest total of 781-7 declared was made at Northampton in 1995 in reply to Nottinghamshire's 527. Northamptonshire dismissed Nottinghamshire for 157 and won by an innings and 97 runs.

Four batsmen scored centuries for Northmaptonshire in their record innings above: Alan Fordham, Allan Lamb, Russell Warren and David Capel.

Northamptonshire did not beat Yorkshire from 1913 to 1953.

Northamptonshire did not beat Leicestershire from 1914 to 1953.

Peter Willey was the youngest player to play for Northamptonshire at 16, against Cambridge University in 1966.

After leaving Northamptonshire in 1971, Peter Lee twice took 100 wickets in a first-class season for Lancashire.

Northamptonshire went 43 points clear in the championship in late June 1995.

After Freddie Brown had scored 122 in 110 minutes for Gentlemen against Players in 1950, he was lying in the bath with a large whisky and water when he was asked by England's chairman of selectors Walter Robins if he would captain England's tour to Australia.

'Lovely lettuces, hearts like Freddie Brown': a Sydney vegetable-seller, 1951.

Between 1947 and 1953 202 first-class batsmen were caught Fiddling. Ken Fiddling had previously kept wicket for Yorkshire.

David Steele was BBC Sports Personality of the Year in 1976.

Colin Milburn scored three first-class centuries before lunch in 1966.

COUNTY • NORTHAMPTONSHIRE

Northamptonshire went 99 championship matches from 1935 to 1939 without a win, a record in the county championship.

Roger Prideaux and his wife Ruth both played cricket for England, the first married couple to do so.

On his debut for Northamptonshire against Dublin University in 1926 Sidney Adams, a leg spin bowler, took two wickets with his first two balls in first-class cricket. One of his victims was Samuel Beckett.

Fred Bakewell scored 246 and 257 in successive innings for Northamptonshire in 1933, both then record scores for the county.

In his six Tests Fred Bakewell scored 9, 27, 40, 107, 85, 4, 63, 54 and 20.

Two Northamptonshire and England batsmen had their careers ruined by car accidents: Alfred Bakewell, whose career was ended by an injury to his right arm just after scoring 241* against Derbyshire, and Colin Milburn, who subsequently made a brief reappearance with one eye.

The New Zealand Test wicket keeper Ken James turned professional and kept wicket for Northamptonshire in the late 1930s.

The New Zealand legspinner Bill Merritt turned professional and played for Northamptonshire in the late 1930s. He also played rugby league for Wigan and Halifax.

Allan Lamb made his highest first-class score of 294 for Orange Free State against Eastern Province in 1987-8.

Tim Lamb dismissed David Gower lbw three times in succession at Northampton in 1981, in the county championship and B&H Cup.

COUNTY • NORTHAMPTONSHIRE

Northamptonshire have finished bottom of the county championship eleven times, equal most.

In 1933 Northamptonshire beat the West Indians by an innings.

Northamptonshire beat the West Indians on two consecutive tours in 1966 and 1969.

Harry Wilson was run out for 0 in both innings of his only first-class match, against the New Zealanders in 1931.

Northamptonshire's Robin Boyd-Moss was the last batsman to score a century in each innings of the Varsity Match, for Cambridge against Oxford in 1983.

Tony Penberthy dismissed Mark Taylor with his first ball in first-class cricket in 1989.

Northamptonshire conceded three consecutive first-class totals over 600 in 1921. In their next innings they conceded 545-9 declared.

After his highly successful season in 1921 the batsman Robert Haywood asked for a pay increase, was turned down, and went to coach at Fettes.

Jim Griffiths took 444 first-class wickets and scored 290 first-class runs.

Frank Tyson and Keith Andrew were both picked up from Lancashire and taken on the 1954-5 England tour of Australia.

When Northamptonshire's captain in 1946, Peter Murray-Willis, was chasing a ball in the match at Kettering and lost his cap, he went back to get his cap before continuing to chase the ball.

COUNTY • NORTHAMPTONSHIRE

For 1947 Northamptonshire signed as their captain Arthur Childs-Clarke, whose last first-class match had been for Middlesex 13 years before.

Only three players have done the double of 1000 runs and 100 wickets in a first-class season for Northamptonshire: Syd Smith, Vallance Jupp and George Tribe.

Vince Broderick performed the double in all first-class matches in 1948.

Keith Andrew was awarded four runs in the match against Hampshire at Southampton in 1967 when he cut the ball towards the boundary and it was stopped by a dog.

Northamptonshire tied with Kent in their championship match at Northampton in 1984.

The last pair of bowlers to bowl throughout both completed innings of a championship match were Brian Crump and Ray Bailey against Glamorgan at Cardiff in 1967.

The only bowler to take four wickets in four balls for Northamptonshire was Sydney Smith, against Warwickshire at Edgbaston in 1914.

In 1914, when Northamptonshire played Somerset, twins opened the batting for each county: Billy and Jack Denton for Northamptonshire, Albert and Arthur Rippon for Somerset.

Northamptonshire won the first domestic one-day tournament when they defeated Leicestershire by five wickets to win the Midlands Knock-Out Cup in 1963. Each side was limited to 65 overs but there was no limit on the number of overs per bowler in the final.

In 1979, when no batsman in the country scored 2000 runs in the first-class season for the first time since 1894, the highest scorer was Northamtonshire's Roy Virgin with 1936.

Alan Fordham averaged 40 for Northamptonshire before retiring to become the ECB's Cricket Operations Manager.

COUNTY • NOTTINGHAMSHIRE

Nottinghamshire were founded in 1841 and were one of the original 'Big Six' in the county championship.

Alf Shaw captained Nottinghamshire to four unofficial championships from 1883 to 1886, and bowled more four-ball overs than he conceded runs.

Nottinghamshire went through the 1967 championship season without a win, one of only four counties to do so since World War II.

Rob Andrew, the England rugby player, scored his only first-class century for Cambridge University against Nottinghamshire.

Alf Shaw took two hat-tricks and three wickets in four balls for Nottinghamshire against Gloucestershire in 1884.

Clive Rice scored 105* out of Nottinghamshire's total of 143 against Hampshire at Bournemouth in 1981, the lowest completed first-class innings to include a century.

When Middlesex had five wickets left with half-an-hour to go at Lord's in 1892, Nottinghamshire's 17-stone wicketkeeper Mordecai Sherwin took off his pads and took two wickets. Nottinghamshire won with four minutes to spare.

Nottinghamshire tied with Worcestershire at Trent Bridge in 1993.

Tom Wass is the only bowler to have taken 17 wickets in a day twice, against Lancashire in 1906 and against Essex in 1908.

Arthur Carr hit 48 sixes in the 1925 season, believed to be a record to that point.

The largest winning margin in England, outside Tests, is an innings and 517 runs by the Australians against Nottinghamshire at Trent Bridge in 1921.

COUNTY • NOTTINGHAMSHIRE

George Gunn scored 35208 first-class runs, his uncle William 25691, his brother John 24557, and his son George 10337.

John Gunn is the only player to have aggregated 20000 runs and 1000 wickets in a first-class career for Nottinghamshire.

The equal highest number of defeats in a championship season is 20 by Nottinghamshire in 1961.

Nottinghamshire scored 527 in their first innings against Northamptonshire at Northampton in 1995 and still lost by an innings and 97 runs. It is the highest total ever made by a first-class team which has gone on to lose the match.

Syd Copley took one of the most famous catches by a substitute when he caught Stan McCabe in the 1930 Ashes Test at Trent Bridge. A groundstaff boy, he later played one match for Nottinghamshire.

When Hampshire needed only one run to win at the start of the third day in 1930, the whole Nottinghamshire team took the field without changing into whites.

George Gunn reached his century without hitting a boundary against Essex at Leyton in 1924, then hit two fours to show he still could.

George Gunn shared 40 century opening partnerships for Nottinghamshire with Dodge Whysall.

William Gunn was co-founder of the bat-making and sports equipment firm Gunn and Moore.

The best analysis in a first-class innings for Nottinghamshire is 10-66 by Ken Smales against Gloucestershire at Stroud in 1956.

COUNTY • NOTTINGHAMSHIRE

The best analysis in a first-class match for Nottinghamshire is 17-89 by Frank Matthews against Northamptonshire at Trent Bridge in 1923.

Clive Rice set a record of 814 runs in the Sunday League in 1977.

William Clarke laid out the Trent Bridge cricket ground, founded the All England Eleven, and was one of the best lob bowlers from the age of 45.

Arthur Jones, who has taken the most first-class catches for Nottinghamshire (466) and captained the county from 1900 to 1914, is credited with developing the position of gully.

Willis Walker, who played for Nottinghamshire from 1913 to 1937 and was a professional goalkeeper, was the oldest living county cricketer at his death in 1991 aged 99.

Harold Larwood scored 6138 first-class runs at 20 for Nottinghamshire in addition to taking 1247 wickets at 16.

Nottinghamshire have finished bottom of the county championship eight times.

In 1929 Nottinghamshire became the first county to have four bowlers who reached 100 wickets in the same first-class season: they were Harold Larwood, Bill Voce, Fred Barratt and Sam Staples.

Bill Voce began as a left-arm spin bowler.

Fred Barratt in 1914 became the first Nottinghamshire bowler to take 100 first-class wickets in his debut season.

Fred Barratt hit 139* against Warwickshire in 1928 in only 84 minutes.

Ted Alletson scored 189* in 90 minutes for Nottinghamshire against Sussex at Hove in 1911. 'Runs kept coming and I cast care aside and hit harder' said Alletson afterwards.

COUNTY • NOTTINGHAMSHIRE

'One of those drives would have smashed a man's hand if he had tried to stop it': George Gunn after Alletson's innings.

The highest score against Nottinghamshire is 345 by Charlie Macartney for the Australians in 1921. It remains the fastest triple-century ever made in Britain, in 205 minutes.

The batsman at the other end when Garfield Sobers hit six sixes off an over at Swansea in 1968 was John Parkin. He played 28 matches for Nottinghamshire as a batsman and averaged 11.

Chris Broad was sacked 24 hours after scoring his fifth century of the 1992 season.

When Nottinghamshire took the Sunday League title in 1991 they had won all four domestic competitions in the space of five years.

George Gunn and his son George hit a century in the same innings for Nottinghamshire against Warwickshire in 1931. George Gunn senior was 52 at the time.

Joe Hardstaff junior won the Lawrence Trophy for scoring the fastest century of the 1937 season, in 51 minutes against Kent at Canterbury.

When Joe Hardstaff junior played for Auckland after World War II while coaching in New Zealand, his qualification to continue playing for Nottinghamshire was questioned.

In 1899, when Nottinghamshire scored 581 against Derbyshire, the highest innings was 90 by William Gunn. It remains the highest total in first-class cricket without a century.

Tim Robinson scored over 400 runs in his first two Test series, and 72 in his third.

John Howarth played 13 first-class matches for Nottinghamshire in 1966 and 1967 without scoring a run.

COUNTY • NOTTINGHAMSHIRE

Alf Shaw bowled WG Grace more often than other bowler in first-class cricket, 20 times.

Six Nottinghamshire players were included in the England side in the Test at Sydney in 1887-8.

Richard Hadlee scored 5854 runs at 38 in addition to taking 622 wickets at 14 in his 148 first-class matches for Nottinghamshire.

John Clay was the first professional captain of Nottinghamshire in this century, in 1961.

John 'Foghorn' Jackson was recognised as the best fast bowler in England – he took 109 wickets at nine runs each in 1860 – before dying in a Liverpool workhouse.

Richard Daft, regarded as the best professional batsman in England in his day, led a tour to North America in 1879.

Ben Lilley was the first Nottinghamshire wicketkeeper to score 1000 runs in a first-class season, in 1925.

Charlie Harris shared 46 century opening stands with Walter Keeton.

Joe Hardstaff senior accompanied England to the West Indies in 1929-30 as their Test umpire. He umpired in 21 Tests in all until his son Joe was selected for England.

When Nottinghamshire won the Sunday League their leading run-scorer was Derek Randall, who made 673 runs at the age of 40.

In the same successful season Kevin Evans set a record for the most runs conceded in a Sunday League season, 679.

Alf Shaw asked to be buried 22 yards from Arthur Shrewsbury 'so I can send him down a ball now and then'.

COUNTY • SOMERSET

Somerset were founded in 1875 at Sidmouth in Devon.

In 1891 Somerset were twice dismissed for 37 by Surrey and lost by an innings and 375 runs.

The first Somerset player to win a cricket medal was Alfred Bowerman who was a member of the Great Britain team which won the 1900 Olympics.

When Yorkshire won the Championship from 1900 to 1902, they lost only two matches, both to Somerset.

In 1901 Somerset, having been dismissed by Yorkshire in their first innings for 87, scored 630 in their second and won by 279 runs.

Somerset finished bottom of the championship three times in four years shortly before the First World War.

'For many of us, who had the luck and the honour to play for Somerset, memory lingers on of a hard but humorous adventure': Raymond Robertson-Glasgow on playing for Somerset between the World Wars.

Ian Botham was BBC Sports Personality of the Year in 1981.

In 1982 Ian Botham scored the fastest century of the season, against Warwickshire in 52 minutes.

Both the highest and the second highest innings in the county championship were made against Somerset: 424 by Archie MacLaren in 1895 and 405* by Graeme Hick in 1988.

In his 23 Tests at the turn of the century Len Braund, one of the best slips of his time, took 39 catches.

Jack White took 17 wickets in a day against Middlesex at Bath in 1919.

Bertie Buse's benefit match against Lancashire at Bath in 1953 was completed on the first day.

In 1974 Bob Clapp took 51 wickets in one day matches. In his first-class career he took 25 wickets.

COUNTY • SOMERSET

Seymour Clarke, a wicket keeper, played nine first-class innings for Somerset in 1930 but did not score a run.

In 1991 Andy Caddick took a record 96 wickets in the Second XI competition.

Somerset beat Derbyshire in 1995 after following on. It was the first time Derbyshire had lost after enforcing the follow-on since 1882.

Reverend Archibald Wickham did not concede a bye when Hampshire scored 672-7 declared at Taunton in 1899, a world record.

A stained glass window in the church at Brent Knoll depicts the two favourite pastimes of Reverend Archibald Wickham: butterflies and wicket keeping.

When Oxford University's wicketkeeper was injured in the match against Somerset in 1901, Reverend Archibald Wickham volunteered to keep wicket for both sides.

Martin Crowe scored 3984 first-class runs at an average of 59.46 for Somerset.

Steve Waugh scored 1654 first-class runs at an average of 78.76 for Somerset.

Jimmy Cook carried his bat through both innings for Somerset against Nottinghamshire at Trent Bridge in 1989.

Bill Alley was first to score two unbeaten centuries in the same first-class match for Somerset when he made 183* and 134* against Surrey at Taunton in 1961.

Bill Alley won all of his 28 professional fights as a welterweight boxer.

COUNTY • SOMERSET

Bill Alley bowled 93 consecutive balls without conceding a run against Essex at Yeovil in 1960.

Horace Hazell bowled 105 balls without conceding a run against Gloucestershire in 1949.

The first international match staged in Somerset was England against Sri Lanka at Taunton in the 1983 World Cup.

At the foundation of Somerset in 1875 it was resolved that there should be no county ground.

In the Headingley Test of 1980 both umpires (Bill Alley and Ken Palmer) had played for Somerset as well as both captains.

When Middlesex won the championship in 1947 Somerset did the double against them.

Somerset's Gillette Cup match against Nottinghamshire at Taunton in 1965 was the first in the competition to be spread over three days.

Micky Walford, who scored 264 for Somerset against Hampshire in 1947, represented Great Britain at hockey in the 1948 Olympics.

Fred Rumsey took 100 wickets in his first full season for Somerset, 1965.

Brian Close scored a century on his debut for Somerset against Leicestershire at Leicester aged 40.

Gary Palmer became Somerset's youngest professional when he was given a contract at 14.

Peter Roebuck became the youngest Second XI player when he represented Somerset II against Devon aged 13.

COUNTY • SOMERSET

Johnny Lawrence took four wickets in five balls including a hat-trick against his native Yorkshire in 1948.

Jack Lee, an allrounder for Somerset from 1925-1936, was killed in action in Normandy in 1944.

Guy Earle hit 59 in 15 minutes against Gloucestershire at Taunton in 1929.

In 1974 Brian Close set a record, since broken, of 19 sixes in a Sunday League season.

At the age of 46 John Daniell scored a century in each innings against Essex at Taunton in 1925.

In addition to captaining Somerset, John Daniell captained England at rugby and became president of the Rugby Football Union.

Colin Atkinson and Ian Lomax were Somerset's last amateurs before that status was abolished in 1962.

In 1895 Somerset conceded consecutive first-class totals of 692 and 801 at Taunton.

When Harold Gimblett scored 143 against Northamptonshire at Bath in 1936, his last 84 runs were all scored in boundaries.

Bill Greswell, who became Somerset's president from 1962-1965, worked in his family's tea business in Ceylon and could only appear for Somerset in his holidays between 1908 and 1930.

Somerset have finished bottom of the championship eleven times, equal most, and shared bottom place once.

In 1986 Ian Botham was suspended from first-class cricket for nine weeks for admitting to the use of cannabis.

COUNTY • SOMERSET

Ian Botham gave the Leukaemia Research Fund £888,000 as a result of walking from John O'Groats to Land's End in 1985.

The captain of England's A team to Holland in 1989 was Peter Roebuck.

Only one first-class match has contained four century opening partnerships: Somerset v Cambridge University in 1960. Graham Atkinson and Roy Virgin were the batsmen for Somerset, Roger Prideaux and Tony Lewis for Cambridge.

Jack and Frank Lee were the first brothers to share a double-century opening stand in the championship, in 1932.

The former Cabinet Minister Geoffrey Rippon is the son of Arthur Rippon who played for Somerset between 1914 and 1937.

In 1977 Viv Richards hit the record of 26 sixes in a Sunday League season.

In his only Test for England in 1924 Jack MacBryan fielded for three hours before the game was rained off and neither batted nor bowled.

Maurice Tremlett became Somerset's first professional captain in 1956.

When playing for an England XI at Scarborough in 1895 Herbert Hewett, who captained Somerset from 1889 to 1893, retired from the game on the first day owing to rude remarks from the crowd and another player illegally took his place.

The best analysis in a first-class innings for Somerset is 10-49 by Edwin Tyler against Surrey at Taunton in 1895.

COUNTY • SURREY

Surrey were founded in 1845 and were one of the original 'Big Six'.

Surrey won the championship five times out of six from 1890 to 1895.

Stuart Surridge had a unique record as captain: five county championships in his five seasons in charge, from 1952 to 1956.

Surrey won 63% of all the matches they played under Stuart Surridge.

When Surrey won the championship in 1971, they finished equal on points with Warwickshire but won by virtue of more victories, 11 against nine.

Jack Hobbs made 99 first-class centuries before the age of 40, and 98 after.

William Roller is the only man to have scored a double-century and taken a hat-trick in the same match, against Sussex at The Oval in 1885.

Ken Barrington scored at least 50 in all ten of his first-class innings at Adelaide.

Tom Richardson reached 1000 wickets in only 134 first-class matches, and 2000 in 327 matches, both records.

At the Test trial match at Bradford in 1950 Alec and Eric Bedser played against each other.

Ben Hollioake was chosen for the 1998-9 tour of Australia before he had scored a century or taken five wickets in an innings in the championship.

The Oval used to be a market garden until 1845.

After Jack Hobbs had equalled WG Grace's record of 126 first-class centuries by scoring 101 against Somerset at Taunton in 1926, he broke it the next day with a century in his second innings.

COUNTY • SURREY

Andy Sandham spent sixty years with Surrey as player, coach and scorer.

Bob Willis left Surrey for Warwickshire when he did not receive his county cap after touring with England in 1970-1.

Graham Roope was the batsman at the other end when John Edrich and Geoff Boycott scored their 100th first-class centuries in 1977.

Jack Hobbs headed the national averages in 1920 – for bowling (17 wickets at 11.82). He only came second in the national batting averages.

Andy Ducat, who scored 52 first-class centuries for Surrey, led Aston Villa to the FA Cup in 1920.

Surrey set a world record in first-class cricket when they conceded 86 extras, including 52 no-balls, against Somerset at the Oval in 1997.

In 1953 Jack Hobbs became the first professional cricketer to be knighted.

William Beldham, widely recognised as the finest batsman of his time, represented Surrey from 1801-1817.

Surrey have never finished bottom of the county championship.

Ali Brown scored the equal fastest championship century in 1998, off 72 balls against Northamptonshire.

Cyril Wilkinson, captain of Surrey from 1914 to 1920, captained Great Britain at hockey in the 1920 Olympics and won a gold medal.

The largest margin of victory in a championship match is an innings and 485 runs by Surrey against Sussex at The Oval in 1888.

COUNTY • SURREY

Surrey beat Hampshire by an innings and 468 runs at The Oval in 1909, the second largest innings victory by any county in the championship.

Bobby Abel was first to score twelve first-class centuries in a season, 1900.

Jack Hobbs was first to score 16 first-class centuries in a season, 1925.

Jim Laker is the only bowler to have taken ten wickets in an innings three times in the same season, 1956.

Julius Caesar played for Surrey from 1849 to 1867 and was one of the best batsmen of his day. He shot a game-keeper and never fully recovered from the shock, dying aged 47.

Jim Laker took 8-2 for England against The Rest at Bradford in 1950.

Bernie Constable played first-class cricket until 1964, longer than any other cricketer who had played before World War II.

Andy Sandham retired ill on 282 against Lancashire at Old Trafford in 1928.

Harry Jupp carried his bat through both innings against Yorkshire at The Oval in 1871.

Surrey scored 645 runs in a day against Hampshire at The Oval in 1909, still the most runs in a day by a county in the championship.

MCC were at one point 0-7 against Surrey at Lord's in 1872. The recovered to reach 16 all out.

The highest innings in the Gentlemen v Players match was 266* by Jack Hobbs in 1925.

COUNTY • SURREY

In 1926 Jack Hobbs scored 316* for Surrey against Middlesex, the highest first-class innings made at Lord's until 1990.

In 1909 Surrey played Lancashire at The Oval and Oxford University at Reigate simultaneously, and both matches were ranked as first-class.

Digby Jephson, who captained Surrey from 1900-1902, took more than 200 first-class wickets with lobs.

Trevor Malony was the last man to play championship cricket as a lob-bowler. He appeared in three matches for Surrey in 1921 and took four wickets.

Sylvester Clarke, rated by many as the most ferocious fast bowler ever to play county cricket, played only 11 Tests for the West Indies. He was banned for going on an unofficial tour of South Africa, and West Indies had many other fast bowlers.

Nick Falkner and Keith Medlycott both hit centuries on their first-class debut against Cambridge University at Banstead.

In 1946 Surrey appointed the wrong captain. They had intended to ask Leo Bennett, but instead asked Nigel Bennett, who had never played first-class cricket before, and they were too polite to withdraw the offer when the mistake was discovered.

The best analysis in a first-class innings for Surrey is 10-43 by Tom Rushby against Somerset at Taunton in 1921.

COUNTY • SURREY

The best analysis in a first-class match for Surrey is 16-83 by Tony Lock against Kent at Blackheath in 1956.

In 1895 Tom Richardson took 290 first-class wickets, a record since surpassed by Tich Freeman alone.

Tom Richardson took the most first-class hat-tricks for Surrey, four.

Tom Richardson took 100 wickets in a first-class season most times for Surrey, 10.

James Southerton is the oldest player to make a Test debut: he was 49 when he played in the first Test match in 1876-7.

In 1974 Robin Jackman and Intikhab Alam ran six runs in the Sunday League match against Yorkshire at The Oval.

Ted Pooley still holds the record for the most dismissals by a wicket keeper in a first-class match for Surrey: 12 against Sussex at The Oval in 1868.

Ted Pooley missed the first Test at Melbourne in 1876-7 because he was detained in New Zealand after a betting incident. He made 607 dismissals for Surrey – 357 caught and 250 stumped – before dying in a workhouse in 1907.

Jack Hobbs shared in 166 century opening partnerships.

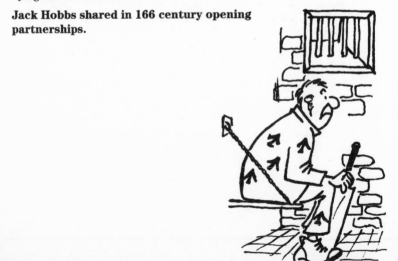

COUNTY • SUSSEX

Sussex were founded in 1839 and were one of the original members of the championship in 1890.

Sussex are one of four counties never to have won the county championship.

Sussex finished bottom of the championship in three of their first seven seasons.

In 1902 and 1903 Sussex were runners-up in the county championship.

Sussex beat the Australians in 1888 largely thanks to the lob bowling of Walter Humphreys.

KS Ranjitsinhji scored 989 Test runs for England at 44.95. His nephew KS Duleepsinhji scored 995 Test runs for England at 58.52.

George Brown bowled so fast for Sussex in the 1820s that his wicketkeeper, Dench, tied a sack stuffed with straw to his chest for protection.

Sussex made their highest total of 705-8 declared against Surrey in 1902. KS Ranjitsinji scored 275 and Charles Fry 139.

In the space of a fortnight in 1924 Maurice Tate and Arthur Gilligan dismissed Surrey for 53 and Middlesex for 41. They also combined for England to dismiss South Africa for 30.

From 1932 to 1934 Sussex were runners-up three times in succession in the championship.

KS Ranjitsinhji scored five double-centuries in 1900, the most in a first-class season after Don Bradman (six) in 1930.

COUNTY • SUSSEX

George Cox senior took five wickets for no runs against Somerset at Weston-super-Mare in 1921.

The highest aggregate for a first-class match in Britain is 1808 runs for 20 wickets in the game between Sussex and Essex at Hove in 1993.

Sussex tied with Kent at Hove in 1991 after scoring 436, the highest fourth innings ever made to tie a first-class match.

Sussex tied with Kent at Hastings in 1984.

Sussex tied with Essex at Hove in 1974.

James Langridge became Sussex's first professional captain in 1950.

James Lillywhite and Richard Fillery bowled unchanged for three consecutive first-class matches for Sussex in 1873.

In addition to all his bowling Maurice Tate shared in the county record second and sixth wicket partnerships, which still stand.

Harold Gilligan scored 1186 first-class runs in 1923 at an average of 17.70 runs per innings. It remains the lowest average by anyone scoring 1000 runs in a first-class season.

In the above season Harold Gilligan had 70 first-class innings, which remains the most in a first-class season.

Sussex have twice been dismissed for a match aggregate of 59 runs, by Yorkshire at Hove in 1878 and by Lancashire at Old Trafford in 1890.

David Sheppard scored the most first-class centuries for Cambridge University, 14, and the most runs in a first-class season, 1581.

COUNTY • SUSSEX

Robin Marlar bowled three deliveries with three different balls in the match against Worcestershire at Hove in 1955. Bob Broadbent hit the first two out of the ground and lost them.

When a Sussex bowler fell ill after bowling three overs in 1897, Lancashire's captain Archie MacLaren permitted a replacement. In 1906 one of Sussex's bowlers was injured after five overs, and again an illegal replacement was permitted.

A fire in the grandstand at Hove held up play during Sussex's match with Gloucestershire in 1947.

Charles Fry was no-balled for throwing more often than any other bowler in first-class cricket.

In the first year of the Gillette Cup, 1963, Sussex's total of 314-7 off 65 overs was the highest total of the first round. Ken Suttle and Ted Dexter hit a century each in taking Sussex to their first trophy.

Warwickshire decided to bat first in the second Gillette Cup final and were dismissed for 127, to lose by eight wickets.

Sussex, as Gillette Cup winners, played the West Indian tourists in September 1963 and beat them. In 1964 they played the Australian tourists and lost, their first defeat in limited-overs cricket.

Ted James was not out in 26 of his 39 first-class innings in 1956.

Walter Humphreys and Vallance Jupp have taken the most first-class hat-tricks for Sussex, three each.

The best analysis in a first-class match for Sussex is 17-106 by George Cox senior against Worcestershire at Horsham in 1926.

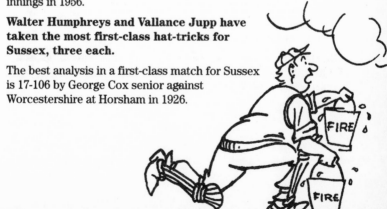

COUNTY • SUSSEX

The second best analysis is 16-100 by John Elicius Benedict Bernard Placid Quirk Carrington Dwyer, an Australian professional of Irish ancestry, in 1906.

KS Ranjitsinhji hit 14 first-class double-centuries for Sussex.

KS Ranjitsinhji's first-class career average of 56.37 was the highest of any batsman whose career was based in England until it was just overtaken by Geoff Boycott.

KS Ranjitsinhji's last games for Sussex in 1920 were played with one eye following a shooting accident during World War I.

Charles Fry represented England at soccer in 1901 and played for Southampton in the 1902 FA Cup final.

Don Smith, who played three Tests for England in 1957, later became coach of Sri Lanka.

Billy Murdoch, who captained Australia in 16 Tests, captained Sussex from 1893 to 1899.

Both of David Sheppard's Test centuries against Australia were innings of 113.

Maurice Tate achieved the double of 1000 runs and 100 wickets on MCC's tour of India and Ceylon in 1926-7.

John Langridge has scored the most first-class centuries, 76, without ever playing a Test match.

William Lillywhite opened the bowling for Sussex in a first-class match at the age of 61.

Tony Greig and Ian Greig both began their Test careers with bowling figures of 4-53 for England.

Charles Fry not only scored a century in each innings of a first-class match five times but missed out on doing so by a single run on three other occasions.

COUNTY • SUSSEX

George Street, Sussex's wicketkeeper from 1909 to 1923, was killed in a motorcycle accident aged 34 in 1924.

Both James and John Langridge scored over 2000 first-class runs for Sussex in 1937.

When Sussex played Warwickshire in 1939, they had three sets of brothers in their side: James and John Langridge, Charles and Jack Oakes, and James and Harry Parks.

Albert 'Jack' Holmes managed England's 1938-9 tour of South Africa and was to have captained the 1939-40 tour of India which had to be abandoned.

'Jack' Holmes was chairman of the England Test selection committee from 1946 to 1949, although he never played a Test. He was also a pioneer of mink farming in England.

Sussex have finished bottom of the championship seven times.

Ted Dexter was the first chairman of England's selectors to be paid.

In 1964 Ted Dexter stood as the Conservative candidate for Cardiff South East. He lost to the Labour candidate Jim Callaghan.

Robin Marlar contested the seat of Bolsover in the 1959 General Election and North East Leicester in a 1962 by-election and lost on both occasions.

Harold Heygate is the only batsman to have been dismissed 'timed out' in first-class cricket, while playing for Sussex against Somerset in 1919, and after failing to reach the crease within two minutes of the fall of the previous wicket.

The umpiring decision against Harold Heygate in the above match was a controversial one because Heygate was ill at the time and the match ended in a tie.

COUNTY • SUSSEX

When Sussex scored 278 against Gloucestershire at Eastbourne in 1928, their first six batsmen were dismissed LBW.

Sussex's 321-6 against Warwickshire in 1993 is the highest total by a losing side in the NatWest Trophy final.

Andy Babington's first three wickets for Sussex in 1986 formed a hat-trick.

Jamie Hall set a record for the slowest 50 in a championship match when he took 302 minutes against Surrey at The Oval in 1994.

KS Ranjitsinhji is the only batsman to have scored two first-class centuries on the same day, against Yorkshire at Hove in 1896.

KS Ranjitsinhji scored 180 before lunch for Sussex against Surrey at Hastings in 1902, the highest number of runs before lunch by any batsman in a first-class match in Britain.

The highest sixth wicket partnership in a first-class match in Britain is 428 by Monty Noble and Warwick Armstrong for the Australians against Sussex at Hove in 1902.

Vallance Jupp scored a century and took a hat-trick for Sussex against Essex at Colchester in 1921.

Sussex set a record of 14 wins in the Sunday League in 1982.

Tommy Cook scored 20198 first-class runs at 30 and played centre-forward for England before committing suicide at the age of 48.

COUNTY • WARWICKSHIRE

Warwickshire were founded in 1882 in Coventry and were admitted to the championship in 1895.

Warwickshire were the first county outside the 'Big Six' to win the championship in 1911. They had never previously finished higher than fifth.

Half-way through 1911 Warwickshire were last but one in the championship. At the end of the season Punch celebrated their title win with a cartoon which quoted Shakespeare: 'Warwick, thou art worthy!'

Warwickshire's captain in 1911 was 22 year old Frank Foster. According to Wisden: 'Not since WG Grace in the early days of the Gloucestershire XI has so young a captain been such a match-winning force'.

Frank Foster was the first Warwickshire player to do the double of 1000 runs and 100 wickets in a first-class season, in 1911.

In 1914 Foster made his highest score of 305*. He was injured in a motorcycle accident during World War I and had played his last cricket by the age of 25.

As a left-arm pace bowler Frank Foster was one of the first to bowl 'leg-theory' with a packed legside field, the forerunner of 'Bodyline'.

Dick Lilley was given out 'hit the ball twice' in the match against Yorkshire at Edgbaston in 1897.

Khalid Ibadulla was given out 'obstructing the field' in the match against Hampshire at Coventry in 1963.

Septimus Kinneir carried his bat through both innings against Leicestershire at Leicester in 1907.

Percy Jeeves gave his name to PG Wodehouse's butler. 'I suppose that Jeeves's bowling must have impressed me for I remembered him in 1916 when I was in New York and starting the Jeeves and Bertie saga' wrote Wodehouse.

COUNTY • WARWICKSHIRE

Percy Jeeves, who took 199 first-class wickets at 20 before World War I, was killed in action in 1916.

In 1928 Bob Wyatt became the first Warwickshire batsman to score 2000 runs in a season.

Alan Old, the British Lions fly-half, played one first-class match for Warwickshire in 1969.

Chris Old, the Yorkshire and England fast bowler, played for Warwickshire from 1983 to 1985.

Reverend Jack Parsons played for Warwickshire as a professional before becoming a parson. He represented both the Players and the Gentlemen.

In 1925 Warwickshire, set 392 to win in four hours against Sussex, won by nine wickets.

In 1994 Brian Lara became the first batsman to score seven centuries in eight first-class innings.

Brian Lara shared a county record stand of 322* for the fifth wicket with Keith Piper against Durham in 1994.

Bryan Richardson played 40 first-class matches for Warwickshire in the 1960s before becoming chairman of Coventry FC.

Syd Barnes, widely recognised as the best bowler England has produced, played four matches for Warwickshire between 1894 and 1896 before giving up county cricket.

Hon Freddie Calthorpe, the uncle of Henry Blofeld, captained Warwickshire from 1920 to 1929.

Warwickshire's lowest total is 16 against Kent at Tonbridge in 1913.

COUNTY • WARWICKSHIRE

The first flood-lit Sunday League match in 1997, between Warwickshire and Somerset at Edgbaston, attracted a crowd of 15,000.

Warwickshire went through the 1982 season without a championship win, one of only four counties to do so since World War II.

Tom Dollery became Warwickshire's first professional in 1948.

Warwickshire's match against the New Zealanders in 1958 was halted because of fog.

Keith Piper was fined £500 and suspended for one match in 1997 after failing a drugs test.

Peter Cranmer, who captained Warwickshire from 1938 to 1947, was a rugby centre for England.

William Quaife scored his last first-class century for Warwickshire in 1928 aged 56.

William Quaife made the most first-class appearances, 665, for Warwickshire between 1894 and 1928.

Michael Edmond has played Indoor Cricket for Australia.

Tom Pritchard, a fast bowler from New Zealand, has taken the most first-class hat-tricks for Warwickshire, three.

John Jameson, who was born in Bombay, turned down an approach for India and played four Tests for England.

Abdul Hafeez Kardar, who captained Pakistan in their first 23 Tests, played as an allrounder for Warwickshire from 1948 to 1950.

Dick Lilley was England's first regular wicket keeper, from 1896 to 1909.

Bob Wyatt, who captained in 16 Tests and had his jaw broken on the 1934-5 tour of the West Indies, scored over 39,000 first-class runs and took over 900 first-class wickets.

COUNTY • WARWICKSHIRE

'Tiger' Smith scored 113 runs and made 20 dismissals in Tests for England.

Alan Smith scored 118 runs and made 20 dismissals in Tests for England.

Sam Hargreave, a left-arm spinner, took the best analysis in a first-class match for Warwickshire of 15-76 against Surrey at The Oval in 1903.

Eric Hollies took more first-class wickets, 2323, than he scored first-class runs, 1673.

Mike Smith played rugby union for England as well as cricket.

The second and third Tests between England and West Indies in 1973-4 contained seven players from Warwickshire.

When Warwickshire scored 392-5 against Oxfordshire in the NatWest Trophy in 1984, two of the opposing bowlers conceded more than 100 runs.

Alan Smith gave up wicket keeping and took a hat-trick against Essex at Clacton in 1965.

Warwickshire's bowlers dismissed eight Oxford University batsmen lbw in the second innings of their match in 1980, a record since equalled.

In the Sunday League in 1982 Warwickshire became the first county to chase 300 and win, when they scored 301-6 against Essex.

When Jim Cumbes played for Warwickshire in the Sunday League, he became the first to represent four counties in that competition.

Asif Din's century off 103 balls in 1993 is the fastest in a NatWest Trophy final.

COUNTY • WARWICKSHIRE

Mike Smith scored a century in the Varsity Match in three consecutive years, from 1954 to 1956.

Jack Bannister took 1181 first-class wickets for Warwickshire before becoming a cricket writer and TV commentator.

Warwickshire have finished bottom of the championship three times.

Eric Hollies took all ten wickets in an innings against Nottinghamshire in 1946 without help from his fielders as seven batsmen were bowled and three lbw.

Eric Hollies was the leading first-class wicket taker in England in 1946 with 184 wickets.

Alvin Kallicharran and Brian Lara have made the most first class centuries in a season for Warwickshire, nine.

Keith Piper has made the most dismissals in a first-class match for Warwickshire, 11.

Warwickshire lost the match against Lancashire in which Alvin Kallicharran and Geoff Humpage added 470.

Tom Pritchard, the fast bowler from New Zealand, was granted a benefit after only five years.

Alvin Kallicharran was the only batsman to score 2000 first-class runs in 1982.

Steve Rouse played for Warwickshire as a left-arm pace bowler from 1970 to 1981 before becoming the Edgbaston groundsman.

Derrick Robins, who later raised his own touring sides, played two matches for Warwickshire in 1947 as a wicketkeeper. He played his last first-class match for his own team in 1971.

COUNTY • WORCESTERSHIRE

Worcestershire were founded in 1865 and were admitted to the county championship in 1899.

Worcestershire were outright winners of the Minor Counties championship in the three seasons before 1899.

In 1907 Worcestershire were runners-up to the county champions Nottinghamshire.

In 1919 Worcestershire could not afford to enter a side in the county championship and only played friendly matches.

On their return to the championship in 1920, they won one of their 18 matches.

Seven members of the Foster family played first-class cricket for Worcestershire, four of them in one match.

Worcestershire tied with the South Africans at Worcester in 1901. Worcestershire's last man was stumped with the scores level.

Worcestershire tied with Somerset at Kidderminster in 1939, when there was only one run between the sides in each innings. Worcestershire scored 130 and 142, Somerset 131 and 141.

In 1961 Worcestershire won seven consecutive championship matches for the first time.

Henry Foster captained Worcestershire from 1899 to 1900, from 1902 to 1910 and again in 1913. He was also an England Test selector though he did not play Test cricket.

Besides scoring the first double-century for Worcestershire in 1903, Henry Foster was the English Amateur Rackets champion.

Reggie Foster could only afford the time to play one full season of county cricket, in 1901, when he became the first Worcestershire batsman to score 2000 runs in a first-class season.

COUNTY • WORCESTERSHIRE

Reggie Foster played soccer for Corinthians and England.

No other batsman made 2000 runs in a first-class season for Worcestershire until 1933, when three did so: Doc Gibbons, Maurice Nichol and Cyril Walters.

Maurice Nichol scored a century on his first-class debut for Worcestershire against the West Indians in 1928.

Maurice Nichol was found dead in bed on the second morning of the Essex v Worcestershire match at Chelmsford in 1934, aged 29.

In 1995 Parvaz Mirza was found dead in his Birmingham home, a week after playing a Sunday League match against Glamorgan.

The first Worcestershire batsmen to hit a century in each innings of a first-class match were Reggie and Wilfred Foster, against Hampshire in 1899.

The first four instances of a Worcestershire batsman scoring a century in each innings of a championship match were all recorded against Hampshire.

When Worcestershire were set 131 in 40 minutes by Nottinghamshire in 1951, they knocked off the runs in 12.1 overs and won by nine wickets with five minutes to spare.

The stand of 393 for the fifth wicket by Ted Arnold and William Burns against Warwickshire in 1909, which set a record for the fifth wicket in English first-class cricket, was compiled in only 255 minutes.

Besides scoring 200* in the above match, Ted Arnold also took ten wickets in the match for 114 runs.

Sir George Abell, who played 34 matches for Worcestershire, scored 210 on his debut in the Ranji Trophy for Northern India against the Army at Lahore in 1934-5.

COUNTY • WORCESTERSHIRE

Alfred Archer played one Test for England in South Africa in 1898-9, before playing four matches for Worcestershire. At Haileybury he was not in the first XI.

George Brock took 132 first-class wickets in his debut season in 1930, aged 41.

William Burns scored a century and took a hat-trick for Worcestershire against Gloucestershire at Worcester in 1913.

The Worcestershire wicket keeper Tom Straw is the only batsman who has been given out 'obstructing the field' twice.

Worcestershire have finished bottom of the championship three times.

Fred Root was a leading pioneer of 'leg-theory', bowling inswing to a predominantly legside field.

Reg Perks became Worcestershire's first professional captain in 1955.

In the match against Yorkshire in 1933 Frank Ahl kept wicket until he took his pads off and bowled four batsmen.

John Inchmore scored 30 in five minutes against Gloucestershire at Cheltenham in 1973.

When Worcestershire's captain Norman Gifford declared at 146-6 in reply to Northamptonshire's 294 at Worcester in 1979, he had forgotten that it was a two-day match and the follow-on was 100, not 150.

Worcestershire's match against Oxford University at Oxford in 1962 was suspended because of bees.

Doc Gibbons scored two not-out centuries in one match in 1939 and was bowled for two ducks in the next.

In 1971 Worcestershire took the Sunday League title from Essex by virtue of faster run-rate. The difference was 0.003 per over.

COUNTY • WORCESTERSHIRE

Although they won the Sunday League in 1971, Worcestershire hit the fewest sixes in the League in that season, only 12.

George Simpson-Hayward took 68 first-class wickets with lobs in 1908, and was the last lob bowler to have any success in a Test series, taking 23 wickets at 18 runs each in South Africa in 1909-10.

Tom Moody reached 4000 runs in the Sunday League in fewer innings than any other batsman, 100.

Nawab of Pataudi senior scored the most runs in a first-class season for Oxford University, 1307.

Arthur Conway took only 57 wickets at an average of 35 in his first-class career, but against Gloucestershire at Moreton-in-Marsh in 1914 he took 15-87, still the best match analysis for Worcestershire.

Derek Pearson was no-balled for throwing in 1954, twice in 1959, and in 1960.

Keith Aldridge was no-balled for throwing twice in 1959, and in 1960.

Tom Moody scored 160 on his Worcestershire debut in the Sunday League against Kent in 1991.

Bob Carter scored 317 first-class runs for Worcestershire and took 521 first-class wickets.

Ted Arnold took a wicket with his first ball in Test cricket in 1903-4. Two other Worcestershire bowlers have done so for England, more than any other county.

John Cuffe, an Australian professional who did the double of 1000 runs and 100 wickets for Worcestershire in 1911, drowned himself aged 50.

Glenn Turner's 141 against Glamorgan in 1977 was scored out of a total of 169 all out, the highest proportion by any batsman in a first-class innings (83.4%)

Graeme Hick scored 645 runs without being dismissed in 1990, a record for English first-class cricket.

COUNTY • WORCESTERSHIRE

Doc Gibbons scored the first two centuries of his first-class career before lunch in 1928.

Reverend Reginald Moss made his first-class debut for Worcestershire in 1925 aged 57. His previous first-class match had been for Liverpool and District against the Australians in 1893.

Steve Perryman did not score a run in his eight first-class innings in 1982.

Hon. Charles Lyttelton, later Viscount Cobham, who played for Worcestershire from 1932 to 1939, toured New Zealand with MCC in 1935-6 and later returned as Governor General.

Jack Flavell took the second first-class hat-trick of lbws against Lancashire in 1963.

Robert Burrows, a fast bowler, sent a bail 67 yards and six inches when bowling for Worcestershire against Lancashire in 1911.

In 1901 Robert Burrows sent a bail 64 yards and six inches when bowling Archie MacLaren.

Three generations of the Fosters have played for Worcestershire, the descendants of a master at Malvern College.

In 1961 Jack Flavell, Len Coldwell, Norman Gifford and Martin Horton all took over 100 first-class wickets. It was the first time that any county had achieved this feat twice.

COUNTY • YORKSHIRE

The record number of championship wins in a season is 25 by Yorkshire in 1923, out of 32 matches.

The longest unbeaten run in the championship is 70 matches by Yorkshire from August 1924 to May 1927.

When Yorkshire scored 887 against Warwickshire at Edgbaston in 1896, it was the first time four batsmen had scored centuries in the same first-class innings.

Tom Armitage, an allrounder, bowled lobs for England in the first Test against Australia in 1876-7 to much amusement. In the previous summer he had taken 13-46 for Yorkshire against Surrey.

Arthur Booth headed the national first-class bowling averages in 1946 with 111 wickets at 11.61, but took only 131 wickets in his whole first-class career.

Major Booth, who took 603 first-class wickets at 19, was killed in action in 1916 aged 29.

The highest number of catches in a first-class season by any wicket keeper is 96 by Jimmy Binks in 1960.

Vic Wilson became Yorkshire's first professional captain of the twentieth century in 1960.

In June 1949, when he set a record for the most runs in June, Len Hutton also made a pair against Worcestershire.

Honourable Stanley Jackson, who captained England but not Yorkshire, became Governor of Bengal.

John Wilson, the brother-in-law of Stanley Jackson, was a steeple chase jockey who won the Grand National on Double Chance in 1925.

COUNTY • YORKSHIRE

Horace Fisher took a hat-trick of lbws against Somerset at Sheffield in 1932.

Cecil Tyson scored his first and only championship century on his debut against Hampshire in 1921.

When England played Australia at Melbourne in 1920-1, both wicket keepers – Arthur Dolphin and Hanson Carter – were Yorkshire-born.

Yorkshire's match against Kent at Harrogate in 1904 had to be abandoned on the second day because the pitch had been tampered with during the night.

Captain Ronnie Stanyforth captained England in South Africa in 1927-8 before he had played any county cricket.

Paul Jarvis made his championship debut against Sussex at Hove aged 16.

The highest score made against Yorkshire is 318* by WG Grace.

Yorkshire's lowest first-class total is 23 against Hampshire at Middlesbrough in 1965.

Yorkshire were undefeated in the championship in 1900, 1908, 1925, 1926 and 1928.

Of Geoff Boycott's 151 first-class centuries, 68 were unbeaten, the most by any batsman.

Bill Bowes took more first-class wickets, 1638, than he scored runs, 1529.

The cricket journalist Michael Carey defined a Yorkshireman as someone who was born within sound of Bill Bowes.

COUNTY • YORKSHIRE

Louis Hall has carried his bat through a first-class innings most times for Yorkshire, 14.

David Bairstow is the only Yorkshire wicketkeeper to have scored 10,000 runs and made 1000 dismissals in first-class cricket.

In the match against Derbyshire at Scarborough in 1982 David Bairstow set the record for the most dismissals in a first-class innings and match – 7 and 11 – by a Yorkshire wicketkeeper.

Wilfred Rhodes has made the most first-class appearances for Yorkshire, 883.

John Tunnicliffe has taken more catches than any other fielder for Yorkshire other than wicketkeepers, 665.

The best analysis in a first-class match for Yorkshire is 17-91 by Hedley Verity against Essex at Leyton in 1933.

Hedley Verity was killed in action in Italy during World War II aged 38.

The Hutton who scored a 50 on his Test debut was Richard, against Pakistan at Lord's in 1971. Len Hutton scored 0 and 1.

Yorkshire dismissed Middlesex for 23 at Headingley in the Sunday League in 1974.

Only once have Yorkshire finished bottom of the county championship.

Lord Hawke was not born in Yorkshire but in Lincolnshire, at Gainsborough.

William Keighley was the most recent Yorkshire player not to have been born in Yorkshire, before Richard Stemp. He was born in Nice, France.

COUNTY • YORKSHIRE

Jack Hobbs scored the most first-class centuries against Yorkshire, 11.

Hedley Verity took nine wickets in a first-class innings seven times for Yorkshire.

Although Yorkshire were dismissed for 46 in their first innings by Nottinghamshire at Sheffield in 1888, they still won by ten wickets.

Yorkshire's largest first-class victory was by an innings and 397 runs against Northamptonshire at Harrogate in 1921.

Percy Holmes and Herbert Sutcliffe put on a century opening partnership for Yorkshire on 69 occasions, and 74 times in all first-class cricket.

In 1902 at Headingley Yorkshire dismissed the Australians for 23.

George Deyes scored only three runs in 14 first-class innings in 1907.

Phil Robinson faced only one ball in being dismissed for a pair against Kent in 1988. In the first innings he was run out without facing a ball.

On 2 February 1974 Chris and Alan Old played for England at cricket and rugby respectively.

Graham Stevenson scored 115* at number 11 against Warwickshire in 1982.

Six Yorkshire players represented England in 1935 – and Yorkshire still won the championship.

The highest aggregate in a first-class debut season is 1839 by Herbert Sutcliffe in 1919.

COUNTY • YORKSHIRE

Wilfred Rhodes has taken the most wickets in a first-class debut season, 154.

George Hirst did the double of 1000 runs and 100 wickets in 11 consecutive first-class seasons, a record.

The highest score for Yorkshire is 341 by George Hirst against Leicestershire at Leicester in 1905.

The best analysis in a first-class innings against Yorkshire is 10-37 by Clarrie Grimmett for the Australians at Sheffield in 1930.

Yorkshire were runners-up in the county championship four times in the 1950s.

In 1959 Yorkshire recovered the title when they defeated Sussex at Hove by knocking off 215 in 105 minutes.

Geoff Boycott's 146 against Surrey in 1965 remains the highest score in a Gillette/NatWest final.

The left-arm spinner Ted Peate took 8-5 against Surrey at Holbeck in 1883.

Maurice Leyland was one of the first left-arm spinners to bowl chinamen.

The last Yorkshire bowler to be the leading wicket taker in an English first-class season was Geoff Cope, who took 93 first-class wickets in 1976.

The only bowler to take four wickets in four balls for Yorkshire was Alonzo Drake, against Derbyshire at Chesterfield in 1914.

Darren Gough took a wicket with his sixth ball in Tests and ODIs, both against New Zealand in 1994.

Gavin Hamilton played for Scotland, for whom he was qualified by birth, in 1998.

The best analysis for Yorkshire in the Sunday League is 7-15 by Richard Hutton against Worcestershire at Headingley in 1969.

EXTRAS

EXTRAS • GROUNDS

1   For what sporting purpose was the County Ground at Derby originally laid out?

2   Which ground did Essex use as its headquarters until 1933?

3   Where in Cardiff is the Glamorgan County Ground?

4   On which Public School Ground have Gloucestershire played Championship matches since 1872?

5   Where is Hampshire's United Services Ground situated?

6   What unique feature, for main county grounds, does the St Lawrence Ground at Canterbury possess?

7   Name the county ground at Liverpool?

8   Prom 1946 to 1965 which county cricket headquarters was owned by the local eduction authority?

9   Where did Middlesex play their home matches in the seasons just prior to their move to Lord's.

10 At which school ground have Northants staged regular Championship matches?

11 Where, apart from Trent Bridge, did Notts play Championship cricket in 1998?

12 On which Devon ground was a meeting held to form the present Somerset CCC?

13 To whom are the main gates at Kennington Oval dedicated?

14 Name the present County Ground in Hove?

15 Who was mainly responsible for modernising the Edgbaston Ground in the 1940s and 1950s?

1 Horse Racing. 2 Leyton. 3 Sophia Gardens. 4 Cheltenham. 5 Portsmouth.
6 There is a tree in the playing area. 7 Aigburth. 8 Grace Road, Leicester. 9 Prince's.
10 Wellingborough. 11 Central Avenue, Worksop. 12 Sidmouth. 13 Sir Jack Hobbs.
14 Eaton Road. 15 Leslie Deakins.

Quiz 2

EXTRAS • GROUNDS

1   Which Worcestershire County Ground was abandoned for County matches due to subsidence?

2   Which Yorkshire Test ground is no longer used for cricket?

3   Who was the groundsman mainly responsible for laying out Durham's new ground?

4   There have been two 'Lord's Grounds' used for Test cricket, one is in London, where is the other?

5   Where do the New Zealand side, Canterbury, play their principal matches?

6   On what ground did Gary Sobers hit six sixes in one over?

7   Name the ground used for county cricket in Chesterfield?

8   Which was the only seaside ground Essex used for Championship matches in 1998?

9   What sport is played on Glamorgan's original main ground in Cardiff?

10   Where is Hampshire's Dean Park ground situated?

11   Which Kent ground is famous for its rhododendrons?

12   What or whom connects the pavilion at Old Trafford with that at Kennington Oval?

13   How many post-1946 grounds have staged Championship matches in Loughborough?

14   Where is 'The Walker Cricket Ground'?

15   What fundamental change has taken place in the Northampton County Ground during the 1990s?

1 Dudley. 2 Bramall Lane. 3 T Flintoft. 4 Queen's Park. 5 Lancaster Park, Christchurch.
6 St Helens, Swansea. 7 Queens Park. 8 Southend-on-Sea. 9 Rugby – Cardiff Arms Park.
10 Bournemouth. 11 Tunbridge Wells. 12 F Muirhead, the architect for both. 13 Three.
14 Southgate. 15 Northampton Town PC have moved out.

EXTRAS • GROUNDS

1   After which batsman was the famous elm tree at Trent Bridge named?

2   Who are the freehold owners of Kennington Oval?

3   How many grounds used for major county matches preceded the present ground in Brighton & Hove?

4   Which cricketer, who played more than 440 matches for Warwickshire, was born at the Edgbaston Ground?

5   Which river often floods the Worcester County Ground?

6   What sport apart from cricket is regularly played at Headingley?

7   Which county has played Championship cricket at Grangefield Road in the 1990s?

8   On which ground did South Africa play its first Test?

9   Where was the venue for the last County Championship match, where the whole game was complete on the first day?

10 At which border town did Derbyshire oppose Notts in most season between 1925 and 1994?

11 In which town has Essex used two separate venues for cricket since 1946?

12 Where on the North Wales coast have Glamorgan staged Championship games in the 1990s?

13 Which engineering firm's ground have Gloucestershire used in Gloucester?

14 Where's May's Bounty?

15 Where did Kent establish their first nursery for young players?

EXTRAS • GROUNDS

1   Which ground did Lancashire use for Championship games for the first time in 1985?

2   Where is or was Snibston Colliery Ground?

3   Where are Brearley Close and Gatting Way?

4   Three sports other than cricket were played on the Northampton ground, one was soccer, name the other two?

5   After whom are the two new indoor net areas at Trent Bridge named?

6   Which county has played Championship matches at Clarence Park in recent years?

7   Who was the Surrey Poet – he hawked his cricket verses round the Oval?

8   Where's the Dripping Pan?

9   Which ground has the SF Barnes' Gate?

10   Which ground is entered from Offmoor Lane?

11   Which 1980s Yorkshire home ground used to be in Derbyshire?

12   Where was the first ever Test Match in England played?

13   Three grounds in Bombay have been used for Test Matches, Wankhede and Brabourne are two, name the third?

14   Where is the Queen's Park Oval Test Ground?

15   Which Test ground is no longer in a Test playing country?

15 Dacca Stadium, now in Bangladesh.
12 Kennington Oval. 13 Gymkhana Ground. 14 Port of Spain, Trinidad.
8 Lewes Cricket Ground. 9 Edgbaston. 10 Kidderminster. 11 Abbeydale Park, Sheffield.
5 Sir Richard Hadlee and Sir Garfield Sobers. 6 Somerset. 7 Albert Craig.
1 Lytham. 2 Coalville. 3 Adjacent to the Uxbridge ground. 4 Tennis and bowls.

EXTRAS • GROUNDS

1   Name the former head groundsman at Derby who now holds the same post at Trent Bridge?

2   Which is Essex's present headquarters ground?

3   Which ground in Aberystwyth have Glamorgan used in the 1990s?

4   Gloucestershire have used two Wiltshire Grounds for Limited Overs matches in the 1990s, which are they?

5   On which ground is the Phil Mead stand?

6   Which town possesses the Crabble Ground?

7   Which ground was dropped from the county circuit because it staged a benefit match for Boycott and Botham?

8   Name Leicestershire's inter-war headquarters?

9   Which first-class county have staged matches at Tring?

10 Which family has worked on the ground at Trent Bridge since 1920 continuously until the present day?

11 Past which current Championship ground does the River Avon flow?

12 Where is the Ken Barrington Centre?

13 On which ground did Sussex stage Championship matches for the first time in the 1990s?

14 Where is the Courtaulds Ground, which has been used for Championship matches since 1945?

15 Which first-class county has played matches on Hereford Racecourse?

Quiz 6

EXTRAS • GROUNDS

1. Where is Acklam Park?

2. What sport is now played on the former Test Ground at Ellis Park, Johannesburg?

3. Where is the Woolloongabba Test Ground?

4. Which former Indian Test Ground is now partially the course of a river?

5. On what English county ground did first-class tourists traditionally play their initial three-day game?

6. Which county have played Sunday League matches at Knypersley?

7. In which Essex town is Valentine's Park?

8. Three Glamorgan venues have staged more than 20 Sunday League games, Cardiff and Swansea are two, where's the third?

9. Which ground was very famous for its 5.5 ton heavy roller?

10. Which Kent seaside town used to have a cricket festival, which included Gentlemen v Players matches?

11. Adjacent to which ground was Warwick Road railway station?

12. At which venue outside the county have Leicestershire played home Championship games?

13. After whom were the two stands, which were officially opened at Lord's in May 1991, named?

14. Which county use Wardown Park has a home venue for first-class matches?

15. Which of these three pavilions is the oldest, Lord's, Old Trafford or Trent Bridge?

EXTRAS • DATES

1 In which year was the first Wisden Cricketers' Almanack published?

2 When did England first play a Test Match v New Zealand?

3 When was the final match in the Gentlemen v Players series played?

4 In which season did the John player Sunday League commence?

5 Which countries joined the ICC in 1966?

6 Allan Border captained Australia in six Ashes series – between what dates?

7 In what season did Sri Lanka played their first Test?

8 When did Glamorgan join the County Championship?

9 Which county won the Championship most times in the 1980s?

10 In which season was the Sheffield Shield inaugurated?

11 In which year was the feat of scoring 2,000 runs and taking 200 wickets performed by a single individual?

12 Who scored two separate hundreds in a county match and took 11 wickets in 1988?

13 What Test Match in 1956 did Australia play, without any preparation on a matting wicket?

14 When was the Australian Cricket Board of Control set up?

15 What fundamental law concerning the equipment of the game was laid down in 1771 and still holds good?

---

15 Maximum width of a bat shall be four and a quarter inches.
Yorkshire. 12 Franklyn Stephenson Notts v Yorkshire. 13 v Pakistan in Karachi. 14 1905.
8 1921. 9 Both Essex and Middlesex won three titles. 10 1892/93. 11 1906, George Hirst of
5 Bermuda, Denmark, East Africa and Netherlands. 6 1985 to 1993 inclusive. 7 1981/82.
1 1864. 2 January10-13, 1930. 3 September 8-11, 1962 at Scarborough. 4 1969.

Quiz 2

EXTRAS • DATES

1 In which seasons did Don Bradman come to England with the Australian Tourists?

2 When did a cricketer's benefit receipts top £100,000 for the first time?

3 When and by whom was the Benson & Hedges Cup first won?

4 The Birmingham League is reputed to be the oldest in England, in which year did it commence?

5 In which season did the famous 'Bodyline' tour of Australia take place?

6 The Bombay Tournament was for many year the major first-class competition in India, in which season was it last played?

7 In international cricket what is significant about the year 1844?

8 Only one Test Match has been cancelled just a day or two prior to the match. Which match and when?

9 Which national competition involving 256 teams was begun in 1969?

10 When was the year of Compton's knee?

11 Which famous West Indian player was made a Life Peer in 1969?

12 Which county joined the Minor Counties in 1955 and won the title for the first time in 1986?

13 Who were the two Danish cricketers appearing in the County Championship in the 1980s?

14 In which year was the is Deodhar Trophy established?

15 When did MCC cancel their projected tour to South Africa, because the host country objected to the inclusion of Basil d'Oliveira?

DAILY NEWS
COMPTONS
KNEE
LATEST

12 Cumberland. 13 Ole Mortensen and Soren Henriksen. 14 1973/74. 15 1968/69.
Tournament. 10 1950 – Denis Compton's knee injury was reported constantly. 11 Learie Constantine.
8 West Indies v England at Georgetown in 1981 1980/81. 9 National Club Cricket Knock-Out
4 1888. 5 1932/33. 6 1947/48. 7 The first ever international match was staged: Canada v United States.
1 1930, 1934, 1938 and 1948. 2 1980, Jack Simmons received £128,000. 3 1972 by Leicestershire.

EXTRAS • DATES

1 When was the longest Test Match staged?

2 When were 'fielding circles' introduced into English county cricket?

3 Which country played a handful of first-class matches between 1894/95 and 1953/54, but never played first-class games at home?

4 The Final Test of 1953 had two cricketing connotations – first England beat Australia at The Oval, what was the second?

5 What was significant on the night of December 14, 1977?

6 What period do writers referred to as 'The Golden Age' of cricket?

7 Who was born on July 18, 1848?

8 Who was knighted for his services to cricket in 1953?

9 When was the ICC Trophy first staged?

10 What changed concerning the International Cricket Conference in 1965?

11 Between 1910 and 1964 the principal match, Officials v Settlers was played in which country?

12 When did the Lawrence Trophy begin?

13 When was the first major Tournament played in Sharjah?

14 In which year did the Combined Services Team cease to play first-class matches?

15 When was The Cricket Society founded?

EXTRAS • DATES

1 When did Great Britain issue the first postage stamps depicting a cricketer and who was the player?

2 What is significant about Sunday May 15, 1966?

3 Which is the oldest 'wandering' club and when was it founded?

4 Who was the first professional West Indian player to captain an English county?

5 When was over-arm bowling legalised?

6 What basic change occurred for the 1930 England v Australia series of Test Matches?

7 What was triangular about 1912?

8 What was unique about county matches between 1889 and 1899?

9 When did the MCC first send a team to Australia?

10 What new individual batting record was created in 1994?

11 Who made a debut double century in 1997?

12 What did Arthur Fagg achieve in 1938?

13 How many first-class hundreds did Denis Compton hit in 1947.

14 Why was 1928/29 significant in Don Bradman's career?

15 When was The Cricketer magazine founded?

---

1 1973, WG Grace. **2** The first Sunday on which Championship cricket had been played. **3** Zingari in 1845. **4** Garry Sobers of Notts in 1968. **5** 1864 **6** The matches were arranged for four days, instead of three. **7** The first time three sides competed in a Test series in England. **8** Overs consisted of five balls. **9** 1903/04. **10** First score of 500 – by Brian Lara. **11** Michael Powell of Glamorgan. **12** The only player to hit two double hundreds in one match. **13** A record 18. **14** He made the most runs ever recorded in a single Australian season. **15** 1921.

EXTRAS • DATES

1   How does HG Wells link to 1862?

2   What record did WR Hammond achieve in 1928?

3   Why do Dera Ismail Khan try to forget 1964/65?

4   What did SC Ganguly attain at Lord's on June 21/22 1996?

5   Why is the season of 1991/92 important in South African and West Indian cricket?

6   Why do bowlers want to forget 1816?

7   When did the first American cricket team tour England?

8   Who heard what for the first time in 1927?

9   Who in 1947 made both his first-class debut and his England Test debut?

10   Which countries did Ireland play for the first time in 1970?

11   Which present first-class county club was formed in 1882?

12   What in county championship history links 1975, 1996 and 1998?

13   Who won the Sunday League in 1997?

14   What connects the Championship to the NatWest Trophy in 1987?

15   In which season was there a triple tie in the Championship?

---

1 His father was the first first-class bowler to take four wickets in four consecutive balls, in that season. 2 Most catches in a season – 78. 3 They lost by a record innings and 851 runs to Railways. 4 Century on Test debut. 5 The first time the two countries met in a Test Match. 6 Wides were first penalised that year. 7 1884 8 The first running commentary on cricket was broadcast. 9 Kenneth Cranston of Lancashire. 10 Holland and Denmark. 11 Durham. 12 The only times Leics have won the title. 13 Warwickshire. 14 Notts won both titles. 15 1889.

EXTRAS • DATES

1 Which Australian state had a monopoly between 1953/54 and 1961/62?
2 Why was 1947/48 a break with tradition in Australia?
3 What was unusual about Australia's domestic One Day Competition between 1969/70 and 1974/75?
4 Why does the season of 1957/58 stand out in comparison with all the Ranji Trophy seasons between 1955/56 and 1972/73?
5 In which season was the Duleep Trophy instituted?
6 How did the Deodhar Trophy competition change in 1993/94?
7 Which side won both the Ranji Trophy and Wills Trophy in 1996/97?
8 In which season did the Plunket Shield cease to be New Zealand's major first-class trophy?
9 Why did the season of 1978 link three major Test playing countries?
10 How does July 23, 1964 link TW Cartwright and FE Rumsey?
11 In which season did Orange Free State take both major South African Trophies?
12 What links Eastern and Western Province in 1989/90?
13 In what season did Sri Lanka institute a domestic first-class Competition?
14 Who won the Red Stripe Cup in 1996/97?
15 Between 1891/92 and 1938/39 which major West Indian team did not compete in the first-class Tournament?

Currie Cup. **13** 1988/89. **14** Barbados. **15** Jamaica – due to travel problems.
10 They both made their England Test debut that day. **11** 1993/94. **12** They were joint winners of the
9 The principal One Day Trophy in Australia, England and New Zealand was sponsored by Gillette.
to win the title. **5** 1961/62. **6** It was run on a league basis rather than knock-out. **7** Mumbai. **8** 1974/75.
Shield for the first time. **3** New Zealand played in it. **4** It was the only season in which Bombay failed
1 New South Wales won the Sheffield Shield every season. **2** Western Australia won the Sheffield

Quiz 1

EXTRAS • UMPIRES

1   Which Worcestershire bowler lost an arm in the First World War and became the most outstanding umpire of his day?

2   Which county umpire was buried in his umpire's coat and with a cricket ball in his hand?

3   Who umpired himself out of the University team?

4   Name the umpire at the centre of the Gatting incident in Pakistan?

5   Who said that a batsman on going to the crease should ask after the health of the umpire's father and promise the umpire a brace of rabbits?

6   Who umpired in the First Test match?

7   Which umpire no balled Geoff Griffin eleven times at Lord's in 1960?

8   Who said when given out, 'That was either a very ignorant decision or a downright swindle'. The umpire replied, 'A bit of both'.

9   Which umpire ruled CP Foley out for picking up a bails in a Championship match?

10 Who was forced to retire from Test Match umpiring when his son began to play for England?

11 Which umpire refused to officiate on the sixth day of the West Indies v Australia match at Kingston in 1978 – the match was therefore drawn?

12 Which umpires took exception to Gavasker's language in the Pakistan v India Test at Faisalabad in October 1978?

13 Which umpire announced his retirement at Perth in December 1978?

14 Which umpire has officiated in most Tests?

15 Who no-balled David Gower for throwing in a Test on August 12, 1986.

EXTRAS • UMPIRES

1   Who was the first Englishman to umpire a Test in New Zealand?

2   Name the first Test cricketer to umpire a Test?

3   Which player, who was actually playing in a Test, deputised as umpire, when the latter took umbrage?

4   Replying to 'How's That?' which umpire said: 'I'll make a note of it and let you know tomorrow morning'?

5   Which umpire invariably whipped off the bails at the close of play, saying, 'And that concludes the entertainment for the day, Gentlemen'?

6   Who answered a complaint about the light with 'You can see the moon, how far do you want to see?

7   Which umpire was mainly responsible for stamping out 'throwing' during the 1890s epidemic.

8   Which Test umpire possessed the christian names Valentine Adolphus?

9   Which Test umpire was 'related' to Sherlock Holmes?

10 Which Kent cricketer later played for South Africa and went on to umpire in Tests in South Africa?

11 At Lord's in 1909 both umpires, John Moss and Charles Dench, in the Test v Australia, came from the same county, which one?

12 Which Australian umpire was forced to retire due to failing sight and set up a successful bat manufacturing business?

13 In which year did the Laws of Cricket first lay down that a team should, usually, be composed of 11 men?

14 Who was ordered off the field for refusing to bowl during the Derbyshire v Yorkshire game at Chesterfield in 1973?

---

1 Charlie Elliott in 1971. 2 Jim Lillywhite, who was England's first captain. 3 Tom Garrett.
4 Bob Thoms. 5 Alec Skelding. 6 Arthur Jepson. 7 Jim Phillips. 8 VA Titchmarsh.
9 Tom Mycroft – it is said that Conan Doyle named Sherlock's brother after him.
10 Frank Hearne. 11 Nottinghamshire. 12 Bob Crockett. 13 1884 14 Alan Ward.

EXTRAS • UMPIRES

1 Which famous Indian batsman in 1944/5 decided to retire when he had scored 201* and therefore is shown as 'retired out'?

2 What is the correct weight of a cricket ball?

3 In 1978 Malcolm Nash hit a ball which lodged in the visor of the helmet worn by the short leg fielder. What did the umpire rule?

4 Len Braund was no-balled for overstepping the crease, but never released the ball. Did the umpire's call of No-ball stand?

5 Sunil Gavaskar playing for Bombay at Bangalore batted alternately left and right handed. Was his action illegal?

6 What caused James Allen to be no-balled in the Kent v Leics match of 1957? He had not overstepped the crease and his bowling action was entirely legal.

7 Spectators often see batsmen picking up the ball to throw it back to the bowler. If the fielding side appeal, is the batsman out?

8 Tom Pugh ducked low to a full toss from David Larter and was hit on the head. The bowler appealed for leg before wicket was the batsman out?

9 How many runs are added if the fieldsman stops the ball with his cap?

10 After which season were 12-a-side and two-day matches ruled not first-class?

11 Which English current umpire played for Hants, Lancs & Surrey?

12 Which former Test selector was a county umpire in the 1990s?

13 Who was chiefly responsible for the 1980 Code of Laws?

14 Who was the first player to be out 'obstructed field' in English first-class cricket?

15 Which umpire's autobiography was called 'How's That'?

1 Vijay Merchant. 2 Between 5½ and 5¾ ozs. 3 Dead ball. 4 Yes, the MCC ruled that it should be counted as a no-ball. 5 No, but the Indian Board of Control condemned it as a bad example to the young. 6 Too many fielders on the leg-side. 7 Technically yes, but the rule is rarely applied. 8 Yes – unfortunately he had his jaw broken as well. 9 Five. 10 1946. 11 Trevor Jesty. 12 Jack Bond. 13 Billy Griffith. 14 Khalid Ibadulla. 15 Frank Chester.

Quiz 1

EXTRAS • WHO SAID WHAT?

1   Our game has fallen victim to a load of fitness claptrap, theatrical gobbledy-gook and nannying psycho-babble.

2   Hutton was never dull. His bat was part of his nervous system. His play was sculptured.

3   Some decisions were so arbitrary that it was more like watching Russian roulette.

4   All that Jackson did on the cricket field he did so easily that it seemed to be the only thing to do.

5   Jack Russell can wind you up, but you get to the point where you want to take him round the back of the pavilion and slap him.

6   What will become of him? Oh God of cricket, let it be good, for he has given much to your game.

7   A day's cricket is a long time and you can go through periods where you can get lost and bored.

8   He combines an Oriental calm with an Oriental swiftness – the stillness of the panther with the suddenness of its spring.

9   People have lost the art of watching cricket properly.

10   If ever there was a complete cricketer, it was Wilfred Rhodes, batsman, bowler, fielder and strategist.

11   A glorious upstanding batsman of free-flowing beauty of execution.

12   I always feel as though I am stepping into history.

13   Australians will not tolerate class distinction in sport.

14   Oh why don't you take your bra off.

15   Joined together in cricket's manly toil.

1 Tony Lewis. 2 Harold Pinto. 3 Ian Woolridge on Man of the Match Awards in 1998.
4 Edward Sewell on FS Jackson. 5 Adam Hollioake. 6 Robin Marlar on Derek Randall.
7 Chris Lewis. 8 AG Gardiner on Ranjitsinhji. 9 Martin Henderson. 10 AA Thomson.
11 Ronald Mason on Frank Woolley. 12 JM Kilburn at Lord's. 13 Jack Fingleton.
14 Adam Hollioake on Shane Warne. 15 Lord Byron.

Quiz 2

EXTRAS • WHO SAID WHAT?

1   When you have just lost the Ashes is no time to pick a bone with opposing spectators.

2   The only fellow I've met who fell in love with himself at an early age and has remained faithful ever since.

3   Gone for ever are the days when we and Australia thought that we were the only people who could really play cricket.

4   Players will appeal for almost anything... they think that if they can put sufficient pressure on the umpire he may break.

5   I felt that if I put my head up I would be told I was sticking my neck out, and if I looked down, I would be accused of sulking.

6   Lord's cricket, cricket straight from Debrett.

7   Cricket is certainly a very good and wholesome exercise, yet it may be abused if either great or little people make it their business.

8   Bailey awoke from an apparent coma to strike a boundary.

9   David Lloyd. Now there's a name. When I first heard it mooted as the answer to England's woeful fortunes, I thought, 'Good, that's just what we want, a tycoon tennis player as coach.'

10 In Victor Trumper we have seen the very poetry and heard the deep and wonderful music of batsmanship.

11 Verity counted cricket both a privilege and an obligation and bowling a proper subject for serious study.

12 If Geoff Lawson was once a thoroughbred among fast bowlers, it is now time for him to be turned into glue.

13 I've got to lay a good deal of blame at the feet of my old adversary, Ray Illingworth. An awful lot of the mess we're in comes buck to his legacy.

14 Adams' action is like stealing hubcaps off a moving vehicle.

15 It's like starting Tesco all over again. We had a great vision of changing this cheap and cheerful company into something great, and we did.

---

1 Alan Gibson. 2 Dennis Lillee on Geoff Boycott. 3 Pelham Warner in 1951. 4 Steve Bucknor.
5 Adam Parore. 6 Neville Cardus in 1929. 7 Gentleman's Magazine in 1743. 8 PG Wodehouse on
Trevor Bailey. 9 Ingrid Pitt – actress 1996. 10 Albert Knight. 11 JM Kilburn. 12 Sydd Berry 1986.
13 Ian Botham, on being appointed England's technical advisor. 14 Description of South African
Paul Adams. 15 Lord MacLaurin, on his appointment as ECB Chairman.

EXTRAS • WHO SAID WHAT?

1 Atherton leads England's Rearguard action from the Front.

2 In 10 years of being married to Robin Smith, I have not made a habit of writing to the Chairman of the England Selectors.

3 He walked to the wicket like a free man, one going out to a hard, but agreeable task.

4 Nobody was ever bored by what Frank Woolley did or said on a cricket field.

5 I have my opinion and will make it known to the authorities, That is as far as I will go. They have an off-spinner with an unorthodox action, let's find someone like him.

6 The better side on the day won, of that there's no doubt, but it's not particularly nice being humiliated by anyone especially Surrey.

7 This year Tendulkar has been the batsman nobody wanted to bowl at. He took Shane Warne apart in India, which illustrates his genius.

8 Bumble popped for a pee and we agreed Graham should be in. David was relieved.

9 The wicket didn't really do too much, and when it did, it did too much.

10 He loved his cricket with all his heart and soul. He did everything spontaneously and wholeheartedly and he seemed to call to us to come and play with him.

11 He employs his face also to add to the dismay his approach is calculated to inspire.

12 There's not much you can do about Botham in that mood, It might have been a decent game without him.

13 Tufnell did not find India's shortage of creature comforts to his liking, fairly early on, having done the elephants and seen the beggars, he'd rather like to go home.

14 When I started playing Test cricket, my aim was not to make a fool of myself.

15 Border was facing a four-paced prong attack.

---

1 Headline in Daily Telegraph. 2 Mrs Smith – having written to David Graveney. 3 RC Robertson-Glasgow on Cyril Walters 2. 4 CS Marriott. 5 Gus Fraser on M Muralitharan. 6 Matthew Fleming on losing the B&H Final in 1997. 7 Ted Dexter in 1998. 8 Ray Illingworth – David Lloyd leaves the room when his son is chosen for England. 9 Mike Gatting in Perth 1986. 10 Margaret Hughes on Patsy Hendren. 11 Archie MacLaren on Jack Gregory. 12 Allan Border, when England beat Australia at Melbourne in 1987. 13 Martin Johnson, when Tufnell toured India. 14 Sunil Gavaskar. 15 Dave Renneberg.

EXTRAS • WHO SAID WHAT?

1. Perhaps Harris was a bit of a dictator, but he was eminently just and fair.

2. May, I should say, is a cavalier batsman and a roundhead captain.

3. Gatting, caught rumour, bowled hypocrisy 0.

4. That shot's going only three halves of the way to the boundary.

5. The Imran Khans looked as though they had dropped in from Planet Vogue.

6. Gough went, but Gus stayed. Dear loyal big Gus. He bloody well did it.

7. This series could be to cricket's box office what Attack of the Killer Tomatoes was to the cinema industry.

8. I don't like fudged issues... and I've never been one to say something simply to have an easy life.

9. Masculine as Tarzan, he plays lustily.

10. He was far better known by sight than any man in England.

11. Contrary to all belief, popular and learned, Constantine the magician is the product of tradition and training.

12. A captain who makes no allowance for mistakes and is for ever grumbling discourages effort and honest endeavour.

13. I was worried someone would be killed out there. The pitch is not worthy of international cricket. It's a disgrace.

14. The West Indies batting lacked character, heart and quality. Even the high fives are low threes these days.

15. The flash of fire in his eyes was never extinguished. He always believed in his fate and his fate was to play for England.

EXTRAS • ENGLAND OVERSEAS

1 Which was the destination of first English side to travel overseas?

2 How many times did England tour Australia before going on the first Test tour?

3 Who captained the first England 'rebel' team to South Africa?

4 Who topped the first-class batting table for England's 1978/9 tour to Australia?

5 Who hit over 1,000 first-class runs on the 1973/4 visit to West Indies?

6 How many matches did the English side to West Indies in 1947/8 win?

7 Which was the first English team to fly overseas?

8 Who led the 1924/5 team to Australia?

9 In which season did two English sides tour and both played Test Matches?

10 Ray Illingworth, then with Leics, led the 1970/1 team to Australia, name the three Yorkshire players who went with him?

11 Who was top of both the batting and bowling averages on the 1963/4 tour to India?

12 To which destination did Denis Compton lead a side in 1963/4?

13 Which county side toured Bermuda, playing 9 matches, in 1962?

14 Why was Mike Smith the third choice to lead the team to South Africa in 1964/5?

Quiz 2

EXTRAS • ENGLAND OVERSEAS

1   Which was the first English side to fly by jet to Australia?

2   On which tour were Geoff Boycott and Ken Barrington replaced by Colin Milburn and Robin Hobbs prior to travelling?

3   In which season did two rival English sides tour Australia?

4   What fixture was played in place of the Third Test during the 1886/7 English tour to Australia?

5   Who managed the 1962/3 English tour to Australia?

6   Which side did Dennis Silk captain overseas in 1960/1?

7   Which county went round the world in 1964/5 and where was their final match?

8   Which young Surrey bowler flew out to Australia in 1970/1 to replace the injured Alan Ward?

9   What English side went out to Jamaica to mark the 75th anniversary of the Kingston Cricket Club?

10 Why did Denis Compton decline an invitation to tour South Africa in 1938/9?

11 On which tour was Bob Wyatt's 162 the highest individual innings in first-class matches?

12 Who financed private tours from England to Ceylon, New Zealand and West Indies in the 1930s?

13 Who was the reserve wicketkeeper on the tour to West Indies in 1934/5?

14 When did the first English side tour India?

1 1965/6 – they had a stopover in Colombo. 2 1968/9 to Pakistan. 3 1887/8. 4 Smokers v Non-Smokers. 5 Duke of Norfolk. 6 The MCC team to New Zealand. 7 Worcestershire ended in Hollywood. 8 Bob Willis. 9 Combined Oxford and Cambridge in 1938/9. 10 Because of his commitments to Arsenal FC. 11 Sir TEW Brinckman's Tour to South America in 1937/8. 12 Sir Julien Cahn. 13 Bill Farrimond. 14 1889/9.

EXTRAS • ENGLAND OVERSEAS

1 In 1991/2 England went on tour and returned home undefeated, which country did they visit?

2 Who managed the ill-fated England tour to South Africa in 1995/6 – only one victory in 11 first-class matches?

3 Which English Test playing side to Australia 'forgot' to take a specialist wicketkeeper?

4 MCC had arranged to tour Uganda, Zambia and Kenya in 1969/70, where did they end up?

5 Which members of the 1946/7 team to Australia did not play in any Tests?

6 Which batsman captained the side to India and Pakistan in 1951/2?

7 On which tour did Frank Tyson and Brian Statham dominate the England attack?

8 On what tour did Yorkshire refuse to allow Wilfred Rhodes and George Hirst to go?

9 Who topped the first-class batting averages for the 1929/30 tour to Australia and New Zealand?

10 Which famous non-Yorkshireman hit the highest score for Yorkshire in the final match of their 1964 tour to North America?

11 For which tour was Colin Cowdrey appointed captain, withdrew due to injury and was then flown out as a late reinforcement?

12 Where did WG Grace hit the highest individual innings in each of the first three matches by the tourists?

13 Who led the first English side to West Indies?

14 What tour featured a train crash and a plague of locusts?

EXTRAS • FROM THE LIBRARY

1   For which county did John Wisden, the founder of Wisden's Cricketers' Almanack play most of his cricket?

2   Under what nom de plume did AW Pullin write cricket books?

3   Who was the noted cricket historian who wrote the history of Northamptonshire CCC in 1959?

4   Which wicketkeeper's story is told in the book entitled, 'Behind The Stumps'?

5   In which year was the annual 'Indian Cricket' first published?

6   Who was the England cricket captain who became the founding Editor of 'The Cricketer' magazine in 1921?

7   Which English first-class county boasts the longest running cricket annual?

8   The present run of South African cricket annuals was preceded in 1950/1 by a single issue of 'The South African Cricket Almanac', edited by whom?

9   Neville Cardus began is career as a cricketing journalist with which daily morning newspaper?

10 Which famous author founded his own cricket team and for some years arranged matches against the Artists CC?

11 What was the title of the short story written by Conan Doyle and featuring a slow bowler?

12 Who was the author of 'The Valiant Stumper'?

13 Who wrote the introduction to 'Kings of Cricket'. He was a well known poet?

14 Which cricket magazine did Gordon Ross edited for its entire run – between May 1960 and April 1973?

15 What book links Harry Altham, John Arlott, Desmond Edgar and Roy Webber?

Quiz 2

EXTRAS • FROM THE LIBRARY

1. Who edited the first issue of 'The Journal of The Cricket Society'?
2. Which cricket historian wrote a series of booklets collectively entitled 'Old English Cricket' under the initials HPT?
3. What was the title of Jack Fingleton's book which related the 1948 visit of the Australians to England?
4. Who or what were the subject of the book by Basil Haynes and John Lucas, entitled 'The Trent Bridge Battery'?
5. What is the title of the poem which commences: "There's a breathless hush in the close tonight – ten to make and the match to win."
6. Which MP founded a cricket annual in 1980, which is still published?
7. When was the famous match, fictionalised in 'Tom Brown's Schooldays actually played and how many did the author score?
8. Who was 'Happy Go Johnny' according to the title of his autobiography?
9. What was the subject of 'Sketches at Lord's'?
10. Who was the original editor of the Playfair Cricket Annual – he later became a well-known TV presenter?
11. Who wrote about the Reverend Septimus Jones?
12. Who ran the Epworth Secondhand bookshop in City Road, London it was the leading cricket book shop of its day?
13. Which county's history was published in 1906 and has since been updated with a number of supplements?
14. Whose first book was entitled 'Cricket Caravan'?
15. How did John Arlott title his biography of Freddie Trueman?

1 Irving Rosenwater. 2 PF Thomas. 3 Brightly Fades The Don. 4 The four members of the Gunn Family who played county cricket. 5 Vital Lampada. 6 Iain Sproat. 7 1841 – Thomas Hughes made 29 and U. 8 Johnny Wardle. 9 The lithographs of JC Anderson. 10 Peter West. 11 Alan Miller in 'Close of Play'. 12 Leslie Gutteridge. 13 Kent. 14 Keith Miller and Richard Whitington. 15 Fred.

Quiz 3

EXTRAS • FROM THE LIBRARY

1   Which editor of 'Wisden' was 1warded the MBE for his services to cricket?

2   Whose autobiography is entitled 'A Sort of Cricket Person'. He played three matches for Middlesex.

3   What was the subject of 'The International Series' by John Marder?

4   Why is Ranjitsinhji's book "The Jubilee Book of Cricket" so called?

5   Which cartoonist, who worked for the Daily Mail, annually published books of his cartoons featuring sports, with many on cricket?

6   What was William Caffyn's biography appropriately entitled?

7   Which author, when asked to compose a suitable inscription for the memorial gates at Trent Bridge, replied 'I've been asked to write many books, this is the first time I've been asked to write a gate.'

8   Who wrote an essay in 1903 entitled 'Playground Cricket'. He went on to write a world best seller in the 1920s.

9   The biography 'The Captain's Wife' featured which cricketer's better half?

10 Who played hockey and tennis for England and also wrote a famous description of a country house match, titled Fincham v Besterton?

11 Which first class cricketer wrote mystery novels featuring the female detective, Evelyn Humberthorne?

12 The author of 'England Their England' stood as Liberal candidate in two General Elections, name him?

13 For which newspaper did Roy Webber write statistical pieces?

14 Who wrote 'Three Straight Sticks'?

15 What was the title of Don Mosey's autobiography?

DAILY MAIL CARTOONIST

15 'The Alderman's Tale'.
11 R Gorell Barnes. 12 Archie MacDonell. 13 News Chronicle. 14 Bob Wyatt.
age at the time of writing. 7 EV Lucas. 8 TE Lawrence. 9 CB Fry. 10 JC Masterman.
4 It was published in the jubilee year of Queen Victoria. 5 Tom Webster. 6 71 Not Out – his
1 Norman Preston. 2 EW Swanton. 3 The matches between Canada and United States.

EXTRAS • GROUNDS

The Lords Cricket Ground has moved sites twice since it was first laid out, but each time the turf was dug up and moved to the new site.

The Kennington Oval was commandeered by the military authorities during the Second World War and barbed wire cages were erected over the ground to accommodate Prisoners-of-War. In fact no prisoner ever arrived.

The cricket ground at Melbourne was the venue for the 1956 Olympic Games.

The main gates at Trent Bridge were erected in memory of John Augur Dixon, who captained Notts from 1889 to 1899 and then served on the County Committee until his death.

The ground at Wellington, New Zealand was originally a lake. An earthquake removed most of the water, resulting in a swamp. This is now the site of the Basin Reserve Ground.

The present press box at Old Trafford is called the Neville Cardus Suite and was officially opened by John Arlott in 1987.

During the match between MCC and Cambridge University at Lord's in 1936, a ball being bowled by Jahangir Khan hit and killed a sparrow – TN Pearce was the batsman at the crease.

William Clarke married the landlady of the Trent Bridge Inn in December 1817 11nd in May 1838 laid out the present cricket ground in the field at the rear of the inn.

The Old Trafford Ground is the only one in England where a Test Match has been totally washed out and this happened twice – in 1890 and 1938.

The Derbyshire County Ground at Derby was once the home of Derby County FC and staged one FA Cup Final replay and several FA Cup semi-finals. Derby County FC moved on in 1891.

EXTRAS • GROUNDS

The new Durham County Cricket Club ground – Riverside at Chester-le-Street – was officially opened for the Championship match v Warwickshire on May 18 to 22, 1995. Unfortunately the weather was bitterly cold and only about 4,000 spectators witnessed the historic occasion.

In an effort to secure more members Essex sold their ground at Leyton in 1933 and for the 1934 season played their home matches on six other Essex grounds. They lost 500 members as a result, but gained 1,000 new subscribers.

One of the major cricket grounds in Kent was The Angel Ground at Tonbridge. County cricket ceased there in 1939. In the 1950s it was used by the local soccer club, but that went bankrupt and the ground is now a supermarket carpark.

Because MCC had arranged for Eton to play Harrow at Lord's and the dates which clashed with Middlesex v Notts, the latter game, in 1939, was moved to Kennington Oval.

The cricket ground used by Cambridge University was laid out by FP Fenner in 1846, being described shortly after as perhaps the smoothest ground in England – being in fact too easy and causing too much run-getting.

Thomas Lord, who laid out the famous Lord's Ground in London, was a Yorkshireman, born in Thirsk, who spent much of his youth in Norfolk.

Two early cricket grounds in Sheffield were the New Ground at Darnall and the Hyde Dark Ground. The first is now a cemetery, the second a housing estate.

The first first-class match in Australia was played on the Racecourse at Launceston. The ground was reported as so rough that the umpires had difficulty selecting a suitable place for the pitch. The date of the game was Feb 11 and 12 1851.

The main pavilion on the Saffrons Ground at Eastbourne was destroyed by fire in 1947, rebuilt and again damaged by fire in 1977.

EXTRAS • GROUNDS

The present cricket ground at Arundel Castle was laid out under the instructions of the 15th Duke of Norfolk in 1894-5. The 16th Duke was the manager of the 1962-3 England team to Australia.

The Adelaide Oval has been used for first-class cricket since 1877/78 and for Test Matches since 1884/85.

The final first-class match at Bramall Lane – the home of Sheffield United Football Club – was Yorkshire v Lancashire on August 4, 6 and 7, 1973.

The National Stadium in Karachi staged its first Test Match when Pakistan played India there in 1954/55. At that time games were played on matting wickets, grass wickets being introduced in the 1960s.

Gloucestershire played 96 matches on the Clifton College Ground between 1871 and 1932, since when it has not been used for first-class cricket.

After two overs had been bowled in the Derbys v Yorks match at Chesterfield in 1946, it was discovered that the pitch was two yards too long. The pitch was adjusted and the game restarted.

Heavy rain flooded the dressing rooms at Dewsbury during the Derbyshire v Yorkshire match of 1899, as a result Derbyshire players fielded in their ordinary clothes on the last day.

During the Sheffield v Nottingham match at Darnell in 1822, a temporary stand collapsed. Two spectators were killed and between forty and fifty more or less maimed.

In the match between Glamorgan and Cambridge University at Margam, the British Steel Ground neat Port Talbot, the batsmen appealed against the light due to smoke coming from the furnaces.

EXTRAS • GROUNDS

The principal cricket ground in Leicester used to be at Wharf Street. Apart from cricket it staged pony races, circuses, fireworks displays and even public dinners. The ground disappeared under bricks and mortar in the 1860s.

The only first-class match at Stratford-on-Avon was Warwicks v Oxford University in 1951. It was promoted as part of the 'Festival of Britain.'

A first-class match involving the Australians was once played at Wembley. The game took place in 1896, but the ground was described as totally unsuitable of cricket – the venue was roughly where Wembley Stadium stands today.

The Bournville cricket pavilion, a large Tudor style building with a turret and gable was opened to celebrate the coronation of Edward VII in 1902 and a gift from the Cadbury Chocolate firm. Worcestershire played two first-class matches on the ground shortly before the First World War.

Hampshire have used two grounds on the Isle of Wight for first-class cricket – at Newport and the Plessey Ground at Cowes.

Fire destroyed the pavilion at Llandudno in 1973, just four years after Glamorgan staged their only game there.

The mass produced heavy cast iron roller, so common a feature of cricket grounds, came into general use about 1870.

The National Association of Groundsmen was formed by a meeting of 11 groundsmen in 1934.

Albert Trott was the first batsman to hit a ball over the present pavilion at Lord's, a feat he achieved in 1899.

The first Gentlemen v Players match was played at Lord's in 1806.

It was at Kennington Oval in 1948 that Don Bradman made his farewell Test appearance and was bowled out without scoring.

Warwickshire gave Essex an interest free loan, so that the latter could built a new pavilion at Chelmsford.

EXTRAS • GROUNDS

The Essex match v Derbyshire in 1966 was scheduled to be played at Castle Park, Colchester, but when rain prevented any play on the first two days, the game was transferred to the Garrison Ground, in the same town.

The great feature of Canterbury Cricket Week was the theatrical programme arranged by the Old Stagers.

The two old stands on the County Ground at Hove were usually referred to as the chicken-coop and the cow-shed. They finally disappeared in the 1980s.

The erection of the new brick and tile pavilion on the Taunton Ground in 1981 effectively stopped the batsmen hitting the ball into the adjacent river Tone.

Sophia Gardens in Cardiff, which has been the headquarters of Glemorgan cricket since 1967, is named after the wife of the 2nd Marquess of Bute.

The best known Worcester groundsman was the former Kent cricketer, Fred Hunt. He had a farm next to the Worcester County Ground.

The first time a Sheffield Shield match was played outside a major Australian city was in 1977/78 when Tasmania opposed New South Wales at the Devenport Oval.

The first international match played at Trent Bridge was the soccer game between England and Ireland in the 1896/97 season – England won six nil.

The Warner Stand at Lord's is named after Sir Pelham Warner who was captain of Middlesex and of England and later an important figure in cricket administration.

The present Kennington Oval was originally a market garden.

Essex moved their headquarters from the initial site at Brentwood to the Leyton Cricket Ground, which they bought in 1886 from the Lyttelton Estate for £12,000.

EXTRAS • GROUNDS

When the cricket pavilion at Tunbridge Wells was burnt down in 1913 by the suffragettes, the local club, the Bluemantles who had been formed in 1862, lost much of their archive.

The pavilion at Cheriton Road, Folkestone was designed by the well-known architect, Reginald Pope and paid for by the Earl of Radnor.

The scoreboard on the County Ground at Hove was erected in memory of Prince Ranjitsinhji, who had captained the county and played Test cricket for England.

In 1900 as an experiment a net about 2ft high was erected in place of the boundary rope at Lord's. Apart from balls hit over the net, batsmen had to run every hit, whilst the fielder retrieved the ball from the net. The idea was soon abandoned.

When the ground at Sophia Gardens, Cardiff was set out, the drains were incorrectly laid. One drain ran loross the square, causing a ridge just on a fast bowler's length. After many complaints from the batsmen, the drains were dug up and relaid.

Don Bradman scored a hundred on each of his four visits to Worcester, in 1930, 1934, 1938 and 1948.

The last major game to be staged on the Exhibition Ground at Brisbane was the 1930/31 Test Match between Austr:alia and West Indies. The ground in the years immediately after that continued to be used for rugby and speedway racing.

The original doorstep from WG Grace's home at Downend, Bristol, is now a feature of the pavilion at Wellingborough School.

Packer's World Series Cricket 'Super-Tests' of 1977/78 were banned from using the major Australian cricket grounds and forced to use football stadia.

The ground, which has been used for first-class cricket at Neath, is called the Gnoll, after the estate on which it was laid out.

EXTRAS • GROUNDS

In 1976 Gloucestershire County Cricket Club was in financial straits, so much so that it sold the freehold of the County Ground at Bristol to the Phoenix Assurance Company.

Alfred Oakes was for many years the groundsman at Horsham. Both his sons were born in the house attached to the ground and both sons – Charlie and Jack – went on to play for Sussex.

The County Ground at Dartford was given to the local coundil on condition that no alcohol was sold on it. The Council got over the ban by annexing some land adjoining the cricket area and selling drink from the annex.

Worcester is always the County Ground associated with its fine view of the nearby cathedral. The county ground at Guildford also affords spectators of the city's cathedral.

Gubby Allen the famous England and Middlesex fast bowler was the first player to take all ten wickets in a Championship match at Lord's. In later life he moved into a house which backed on to the ground.

Sir Marcus Samuel, who owned the Mote Ground at Maidstone, had his own pavilion built on the ground in order that he could entertain his friends on county match days. The building was known as the Tabernacle.

At Southend in 1948 the Essex side became the only team to bowl out the touring Australians in a single day. The down side to the record was that the tourists scored a record 721.

The entrance gates at Hove were erected in memory of the notable Sussex and England all-rounder, Maurice Tate.

One of the earliest books devoted solely to the preparation and maintenance of cricket grounds was written by the Somerset cricketer JA Gibbs and published in 1895.

When the pavilion was built at Valentine's Park in Ilford, the owner of the park insisted that the building was erected in such a way that trees hid it from her house.

EXTRAS • GROUNDS

The batting and bowling creases were originally cut out of the turf. It is said that Alfred Shaw, the famous slow bowler was the man who suggested the use of whitewash instead.

The first written reference to the word 'pavilion' in connection with cricket occurred in 1825 when a press notice reported a fire in the 'pavilion' at Lord's.

The Saffrons Cricket Ground at Eastbourne, which is used by Sussex for County matches also possesses a croquet lawn.

Until 1934 all the pitches at Port of Spain's Test ground were of coconut matting; this was then changed to jute matting and not until the 1950s did grass wickets appear.

Administered by a Board of Trustees, the Sydney Cricket Ground, home of the New South Wales Cricket Association, was opened in 1877 and the first first-class game was played there in 1877/78 when Victoria were the opponents.

When the Australians opposed Somerset on the ground at Bath in 1977, the two captains each planted a tree adjacent to the ground to commemorate the match.

In the days when Essex travelled extensively round the county for their home matches, the club used a large lorry, one side of which converted into the scoreboard and scorers' Box.

The first Test Match ever played by New Zealand was staged at Lancaster Park, Christchurch on January 10 to 13, 1930 with England as the opponents.

EXTRAS • DATES

On June 13 and 14, 1825 Sussex played Kent at Ireland's Gardens, Brighton, the game was the genesis of the modern County Championship.

Thomas Lord, the founder of Lord's Cricket Ground died at West Meon Cottage in Hampshire on January 13, 1832.

The County Championship was sponsored by Schweppes from 1977 to 1983.

The earliest known scorecards were printed by T Pratt of Sevenoaks in 1776.

Charles Buchwald recorded the first century ever made in Denmark in 1896.

The Kenya Cricket Association was founded in 1953.

The Redpath Cup, which is awarded to the New Zealand batsman for the best record in first-class cricket was awarded for the first time in 1920/21 to AH Anthony of Auckland.

In 1919 the County Championship matches were arranged to be played over two days, rather than three. The system led to so many draws that in 1920 three day games were re-introduced.

W Rhodes of Yorkshire completed the cricketers 'Double' of 1,000 runs and 100 wickets 16 times between 1903 and 1926.

Tich Freeman of Kent in 1928 became the only bowler in history to capture more than 300 wickets in a first-class season. Because of the reduction in first-class matches this is likely to remain a record.

HJ Knutton created a sensation in June 1902 when he took nine wickets in a single innings against the Australians at Bradford – it was Knutton's second and last first-class match!

EXTRAS • DATES

Paul Hugo in a school game in South Africa in 1931, playing for Smithfield v Alwal North, took nine wickets in nine successive balls.

On February 26, 1930 West Indies beat England for the first time in a Test Match – George Headley hit centuries in both innings for the winners.

The first reference to cricket in the West Indies occurred in 1806 – the St Anne's Club of Barbados met on May 12.

The Barbados Cricket Annual was first issued in 1894/95 – it continued in production until 1913/14.

The first recorded century was made in 1769 by J Minshull for the Duke of Dorset's Team v Wrotham.

Don Bradman broke the individual Test Match record in 1930, when he scored 334 v England at Headingley. 309 of these runs were made in a single day – another Test record.

The Imperial Cricket Conference was instituted in 1909; the original members were MCC, Australia and South Africa.

Don Tallon playing for Queensland v New South Wales at Sydney in January 1939 equalled the first-class wicketkeeping record, when he caught nine and stumped three batsmen.

Garry Sobers scored 1,000 runs in the 1962/63 Australian season. He thus became the first batsman to hit over 1,000 runs in a season in four different countries.

The first five match series of Tests in England was played against Australia in 1899. Four games were drawn, Australia won at Lord's by 10 wickets.

PAVILION

EXTRAS • DATES

The heavy roller was used at Lord's for the first time during the 1870 season.

John Benaud hit a century for Australia v Pakistan at Melbourne in January 1973 – unfortunately before he had a chance to play his innings, the Test selectors had announced that he had been dropped from the next Test.

In 1932 Australia made a tour of the United States and Canada. The games were not considered first-class and the tourists completely overwhelmed the opposition in most of the matches.

For the 1931 season the size of wickets was increased, from 27 inches high and 8 inches wide to 28 inches and 9 inches. The wicket has remained unchanged in size since then.

JB Stollmeyer and Gerry Gomez added 434 for the 3rd wicket during the Trinidad v British Guiana match in 1947. This created a new record partnership for West Indies cricket.

On January 7, 1987 Kapil Dev playing for India v Sri Lanka at Cuttack took his 300th Test wicket, thus completing the 'Double of 300 wickets and 3,000 runs – the second player to record the twin milestone.

ACS Pigott was co-opted into the England team for the Test against New Zealand, commencing at Christchurch on February 3, 1984. It was to prove his only Test appearance for England.

Sir C Aubrey Smith, later a well-known film star, captained England in March 1889 v South Africa. It was his only Test appearance.

Two Surrey players, Laurie Fishlock and Alf Gover, made their England Test debut v India on July 25, 1936.

EXTRAS • DATES

The present pavilion at Lord's had its foundation stone laid by Sir Spencer Ponsonby-Fane on September 17, 1889.

The last season in which matches by Dublin University were ranked first-class was 1926.

When Wales opposed Scotland in a first-class match for the first time, in 1923, the whole of the Welsh side had played first-class cricket for Glamorgan.

There were major revisions to the Laws in 1835, round-arm bowling was legalised, the length of a bat was set down as 38 inches and the follow on law was introduced.

Derbyshire's status as a first-class county ceased at the close of the 1887 season. The county was reinstated in 1894.

After several seasons when batsmen deliberately got themselves out, in order to force their opponents to bat a second time, in 1889 declarations were legalised, but only on the third day of a match.

Salim Malik hit a century on his debut for Pakistan v Sri Lanka at Karachi in March 1982 – he was reportedly the youngest player to achieve this feat.

FE Woolley hit 305* for MCC v Tasmania in January 1912 the first time an Englishman had hit a triple hundred in Australia.

King George V watched Australia play South Africa at Lord's in 1912, the first time a sovereign had attended a Test Match.

Miss F Tumsett hit 1,009 runs and took 159 wickets in Australia in the 1929/30 season, the first lady cricketer to perform the 'Double'.

PJ Allan took all ten wickets in an innings for Queensland v Victoria at Melbourne in 1965/66, only the second bowler to record the feat in Sheffield Shield matches.

EXTRAS • DATES

The first wireless commentary of a cricket match in the world occurred during a Testimonial game in November 1922 for the Test veteran Charles Bannerman.

The first first-class match at Amblecote, Stourbridge took place on June 26 and 27, 1905, Worcestershire playing Leicestershire.

Ian Botham was born in Heswall, Cheshire on November 24, 1955.

Mark Butcher made his debut for England v Australia on June 5, 1997 at Edgbaston.

The record number of runs in a season for Gloucestershire were scored by Walter Hammond in 1933. He hit 2,860 runs for the county that year.

Sir Francis Lacey was the first man to be knighted for his services to cricket. The honour was bestowed on him in 1926, when he retired as Secretary of MCC after 28 years.

Arthur Heygarth who compiled the monumental 'Scores and Biographies in 15 volumes died on May 1, 1903.

The largest recorded victory in a first-class match was by an innings and 851 runs when Railways played Dera Ismail Khan at Lahore in 1964/65.

When Border played Natal at East London in 1959/60 they could only manage an aggregate of 34 in their two innings.

Percy Mills, playing for Gloucestershire v Somerset at Bristol in 1928 returned the remarkable figures of 6-4-6-0-5.

The first player to be killed whilst taking part in a game was Jasper Vinall in 1624. He attempted to catch the ball at the same time as the batsman tried to hit it and was struck on the head with the bat. The game was at Horsted Keynes.

The All England XI founded and run by William Clarke played its first match in Sheffield in August and September 1846.

EXTRAS • DATES

WT Greswell took 232 wickets in Ceylon during the 1911 season. He played for Somerset when home on leave.

Charles Packe captained Leicestershire in 1932, but only played in 21 matches for the county between 1929 and 1934.

Air Chief Marshall Sir Edmund Hudleston, who was Commander Allied Air Forces Central Europe between 1964 and 1967, played in four first-class matches commencing in 1929.

Peter Hill-Wood, subsequently Chairman of Arsenal in the 1980s , played a single first-class match in 1960.

William Gunn, who founded the bat makers Gunn & Moore hit his highest score of 273 for Notts v Derbyshire at Derby in 1901.

Vivian Jenkins, who played rugby for Wales and became a well-known sports commentator, gained a cricket blue at Oxford in 1933 and played 44 matches for Glamorgan between 1931 and 1937.

Eton opposed Westminster in a school match in 1796 – when the Eton boys returned to college, the headmaster flogged the entire eleven.

WG Grace in 1871 was the first batsman to hit 2,000 runs in a season. It was not until 1893 that the feat was repeated and his 1871 average of 78.25 remained a record for almost as long.

In 1881 the first instructional book on cricket written in Spanish was published. It was issued in Buenos Aires.

In 1890 a Parsi Cricket Club was established in Shanghai the first Indian cricket club to be formed outside the subcontinent.

EXTRAS • DATES

The youngest batsman to score a century for Gloucestershire was Mark Alleyne. He was aged 18yrs and 54 days when he hit 116 not out v Sussex at Bristol in 1986.

Harlequins Cricket Club was founded in 1852 – the most famous of its players was probably Douglas Jardine, who upset the Australians by wearing the Harlequins multi-coloured cap during Test Matches.

Abdul Hafeez played Test cricket for India in 1946, then to the confusion of the unwary cricket statistician, reappeared as AH Kardar when playing for Pakistan.

The first known century in Ceylon was scored by Charles Ross for Dikoya v Dimbula at Radella in 1878/79.

The only cricket match to be part of the Olympic Games was played in Paris in 1900, Devon County Wanderers represented England, whilst All-Paris represented France.

The first five wickets in an innings in the ICC Trophy was by Leonard Young for Singapore v Argentina in 1979.

William Ferguson, the famous scorer, first toured with the 1905 Australian side to England. In all he scored 208 Test Matches and retired in 1957.

Fred Spofforth, the tearaway Australia fast bowler took all 20 wickets in a match, whilst playing in Bendigo in 1881/82.

The Somerset Stragglers were founded in 1900 at the suggestion of Edward Spurway, who played his final first class match for Somerset in 1898.

Sidney Kitcat played county cricket for Gloucestershire from 1892 to 1904, but rather oddly he played hockey for Middlesex and Surrey.

EXTRAS • DATES

Edgar Killick hit 206 for Middlesex v Warwickshire at Lord's in 1931 – it proved to be the only Championship innings he played for the county during the whole of that season.

Roy Genders, who wrote books on gardening, played 3 matches for Derbyshire in 1946, 5 for 'Worcestershire in 1947 and 1948 and 2 for Somerset in 1949. He went to Cambridge University, but never chosen by the university for a first-class game.

In 1751 it was reported that the Prince of Wales' death was caused by being hit by a cricket ball – other accounts name the culprit as a tennis ball.

The first comprehensive book of cricket records was published in 1951, the author was Roy Webber.

Rhodesia played in the Currie Cup competition for the first time in 1904/05 – they did not make a second appearance until 1929/30.

Tom Hayward scored 3,518 runs in first-class cricket in 1906. This new record aggregate stood until 1947.

A team of American baseball players toured England in 1874 and also tried their hand at cricket – not very successfully.

The last first-class match, to date, played in Canada was MCC v Canada in Toronto on Sept 8 to 10, 1951.

Between 1801 and April 1998, according to the record kept by the Association of Cricket Statisticians and Historians, no less than 43,220 first-class matches have been staged.

In 1810 the Bs were dismissed by the Rest of England at Lord's for 6, the lowest total ever recorded in a major cricket match.

On June 12, 1815, just prior to the Battle of Waterloo, the Brigade of Guards played a cricket match in Brussels.

EXTRAS • UMPIRES

Morris Nichols, during the Yorkshire v Essex match at Colchester in 1935 hit a ball for six – it was declared void, when the umpires realised that there was no batsman at the other end, a wicket having fallen the previous ball.

Completely against the laws the National Bank captain, in the match against Rawalpindi in 1981/2, changed some of his team at lunch on the first day, when he realised the state of the pitch.

Don Topley, fielding sub for England v West Indies at Lord's in 1984 took a brilliant catch, but he stumbled over the boundary rope in the process and the catch became a six.

Pelham Warner retired out during the Middlesex v Essex match at Leyton in 1920, because he had to go to Lord's to attend a selectors' meeting.

George Hunt of Somerset, playing against Notts at Taunton in 1930 batted left handed against the bowling of Bill Voce and right handed against the rest of the attack.

Richard Hadlee's grunt as he delivered the ball during the New Zealand v pakistan match in 1978/9 was mistaken for the umpire's shout of 'No-ball', the batsman, Talat Ali took a swipe and was clean bowled.

During the Oxford University v Pakistani game at The Parks in 1963, Shafqat Rana complained of sun reflecting into his eyes it was discovered to be the metal clips of a spectator's braces.

In 1922 during the Cambridge University v Lancs match, Lawrie Cook bowled a ball to Hubert Ashton. The ball hit the stumps causing the bails to jump up, but they resettled in their grooves – Ashton was judged 'not out'.

At the close of the Smokers v Non-Smokers game at East Melbourne in 1886/7, William Scotton, the batsman who faced the final ball, picked up the ball as a souvenir and was given out 'handled ball'.

EXTRAS • UMPIRES

Harold Day, whilst butting for Hants v Notts at Trent Bridge in 1924, drove the ball straight at the non-striker's wicket, the bails flew in the air and struck umpire, Phillips, in the face. He was so badly hurt that he had to retire.

The ancient custom of umpires officiating armed with a bat, continued until the 1930s. Whether the original reason was to replace a bat broken during play, or to protect the umpire from outraged fielders is unknown.

For many years umpires were not allowed to officiate in matches involving their own county, but Frank Chester, with permission from the captains, stood in the Worcs v Essex match of 1925, when West had to leave suddenly due to a death in the family.

At Parramatta Oval in 1927/8, C Cant hit a ball to square leg during the Manly v Central Cumberland match. The umpire caught it in self-protection.

'The Umpire's Register' was in common use in the 1920s. It was a metal device about 2¼ ins by 1½ ins with keys. The umpire clicked a key for each ball bowled.

In 1936, Claude Woolley umpired in a Kent Championship game, whilst his brother, Frank, was playing for the Hop County.

DC Cleverley in the North Shore v King's Old Boys Match in Auckland was banned from bowling in the middle of his over, because the excessively long spikes on his boots were causing too much damage to the turf.

It is believed that the first instant of umpires wearing white coats occurred during the United Eleven's match v Free Foresters in 1861.

The fashion of umpires pocketing the bails at close of play was first mentioned in 1857.

EXTRAS • UMPIRES

When George Duckworth whipped off the bails to dismiss the last man stumped in the Lancs v Yorks match, when the latter were all out 33, he yelled 'Hooray'. The umpire refused to give the man out until the correct 'How's That' was called.

During the Lancs v Leics game at Old Trafford in 1935, a storm of booing greeted the umpire's decision to judge a batsman 'run out'. The umpires sat down and refused to continue until the noise had ceased.

In the Northants v Indians match at Kettering in 1932, the overnight batsman, Vince Jupp, did not arrive on time to continue his innings. CK Nayudu the Indian captain demanded that he be judged 'retired out'.

In the Leics v Lancs game of 1947, Gerry Lester had completed a run, but stood outside the crease. When the ball returned to the bowler, he lost grip of his bat for a second, the bowler broken the wicket and Lester was given 'run out'.

Stan Squires appealed for lbw in the Surrey v Lancs game. The umpire disallowed it, but slip fielder then appealed for a catch, which was allowed, the ball had gone from bat to pad and then to slips.

Doug Insole, on appeal, was given out lbw in the England v West Indies Test at Lord's in 1950. The ball then trickled on to the wicket, knocking off a bail. The umpire insisted that the lbw decision stood, but MCC ruled later that 'bowled' was correct.

Fielders heard a distinct click as Herbert Sutcliffe played at a ball in a Middlesex v Yorks match. The wicketkeeper, Freddie Price appealed, but was turned down. On inspection it was found that the ball clipped the stumps, but failed to disturb them.

EXTRAS • UMPIRES

The Australian batsman hit what he thought was the winning boundary in the 1948 Trent Bridge Test. He grabbed a stump and ran for the pavilion, only to discover that another run was required.

The rule preventing umpires from officiating in matches involving their own counties was removed in 1948.

Bill Reeves asked Frank Chester to umpire in a Surrey match at the end from which Alf Gover bowled. Chester thought Reeves had a problem with 'throwing', but Reeves said that Gover bowled so many no balls it made him, Reeves, hoarse.

When John Lillywhite no-balled Ted Willsher for throwing in 1862 the fielding team walked off, and refused to continue unless Lillywhite was replaced – he was on the next day.

A batsman hits the ball a few yards, commences to run, but seeing the non-striker not moving, turns back and accidentally kicks the ball into the stumps. Is he out? MCC ruled no.

If the batsmen run five and the ball then trickled over the boundary how many runs are scored? The answer is five.

If a spectator stops the ball inside the boundary, the ball is then returned to the wicket and the batsman is out of his crease, what is the umpire's verdict. Award four and allow the batsman to continue.

A foolish batsman snicked the ball on to his chest, caught it and threw it back to the bowler. How is he out – Caught, obstructed field or handled ball? Handled ball.

How many runs are allowed if a batsman hits a no-ball and is then run out before completing his run? One no-ball.

How can a batsman score runs off a ball he hits twice? If the fielder misfields and gives away overthrows.

Sam Loxton, Australian manager on tour in Pakistan, when Hanif Mohammad had been given 'not out' for the umpteenth time, said 'See those vultures up there. There waiting for that bloody umpire, he's got to be dead.'

EXTRAS • WHO SAID WHAT

Greatbatch is a big, brawny man with a Cinemascope backside and a career potential to match. *Terry Brindle.*

He has directed his expedition with the bewildered air of a man leading a concert party through the trenches. *Patrick Collins on Mike Gatting's 1990 tour to South Africa.*

When a confident appeal for lbw against Richards was turned down he threatened physical punishment to our wicketkeeper for daring to appeal against him. *Imran Khan during the Pakistan v West Indies series of 1988.*

Javed Miandad is something special, an alley cat of a batsman, most dangerous when cornered. *Tony Lewis.*

It might reasonably be argued that once no one has anything to contribute about cricket, the discussion ought to end. *John Arlott.*

Where his first wicket had been a full toss, this one was a love hop. *Misprint in The Observer.*

He is a thoughtful, calculating batsman, shrewdly assessing the dangers and requirements of the situation at all times. *Ian Pebbles of Len Hutton.*

Boycott's idea of bliss might be to bat all night (so long as it was not for Mr Packer), having batted all day. *John Woodcock in 1980.*

He is one who gives an enabling strength to those prepared to fail around him rather than an arresting figure to those who compile the averages. *RC Robertson-Glasgow on Les Berry.*

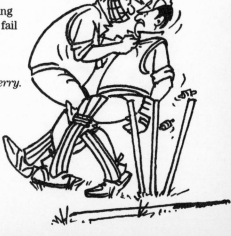

EXTRAS • WHO SAID WHAT

And finally should you ever reach the dizzy heights of County cricket always reserve your best efforts for Saturday. You will get your name in the papers twice, on Sunday and Monday. *John Clay in 1936.*

The triviality of the cause and the violent verbal aftermath sum up the powder-keg on which this three match series sits. *Michael Austin after Mike Gatting's argument with Shakoor Rana.*

They know their onions and with a small chew of humble pie could work together. *Mark Nicholas on Mike Smith and Ray Illingworth.*

England must have had worse captains, but I would be hard put to it to name two or three. *Alan Gibson on Archie MacLaren.*

Only two problems with our team. Brewers' droop and financial cramp. Apart from that we ain't bloody good enough. *Charlie Parker on Gloucestershire in the 1920s.*

I don't go as far as that on my holidays. *Spectator watching Bob Willis's run up.*

He is as untidy as an unmade bed, as devastating as a hand grenade. *Clive Taylor on Colin Milburn.*

The only man that Botham can motivate is himself. *Alec Bedser when Botham is proposed as England couch.*

Lord Archer has declared that he was positively eager to sponsor the application of Rachael Heyhoe Flint. It was an earth trembling prospect: the silliest woman in England proposed by the cheesiest chancellor in Britain. *Patrick Collins – on women joining the MCC.*

Drinking the best tea in the world on an empty cricket ground that, I think, is the final pleasure left to man. *Lord Snow.*

EXTRAS • WHO SAID WHAT

No disrespect but playing for Surrey Seconds against Sussex Seconds at Hove this week in front of a few dogs and coffin-dodgers is quite a different experience to playing to packed houses at The Oval.
Alistair Brown in 1997.

David Lloyd's got more mouth on him than most people in cricket, but doesn't talk a lot of sense. *Godfrey Evans.*

In the cricket season I learned there was a safe and far-away place on the field called 'deep' which I always chose. When 'Over' was called I simply went more and more 'deep' until I was sitting on the steps of the pavilion reading the plays of Noel Coward. *John Mortimer.*

Cricket is an altogether too sacred thing to him to be tampered with on merely religious grounds. *HG Wells.*

We could feel each delivery double declutch on pitching. *Colin Cowdrey in India.*

Was it not Groucho Marx, who, when watching his first match of cricket at Lord's, remarked to his companion and guide, 'But say, when's the game itself going to begin.' *RC Robertson-Glasgow.*

Cricket is an ancient pastime : it ripened sweetly, it has endured nobly. *Thomas Moult.*

Real old-fashioned village cricket is a serious matter for the villager and immense fun for the visitor. *Ian Peebles.*

For six days thou shalt push up and down the line, but on the seventh day thou shalt swipe. *Doug Padgett greeting the start of Sunday League County cricket.*

I'll go and have a fag and a cup of tea.
Phil Tufnell on being asked how he would celebrate a brilliant bowling spell.

EXTRAS • WHO SAID WHAT

To have seen Larwood in Australia is to have witnessed one of the greatest of all sporting occasions. *Bill Bowes.*

He seems to withdraw himself altogether from the conflict round him and to be engaged in some solitary meditation of his own. *Dudley Carew on Maurice Leyland.*

Small, perky, alert as a cat, he is unmistakable from the farthest corner of the ground, whether crouching low beside the stumps, or poised wide-eyed in front of them, handle of the bat thrust forward. *John Thicknesse.*

When he came in to bat the whole crowd broke out into an audible grin, a fever of expectation which made many spectators almost afraid to look in case something went wrong. *Gerald Brodribb.*

The old petrol light has been flashing for about five years and now I know the tank is empty.
Graham Gooch announcing his retirement.

Barbadians come not to see if the West Indies win, but rather like informed spectators round the Madrid bullring, to judge the style and efficiency with which it is done. *Robin Marlar in Bridgetown in March 1986.*

In only two of their last 12 innings have England made more than 200 – at £1,500 per man per match. Professional golfers playing as unsuccessfully as that would be sleeping under the hedges by now. *John Woodcock.*

The good people of St Vincent, who have suffered a volcanic eruption in 1979 and a hurricane last August, will be spared a long innings by Boycott. *Michael Melford in West Indies in 1981.*

Undemonstrative, laconic in speech, he was a man of mighty gusto; inveterate hitter of sixes, but firmly disinclined to discuss them. *John Arlott on Arthur Wellard.*

I used to bowl tripe, then I wrote it, now I sell it. *Notice over Arthur Mailey's butcher's shop.*

EXTRAS • WHO SAID WHAT

When I first picked up a bat as a child, politics and sport were simply two subjects at opposite ends of a newspaper.
Barry Richards.

Don't give advice to a batsman going in; if he's inexperienced it will only make him nervous; if he's an old hand, it's generally unnecessary. Gilbert Jessop.

There is no doubt that Dexter can handle a bat, but who's going to handle Dexter?
Comment after Ted Dexter was appointed England's captain.

**It's all tommy-rot this talk about dropping a ball on a sixpence. Let 'em try and hit a kitchen hearth-rug.
Ted Peate.**

Very few chances were given, but I think a chap in a tweed coat dropped Jack Ryder near the shilling end.
Arthur Mailey, when Victoria hit 1,107.

Many great players have illustrated the game of cricket : of Trumper, more than anyone, it may be said that he adorned it. Alan Gibson.

He lived a corporate life in splendid isolation.
JM Kilburn on Herbert Sutcliffe.

As Shakespeare said – some men in their lives play many parts. Worrell was one of the few to do it all at the same time. Clayton Goodwin.

Few of the great players are deep theorists on cricket, probably because the game has come to them too naturally to need any very close analaysis. *EW Swanton.*

**Do not go into the field with a cigarette or a pipe in your mouth.
WG Grace's advise to fielders.**

EXTRAS • WHO SAID WHAT

I have known cricketers who stood head and shoulder above everyone else at net practice, but rarely were able to do themselves justice in a match. Their mental approach to the game was unequal to their natural physical talents. *Len Hutton.*

I find it mystifying that England produces any cricketers at all. *Colin McCool.*

I'm going to make them wear caps this season. After all you don't get awarded your county floppy hat, do you?
Jack Bond, manager of Lancashire.

People don't pay to watch me any more. They come to see me drop dead from exhaustion or old age.
Bill Alley, playing for Somerset aged 48.

Don Bradman has made so much cricket history of the marvellous sort that one scarcely ventures to speak of him.
Edmund Blunden.

To young eyes, quickest to perceive the things that make cricket, Miller is as an Olympian god among mortals.
Ray Robinson on Keith Miller.

The Aristotle to Ranji's Alexander as he conquered new worlds was, of course, CB Fry. *Neville Cardus.*

Above all, Maurice Tate was unique in that he made the ball leave the ground faster, in relation to its speed through the air, than other other pace bowler in the history of the game. *John Arlott.*

Herbert Sutcliffe is the serenest batsmen I have known. Whatever may have passed under that calm brow – anger, joy, disagreement, surprise, relief, triumph – no outward sign was betrayed on the field of play. *RC Robertson-Glasgow.*

What grace – what elegance – one saw when Arthur was at the wicket. His batting was the poetry of cricket. There was nothing violent or forcible about it, but every stroke was so finished – with such an of polish and mastery.
The Country Vicar on Arthur Shrewsbury.

EXTRAS • ENGLAND OVERSEAS

Jemmy Grundy declared we should never see land again; poor George Parr was nearly out of his mind; old Jackson dropped to his knees. William Caffyn's description of the 1859 England's rough voyage home.

Even when the side landed, the Communist Party of India called for a boycott of the Tests, but the anti-tour faction soon evaporated. England to India 1981/2.

Each of the English eleven was issued with a hat with a ribbon, and also a coloured sash, each man having a different colour and these colours were printed against each player's name on the scorecard. Report of the first match of the 1861/2 tour to Australia.

The Minor Counties first sent a representative team overseas in 1977/78, the side played seven matches in Kenya.

When Sir Julien Cahn took his 1928/9 side to Jamaica, the professionals travelled from Bristol by banana boat, the amateurs went on the Mauretania via New York.

The MCC team arranged for the 1926/27 trip to Argentina, also visited Uruguay, Chile and Peru.

The 1881/2 tour to Australia began with a trip to America. The game in San Francisco was a farce and the only person watching who knew much about cricket demanded his money back.

Lord Sheffield lost £2,000 on the 1891/2 tour to Australia, which he financed, because the usual speculators wouldn't take the risk.

The 1882/3 trip to Australia got off to a bad start when the ship carrying the team collided with another near Colombo. Fred Morley was badly injured, though he played in the tourists matches – he died in September 1884 aged 35.

The first time a team of selectors, rather than the MCC Committee picked an MCC side to go to Australia was in 1928/29.

EXTRAS • ENGLAND OVERSEAS

No less than 50 bags of sawdust were spread on the wicket after rain stopped play in the MCC v Western Province game of 1927/8.

The only two first-class matches ever played in Burma took place during the 1926/27 tour by the MCC

Maurice Tate took 77 wickets at a cost of 19.01 runs each on the 1924/25 tour to Australia, no one else managed more than 40.

George Gunn, who was in Australia for his health, was co-opted into the England side for the First Test of the 1907/08 series and hit the highest scores in each England innings.

On the 1946/7 tour of Australia, the England Captain, Wally Hammond travelled everywhere by car, the rest of the side went by rail.

Mickey Stewart, the England manager, was involved in a scuffle with a TV cameraman, as he tried to take pictures of the seriously injured Syd Lawrence, when the latter broke his kneecap on the 1991/2 tour of New Zealand.

Fumes from a nearby oil refinery produced a dreadful smell and affected the eyes of the fielders during the England v Trinidad match at Pointe-a-Pierre in 1991/2.

The third morning's play between the England touring side and Transvaal in 1993/4 had to be abandoned as England, due to sickness, only had four fit players. Play resumed after lunch with five substitute fielders, including the England physio.

When one of the revolving sightscreens got stuck, 45 minutes play was lost, during the England v Eastern Province game at Port Elizabeth in 1993/4.

EXTRAS • ENGLAND OVERSEAS

Playing for Canterbury against the English touring side in 1977/8, Peter Coman when fielding was hit on the chin by the ball and, rather like a boxer knocked out. He took 20 minutes to come round.

It was estimated that over 2,000,000 spectators watched the 24 matches which MCC played on their 1961/2 tour of the Indian sub-continent.

Scott Ledger playing against the England touring side at Bundaberg in November 2 1978, was hit on the head by John Lever whilst batting; retired to have stitches in the wound; returned only to be hit again in the same place by the first ball he faced. He retired again.

A lone trumpeter sounded the Last Post from the Hill at Sydney as England won the 1978/9 Test series five matches to one.

During the 1979/80 tour of Australia, Geoff Boycott hit his 117th first-class 100, equalling Don Bradman's record – Boycott's score was made on Bradman's home ground of Adelaide.

On the first English tour to India no less than 14 players were co-opted into the side at various times, due to illness or injury.

Confusion reigned over arrangements for an English tour to West Indies in 1896/7. Lord Hawke wanted to take a team, but his telegram confirming the fixtures went astray and a second team was invited. Hawke tried to persuade the organiser of the second side to withdrew. He would not, and two rival teams toured.

Each season from 1929 to 1959 an English side of county standard toured Egypt.

During the MCC to Pakistan tour of 1955/6, some of the English players, as a prank, poured cold water over one of the umpires, Idris Begh. The prank misfired and only high level diplomacy saved the day.

EXTRAS • ENGLAND OVERSEAS

Capt RT Stansyforth, who led the 1927/8 MCC side to South Africa, had never played in first-class county cricket at the time of the tour – he later played for Yorkshire – just three times.

One of the most unpleasant tours of recent times was to New Zealand and Pakistan in 1983/4. London newspapers accused some of the team of smoking 'pot' during the tour, which caused friction between press and players. A later enquiry cleared the players.

On the 1985/6 tour to Sri Lanka, contrary to England management instructions, the team for the third 'Test' included Norman Gifford, the assistant manager – he took seven wickets.

For the England tour of Australia in 1886/7, half the side were Nottinghamshire players.

Dominic Cork was forced to fly back to England in the middle of the 1993/4 match v Border, due to a family illness.

The first match played abroad by MCC was in Paris in April 1867.

The highest scorer in the England v Gymie match of the 1884/5 tour was awarded with gold mining shares.

EXTRAS • FROM THE LIBRARY

The first detailed description of a cricket match was written the Rev William Goldwin and published in 1706. The fact that it was written in Latin has made life a little difficult for cricket historians.

Neville Cardus's first cricket related job was as assistant coach at Shrewsbury School.

The popular Playfair Cricket Annual has been edited by Bill Frindall since 1986.

One of the largest histories of a 'local' cricket club – it runs to 444 pages – is that devoted to Drumpellier CC of Scotland, published in 1908.

A major rival to Wisden was for almost 30 years, James Lillywhite's Cricketers' Annual. It ceased publication in 1900.

After the battering he received from the West Indian fast bowlers when he played for England, Brian Close entitled his memoirs, "I don't Bruise Easily".

Frederick Gale, who wrote cricket articles and books under the nom de plume 'The Old Buffer' took John Ruskin to watch the Australians at The Oval in 1882.

The first history of the County Cricket Championship was published in 1895 and ran to 148 pages.

Henry Thomas Waghorn, who was employed in the British Museum Library, spent much of his time combing old newspapers for cricket references and two volumes of his discoveries were published.

Thomas Turner a shopkeeper of East Hoathly kept a diary from 1754 to 1765. This contains many references to village cricket and a book containing extracts from the diary is currently available.

FS Ashley-Cooper, the noted cricket historian, was appointed Secretary of Notts CCC in 1920, but only survived a season. He did however write the History of the County Club which came out in 1923.

EXTRAS • FROM THE LIBRARY

The first full time librarian at Lord's Cricket Ground was Diana Rait-Kerr, whose father was MCC Secretary at the time of her appointment.

The famous Bodyline Tour to Australia in 1932/3 has inspired about 40 books and they still seem to be appearing!

One of the rarest books relating to an overseas tour by an English team is simply entitled 'The Log of the Old Un', and refers to the tour to North America in 1886. The author was WC Sim, the Secretary of Devonshire CCC.

For many years regular articles appeared in The Cricketer written by 'A Country Vicar'. He was the Rev RL Hodgson, who had been Secretary to Suffolk CCC before the First World War.

David Frith founded the Wisden Cricket monthly magazine in 1979. He continued as Editor until March 1996.

Trevor McDonald, the TV newscaster, wrote the authorised biography of Clive Lloyd, the West Indian cricket captain.

The Cricket Society determined as one of its early aims to compile a bibliography of cricket. This was finally published in conjunction with the Library Association in 1977.

The most attractive of the early instructional books on cricket was 'Felix on the Bat', sub-titled 'being a scientific inquiry into the use of the cricket bat'.

The most perceptive of cricket historians was Rowland Bowen, the culmination of his researches was 'Cricket: A History of its growth and Development Throughout The World'. This was published in 1970.

Tony Lewis celebrated the history of Lord's Cricket Ground in 1987 with 'Double Century'. This told the story of the first 200 years of the Ground.

EXTRAS • FROM THE LIBRARY

The scores of the matches played by Middlesex CCC up to 1947 have been published in three volumes by WJ Ford, FS Ashley Cooper and Nigel Haig.

The most authoritative work on the history of cricket in India was written by the journalist Mihir Bose and published in 1990.

Richard Christen's book on Australian cricket grounds is unlikely to be bettered. On several occasions the author flew over grounds in order to take aerial photographs.

The book which contains brief biographies of every first class cricketer to appear in the British Isles was first published in 1984 and reissued in 1993.

The first English tour overseas also saw the publication of the first 'tour' book : 'The English Cricketers Trip to Canada and the United States', published in 1860.

One of the oddest of 'tour' books is EHD Sewell's 'From A Window at Lords'. This describes the MCC 1936/7 tour to Australia, but was written as soon as the tour ended without the author leaving England.

Vic Lewis better known as a musician – he ran the Vic Lewis Orchestra from 1947 to 1960 – wrote a book entitled 'Cricket Ties'. He had managed to collect about 3,000 ties.

David Rayvern Allen, a diligent researcher into cricketing byways, published in 1981, 'A Song for Cricket', a book which listed all the songs with cricketing connections and illustrated with sheet music.

Charles Dickens was a cricket enthusiast – there is an oil painting supposedly showing him as an umpire. His most famous piece of cricket writing is in Pickwick Papers, the game descrmbed being Dingley Dell v All Muggleton.

EXTRAS • FROM THE LIBRARY

The most prolific of modern cricketing authors was David
Lemmon, who wrote many biographies and County Histories, as
well as being Editor of the Benson & Hedges Cricket Year.

**Whilst the individual Australian states have regularly
issued cricket annuals, national Australian annuals have
usually been short lived. The present Allan's Australian
Cricket Annual is now in its 11th year which is a record!**

Arthur Mailey, the Australian leg break bowler, wrote his
autobiography '10 for 66 and all that' and as a talented cartoonist
supplied his own illustrations.

**Lord Tennyson, grandson of the poet, captained Hampshire
and frequently went overseas on cricketing tours. He
entitled his autobiography, 'From Verse to Worse'.**

The American Cricketer, a monthly magazine published in the
United States ran from 1877 to 1929 – a complete set is very rare.

**A book giving a detailed description of how to play cricket,
written in German, was published in Hamburg in 1796;
it was reissued in Danish in 1801.**

QUIZ SCORE SHEETS

QUIZ SCORE SHEETS

QUIZ SCORE SHEETS

QUIZ SCORE SHEETS